DARWIN OVERTHROWN:
HELLO MECHANOBIOLOGY

SUZAN MAZUR

Remembering Jerry Fodor

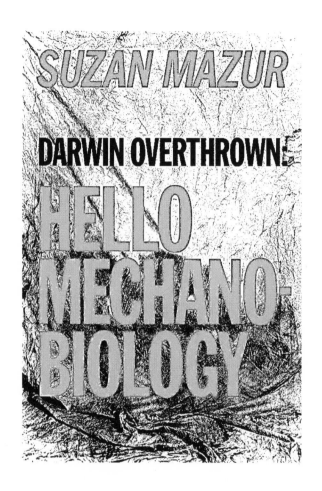

SUZAN MAZUR

DARWIN OVERTHROWN:
HELLO MECHANO-BIOLOGY

CASWELL BOOKS   NEW YORK

Contents

Darwin Overthrown

The Altenberg 16: An Exposé of the Evolution Industry is a book that was welcomed a decade ago by debunkers of Darwinian natural selection and slammed by Darwin stalwarts. In the past 10 years, the debunkers of Darwinian science have prevailed and the term natural selection is now passé, a footnote to what has replaced it: "Mechanobiology."

What exactly is mechanobiology?

Wikipedia defines mechanobiology as the "field of science at the interface of biology and engineering that focuses on how physical forces and changes in the mechanical properties of cells and tissues contribute to development, cell differentiation, physiology and disease."

Indeed, history has shown philosopher Jerry Fodor—who died a little more than a year ago—to be right about Darwin's theory of natural selection being "wrong in a way that can't be fixed."

"It goes deep," Fodor told me over cappuccinos on a snowy Darwin's birthday in 2008.

Fodor joked at the time that he was in the Witness Protection Program because of his challenging remarks about Darwinian science. But it was no joke.

Project grants were at stake for scientists who approached what Fodor termed the "Darwinian government" for money. High profile skeptics of natural selection risked not only rejection for funding but vicious attacks in the media, as high profile skeptics who question official myth have throughout history. And Fodor was majorly high profile, considered even by his peers as the most substantial philosopher of his time.

But evolutionary science is the bedrock of our civilization, and Fodor realized that getting the science right is crucial to life on the planet (Chapter 1)—even as the line between life and non-life is now also under review as we explore Earth's deeper crusts.

1

So, mechanobiology is the new evolutionary science being embraced by the scientific community. And recognizing this—governments worldwide are funding its research.

Mechanobiology goes by assorted names: biophysics, biomechanics, soft matter—as well as "the new condensed matter physics," etc. (Chapter 9).

The French claim Nobel laureate Pierre-Gilles de Gennes pioneered it. The Brits say it was Sir Sam Edwards at Cambridge. But obviously, some of the science dates back a hundred years to D'Arcy Thompson's mathematical biology.

The influence from the East can't be overlooked either. Lev Belousov, Vladimir Voeikov, and their "Osaka Group" colleagues: Mae-Wan Ho, Peter Saunders, Antonio Lima-de-Faria, Brian Goodwin *et al.* Singapore's MechanoBiology Institute is now a central player.

Over the past year or so I've interviewed more of the world's major scientists working in the area of origin and evolution of life—including those looking at microbes and viruses. What life is, is increasingly being described as a process, one whose structure and motion are measurable using neutron scattering, ever more powerful microscopes and other state-of-the-art tools.

Because details of life's process are increasingly readable, synthetic cell designers think that creating life—as they understand it—is technically feasible and they are projecting a new seriousness about getting the job done. And, yes, the term "mechanistic chemistry" has been popping up in the pages of *Nature*.

Naysayers predict the origin of life field will implode and that scientists "can't do it."

Discovery Institute—the politically conservative think tank—in particular, has had a field day lampooning origin of life science, hiring an origin of life cartoonist to satirize efforts.

Nevertheless, a number of synthetic cell collaborations with significant funding have emerged, most post-Harry Lonsdale's 2011 Origin of Life Challenge. Among them:

Simons Collaboration on Origins of Life
Harvard Origins of Life Initiative
Dutch Synthetic Cell initiative
Max Planck Institutes initiative
Ludwig Maxmilians University initiative
National Science Foundation funded collaborations
Chinese Academy of Sciences investigations

Especially empowering the search for understanding life is the ramping up of neutron scattering science in the US, Europe and the Far East, which presents an opportunity to probe biological matter deeper and more precisely than ever before.

Sweden's European Spallation Source (ESS) at Lund University —with construction now nearing 50% completion and the facility operational this year—is slated in the next few years to be the largest neutron science facility in the world. What's more, ESS has passed the test of environmentalists. No nuclear reactor or mercury target is involved in the ESS operation.

Meanwhile, the US remains wedded to a somewhat dicey approach to neutron scattering at its largest facility, Oak Ridge National Laboratory (ORNL), using weapons-grade plutonium for its reactor and liquid mercury to obtain its neutrons for research. ORNL is now expanding its neutron scattering facility.

At the other end of the spectrum, another school of science is pursuing holographic noise, which if detected, could help clarify just how many dimensions we're actually living in—2D, 3D, etc. It's a question D'Arcy Thompson posed to philosopher Alfred North Whitehead a hundred years ago (Chapter 36).

Along with telescopes and microscopes of unprecedented sophistication as well as other technological tools to aid scientific investigation, the thinking about origin and evolution of life is morphing at an unprecedented pace as an ongoing stream of electronic information about experimental results is available to a global audience—open access.

Public curiosity about a scientific explanation for the origin of life as we know it is keener than ever now that Darwinian science has been overthrown and scandal continues to rock organized religion.

The emergence of the Dutch Origins Center, inaugurated in 2017, is evidence of escalating public curiosity about origin of life. Germany's Max Planck Institutes are now offering MScs and PhDs in origin of life science.

And Santa Fe Institute, along the lines of the Dutch initiative, is committed to "massive" public outreach. SFI is designing an online course (MOOC), hosting a series of workshops, as well as festivals—all incorporating the origin of life theme.

Obviously, a new creation myth will not suffice in this electronically connected time of open, democratized science. The days of origin of life "fishing expeditions" are also over as more "experimentally driven" scientists populate the field. So, the bar is higher than ever for scientists, whose academic papers can now be scrutinized by all.

Dialogue with scientists in the pages that follow is largely reflective of a more dynamic and realistic investigation of what life is. But not all the dialogue.

So, as the late television talk show host John McLaughlin used to say: "Let's first review a few statistics of geography."

Let's revisit the politics. . .

Suzan Mazur
January 2019

Part 1

The Controversy

Chapter 1

Jerry Fodor Held High Ground to Evolution's Militant Fundamentalists

"Sometimes when I'm in a mildly bitter mood I think, look the trouble with Darwin is he believes in Intelligent Design. He never really got it clear to himself that there really isn't a designer. So it's questionable whether you can take artificial selection as a model for natural selection the way he did. When you try to do that you can't work it out."—**Jerry Fodor** talking to me in 2008

"Perhaps making all these parallels between natural selection and artificial selection, the way Darwin does in his book, could be somewhat dangerous because in artificial selection there is someone who is selecting, even if unconsciously. In that respect, the evolutionary process is very different in nature where nothing is there to actually select. . . . No one in the mainstream scientific community now takes selection literally."—**Eugene Koonin** in conversation with me in 2017

"The circulation of the proof copy of What Darwin Got Wrong, the product of a noted philosopher and a prominent student of linguistics and cognitive science, has resulted in a volume of

critical comment from biologists and philosophers that has not been seen since 1859. . . . Not to be misunderstood, perhaps biologists should stop referring to "natural selection," and instead talk about differential rates of survival and reproduction."—**Richard Lewontin**, *New York Review of Books*, 2010

12/23/2017

W e are grateful to Jerry Fodor—perhaps the most substantial philosopher of our time, who has now died—for exposing what he called the "empty" Darwinian theory of natural selection and for his courage as well as his superb humor in the face of unrelenting opposition.

"I'm in the Witness Protection Program," Fodor joked when I called him to request an interview following publication of his article in the *London Review of Books* ("Why Pigs Don't Have Wings," October 2007) about problems with Darwin's selectionist theory.

Fodor never claimed to be a biologist. "It's not my field," he told me. But he was the son of a bacteriologist and was comfortable in the science discourse because he didn't see philosophy and science as separate.

Following appearance of his provocative *LRB* article, tenured (and therefore unfireable) academics wanting to make a name for themselves attempted to destroy Fodor's argument that Darwin was wrong about natural selection being the mechanism of evolutionary change. They used venues like the out-of-the-loop *Nation* magazine as well as their own scrappy blogs to do the dirty work, welcoming high school students, undergrads, and misfit Internet trolls to the kill.

But Fodor's plight eventually inspired Richard Lewontin to respond to the distasteful attacks on the philosopher (even though Lewontin told me in a 2008 book interview that he resented biology being "invaded by people like Jerry Fodor and others").

7

In a 2010 Lewontin cover story for the *New York Review of Books* titled: "Not So Natural Selection"—a critique of Fodor's book *What Darwin Got Wrong* co-authored by cognitive scientist Massimo Piattelli-Palmarini—he made the point that Darwin never intended natural selection to be taken literally by generations of scientists who followed, which further infuriated Fodor's assailants.

My only meeting with Jerry Fodor took place on a snowy day in 2008 on the Upper West Side of Manhattan at Le Pain Quotidien. Ironically, it was Darwin's birthday—February 12. Fodor, in the operatic form he so loved, told me over a couple of cappuccinos and in the interview that follows:

> *"All I'm wanting to argue is that whatever the story turns out to be, it's not going to be the selectionist story."*

I'd say Jerry Fodor knew long before he died in late November that he was right about the selectionist story being wrong.

New York, February 12, 2008

Jerry Fodor: One of the reasons why this is so reminiscent of the arguments about behaviorism, 30, 40, 50 years ago is that the Skinnerian kind of story in psychology and the Darwinian story in evolutionary theory are very similar. The basic idea in the case of both is that the environmental variables do most of the work in changing, on the one hand, behavioral structure, and on the other hand, evolutionary structure. So, if you're convinced that that kind of view is essentially right, then the last thing you're inclined to worry about is constraints that come from inside the organism. I think that was a mistake. I think it was a mistake in the Skinnerian case and I think it was a mistake in the Darwinian case. And it seems to me very likely that over time that we will see a shift. But we'll see. I've got tenure, I don't have to worry.

Suzan Mazur: Massimo Pigliucci said that in your *London Review of Books* article you are spectacularly wrong about the big picture.

Jerry Fodor: Who said this?

Suzan Mazur: Massimo Pigliucci.

Jerry Fodor: Oh, that guy. . . .

Here's the evolutionary problem. You've got an organism of a certain kind—suppose you have a population of organisms—and over time various heritable changes occur in this population. Their tails get longer, they get bushier eyebrows, whatever. The question is what is it that occasions such changes. In particular, is it roughly speaking environmental structure or internal structure. . . . Something changes the genome.

Suzan Mazur: What about the ongoing discussion regarding self-organization and form, for instance?

Jerry Fodor: Evolution applies to any generation of organisms that change in a heritable fashion.

Suzan Mazur: What do you see as the main issue?

Jerry Fodor: The Darwin story is the main issue. The heritable traits, features of biological organisms—complex and simple—change over time. They change as a function of some kinds of variables or other god knows what. This would be true of the relation between any generation of the organism and the next generation and the succeeding generation. But the question that evolution theory is about, as opposed to questions about where did life start or something like that—is when you get these changes in the inheritable structures of organisms, where do they come from? What are the controlling variables? It's not whether RNA comes before DNA. The basic question is: Are these changes shaped by environmental factors as in selection theory or are they shaped by some internal factors currently unknown?

Suzan Mazur: You're saying they're shaped by internal factors.

9

Jerry Fodor: I don't even say that. I say there's something wrong with the thesis that they're shaped by environmental factors. And so now there are various other alternatives.

Suzan Mazur: What about the self-organization people— Kauffman and others?

Jerry Fodor: Yes, but the question is, what's the nature and that's—typically these people are seeing natural selection. That there are changes that are brought about in the genetic structure or the RNA structure or whatever.

Suzan Mazur: Some of the self-organization people are rejecting natural selection.

Jerry Fodor: That's what I'm interested in. . . . I think that's right. But what the biologists don't like is the claim that it [natural selection] doesn't work.

Suzan Mazur: I told the science editor from *The Economist* that I was going to see you today. He hadn't read your *LRB* article and didn't know who you were. I was shocked. He's a friend of Richard Dawkins.

Jerry Fodor: Then he probably doesn't read *LRB* as a matter of principle.

Suzan Mazur: I used to write for the old *Economist*. The science now appears affected by politics.

Jerry Fodor: There's internal politics too. But who cares. The question is who's right.

Suzan Mazur: *The Economist* editor said: Can you get him on the phone to have a three-way conversation?—I am not convinced.

Jerry Fodor: I'm not convinced either. But it doesn't matter who believes what. In 50 years we'll all be dead. . .

Suzan Mazur: The *Philadelphia Inquirer* is also interested.

Jerry Fodor: Least of all does one care what the newspapers believe.

There are a couple of theories on the table. One of them says changes of inheritable properties are largely or exclusively—depending on how rigid one's views are—the effect of exogeneous variables. The effect of selection. Who the predators are, whether there gets to be more or less food, etc. That's one kind of view. That's Darwin's view.

Another kind of view is no, the effect is in some way we don't understand—endogenous variables, like laws of form, and stuff like that. . .

All I'm wanting to argue is that whatever the story turns out to be, it's not going to be the selectionist story. There are internal problems, I think, with that, with the selectionist story.

I don't really have a view, if I did it wouldn't be an interesting view. Why would anybody take it seriously? I don't have a view about what the alternatives are. There are these other vague ideas around. Laws of form are one of them. One of them, in fact, that Darwin knew about. I really have nothing of interest to say about that. I don't even know if I have anything of interest to say about the other stuff. I'm simply not concerned. It's not my field.

My problem is what's the status of Darwin's story and that of his followers, that it's variation in the environment—selection by the environment—that accounts for evolutionary variation over time. That's the story I'm interested in. And in particular, the story is that various kinds of ecologies, that is various kinds of surrounds, as it were, select for various kinds of properties of organisms. . . . That's the idea. So, the ecology itself biases the viability of

11

organisms that live in it. And it's that biasing that you're seeing reflected over time in the way that organisms evolve. That's the classical Darwinian picture. It depends on being able to make sense of the notion of traits of one kind or another being selected for.

Suzan Mazur: There's the debate about whether 30,000 genes are driving it.

Jerry Fodor: You get an enormous amount of control out of 30,000 genes or for that matter out of 30 genes. But I don't care. I'm neutral. What I care about is that there aren't one-to-one correspondences between genes and traits. There must be a lot of structure intervening between the genes and the phenotypic expression. So that's one source of endogenous constraints on organisms. But that's not what I'm worried about. I'm worried about whether the source is natural selection. The problem you're talking about is neutral on whether it's natural selection. In fact, most people who are working on that kind of endogenous determination of the phenotype think that it's fully compatible with selection theory.

Suzan Mazur: Scientists are increasingly rejecting the idea of the selfish gene.

Jerry Fodor: If the environment is selecting traits for fitness in that environment, they must change something in the organism. And they must change something in the organism that is heritable. Cause we're only interested in changes from generation to generation, right? Now there's a question about what is it they change. It could be genes, it could be RNA. It could be all sorts of stuff. Fine. Selection is perfectly well accepted. It's different from the question of whether or not there is selection going on that's causing these internal changes that are causing the changes in the features. So fine, let it be the RNA—I don't care. What I care about is not what selection affects but whether or not there is such a phenomenon as selection. If there is, then fine, then maybe it's transmitted.

Suzan Mazur: And if there isn't?

Jerry Fodor: If there isn't, then we need to think of different kinds of theories, and one kind of theory would be to take very seriously the idea that there are only a small number of phenotypes that can occur to an organism with a certain genetic base. In that case, there is not much for selection to do.

Look, Darwin thought roughly—plus or minus a bit—he didn't know about genomes, of course. But he thought in effect that the genome was a random generator of traits. But there are genetic changes—-as I said he didn't know about genes, translation either. That there are changes that occur in the gene structure at random over time. These are expressed by random changes in the phenotype. And now what decides which of those changes becomes characteristic of that kind of organism—answer: the operation of the environment.

Suzan Mazur: So much of science is interpretative. . . .

Jerry Fodor: True, you're involving people. But the way to look at it is, here are the facts and here are the prior theories. What do we have to change to deal with the data. Who cares what people think.

There are things we're not going to find out. The goal is to build a theory. Darwin has one. It's been intact, as it were, for the last 50, 60 years of history. The question is—is what he said true?

Suzan Mazur: Are you saying Darwin's idea is creationist?

Jerry Fodor: Well, it's not creationist in a certain sense that it's a real theory. You can get form by starting with a random generator and biasing and filtering what's out there. A lot of people have thought that's how evolution works, a lot of people have also thought that's how the formation of meaning works. That was the Skinnerian picture.

13

Think about how Skinner thought about language. Organisms dabble at random. Babies dabble at random according to Skinner and the environment comes along—mother or daddy or whatever—and picks out some of the babble that sounds like words or something and reinforces that and the rest of it drops out. And that's how you learn a language.

Well, that's exactly the same picture but only it applies to evolution. Not to learning but to the evolution of heritable change.
. . .

So, Darwin says, okay, how do we get there. Here's a population with a certain phenotype. Look at it a hundred years later, a million years later, whatever, and there's a difference in phenotypic properties in that population. How could this be true? What's the mechanism that takes you from one to another? Answer, well, every organism varies its traits at random. And the environment comes along just like daddy and picks out some of those traits that it likes—it likes the ones that can breathe under water—and throws away the ones it doesn't like. They die. And that's how these variations in phenotypic properties of classes of organisms come about. That's a theory.

It might be right, it might be wrong. But it's perfectly straightforward. There's no doubt that if you start with a random generator, of whatever, anything you like, numbers in a slot machine, you start with a random generator and you have a filter that picks out some of the things that it generates and throws away others, eventually you'll converge on something with structure. Of course you will.

Suzan Mazur: What about neoteny?

Jerry Fodor: That's compatible with either kind of story. What's going on with the Darwinian story is that the genotype is throwing off traits that get expressed in phenotypic properties. Now one of the interesting questions is since organisms develop, they don't exhibit their innate repertoire instantly in the womb, as it were—

organisms develop. What is the impact of development on the expression of the genotype?

One of the reasons that genes aren't in one-to-one correspondence with phenotypic traits is precisely that organisms do develop and that the developmental path of the organism imposes structure on what the genotype started with. So fine. You can imagine all sorts of things that could be involved in getting from a genotype to a phenotype. In fact, it's a very hard question, maybe an unanswerable question, how it's done.

But that's not what Darwin is about. And it's not what the argument about selection is about. The argument about selection is: Look, you start out with a genotype in a certain generation. Something happens to the genotype or to the mechanisms that control its expression or it's both. Something happens to it, such that in the next generation you get a different phenotype. Why is it that this happens? What is it that determines, that mutes the changes in the genotype which leads to these changes in traits? That's what selectionism is about. It doesn't matter to them— obviously very nice to know about—but it doesn't matter to them what the course of development from a genotypic state to its phenotypic expression is. Might be all sorts of things. The simplest model is just one-to-one, each gene makes a trait. We know that's wrong.

Suzan Mazur: Right.

Jerry Fodor: But Darwin didn't even know about genes. Couldn't care less. What he was interested in is when—

Suzan Mazur: Current thinking on evolution includes a sort of Lamarckism.

Jerry Fodor: Right, but that's not— What we now think, probably I suppose rightly, is that heritable traits can only be acquired, can only come into a population as a result of the variation of the genotype. So, you can stop worrying about

Lamarckism. Suppose Darwin was wrong about Lamarckism. It doesn't matter. The same picture still holds, mainly, you've got a genotype in one generation—it's expressed in a phenotype. You've got a genotype in another generation—it's expressed in a different phenotype. What's the mechanism that changes things from one generation to another?

Suzan Mazur: I don't think you're interested in this but regarding the funding. . . . NASA has supported a publication on natural selection and astrobiology by an episcopal priest.

Jerry Fodor: Astrobiology doesn't exist. What are its laws?

Suzan Mazur: He [the priest] is also writing a book for Harvard University Press on astrobiology.

Jerry Fodor: It'll be a short book I should think.

Suzan Mazur: Do you have any objection to the government funding Darwinian science?

Jerry Fodor: The Darwinian government?

Suzan Mazur: Do you object?

Jerry Fodor: Well, object. Government agencies not just here, but elsewhere are extremely conservative. That is, they fund middle-brow science essentially. And that's not surprising. Look—

Suzan Mazur: NAS [National Academy of Sciences] has a sort of defense arm, right? Isn't that why Lewontin resigned from NAS?

Jerry Fodor: I suppose. Look, it doesn't matter to me. I'm interested specifically in the question of whether the selectionist theory is true. Nothing else. There are all these spinouts or

16

consequences of its being too liberal in the polls and they're very important but not for this project.

Suzan Mazur: When is your book coming out?

Jerry Fodor: Soon as it gets written. I don't know. It should be finished I should think. Well, Massimo Piattelli, my co-author, who's doing the biology in the book, is sort of in charge of that. So you have to ask him.

Suzan Mazur: Do you have a publisher?

Jerry Fodor: We haven't got one yet. We've had various offers.

Suzan Mazur: Will the book include a discussion of people who are working on alternatives to the paradigm?

Jerry Fodor: I don't think there are any alternative paradigms. The fact is just as you said the Darwinian theory is essentially the standard view in the business. I'm not in that business fortunately so I don't have to care whether it's the standard theory. But it is. I'm interested in confirming theories. That's what science is about.

There are data. Theories have to correspond to that. Populations shift over time, go in some ways and don't go in other ways. There are laws about this. Whatever the laws are, the story about what's running population change has to account for those data.

Suzan Mazur: You don't see self-organization as a departure from the standard view.

Jerry Fodor: The issue of selection is independent of self-organization, except insofar as something has got to be causing the changes, and if it's not selection, then maybe it's some laws of organization. I have no contention about this. I just don't know how it works. Basically, I don't think anybody knows how evolution works.

17

But here's the hypothesis: It works by selection of traits produced by random variations in the genome. That's the hypothesis. That's essentially Darwin's hypothesis. Is it true? I think not. I think probably it isn't. I think there are problems.

The key notion of a trait being selected or an organism, if you like, being selected because it has a certain trait. In other words, the trait being selected. I think you can make sense out of that relatively complicated argument. It's either right or it's wrong. But it's utterly orthogonal to the issue of self organization.

It's like saying—suppose somebody said: Look here's my theory. Organisms aren't made out of meat, they're made out of metal. And changes in the metal, structures in the metal produce evolutionary changes. All I'm interested in is do these changes in the metal occur as a result of environmental selection of randomly generated phenotypic properties. That's all I care about.

Suzan Mazur: Did you see the email chain Stan Salthe sent around about your *LBR* article with comments from Michael Ruse, Elliot Sober and others?

Jerry Fodor: There have been so many email exchanges. I don't think I have seen this one. Look, nobody knows what's right.

Suzan Mazur: Have you heard from Richard Lewontin?

Jerry Fodor: I had a brief exchange with Lewontin.

Suzan Mazur: Can you share with me what he said?

Jerry Fodor: Well, Lewontin has been playing with this kind of proposal conservatively. He's basically a Darwinian who says: Look there are other things happening beside natural selection. There are other kinds of variables you have to contend with.

Suzan Mazur: In what sense do you see him as a Darwinian.

18

Jerry Fodor: He thinks the basic mechanism is variation in the genome producing variation in the phenotype and selection from the environment determines fitness. However, he thinks that's only a first approximation for the right picture. Another approximation says, well look—something that I think is very likely true—look one reason that it can't be right is that we know that variation in the genome isn't random. If some genotypic traits change, then others change with them. And that's not a matter of law, that's a matter of interconnections at the genetic level. Some of what happens in evolution is a forced option. It's forced by the fact that the behavior of the genome is not random.

Okay it's perfectly possible to say that, which is what Lewontin says—and I think rightly. And also to think that okay the rest of the story is the selection of traits by the environment. I think that's essentially what Lewontin says.

Suzan Mazur: In Lewontin's *New York Review of Books* article ["The Triumph of Stephen Jay Gould"] he said Gould wanted to "put a noticeable crack" in the "Darwinian icon" but couldn't hope to smash it.

Jerry Fodor: I think there's something wrong with the theory [of natural selection]. It goes deep. . . .

Look, Darwin's a very smart guy. Darwin says we know there are cases, we know that various traits that constitute a phenotype don't vary at random. We know that some of them are connected. So if you have variation in color of the organism, you have variation in its size—that's not a function of natural selection. That's just the structure of the space of possibilities that natural selection has to choose among. Darwin was thoroughly aware of it. And what he said was rightly, this must be very important, but we don't know anything about it, so we'll just proceed as though it weren't there. Perfectly reasonable.

Suzan Mazur: So it wasn't really explored.

Jerry Fodor: Well, it wasn't explored until you have some notion of what the carrier of traits from generation-to-generation is, until you have some notion of the genome, there's no way to explore it. So Darwin said, however, we don't know anything about that so let's keep the genome as in effect varying randomly from generation-to-generation and just look at the effects of the environment on the results of that variation. Perfectly reasonable.

The question, however, is whether one can actually make sense of the notion of the environment selecting for traits as a feature. Darwin took it as obviously you could and actually there are ironies in every direction. I think the reason he took it as obvious that you could make sense of the notion of the environment selecting traits of features, the reason I'm saying he had no problem with that is that he had very explicitly in mind as a model for natural selection—breeding. And in the case of breeding, that's just what goes on.

The breeder says to himself, look I want fat fish not goldfish. So, they throw away the goldfish and they keep the fat fish and breed them with one another. So, Darwin says, explicitly, look natural selection is just like that. But there's no breeder.

Well it's not clear what the position is. The question you want to raise for Darwin is—how does the thing work without a breeder? Because when there is a breeder in artificial selection, what he decides to do is crucial to what phenotype fits the individual.

Sometimes when I'm in a mildly bitter mood I think, look, the trouble with Darwin is he believes in Intelligent Design. He never really got it clear to himself that there really isn't a designer in nature. So, it's questionable whether you can take artificial selection as a model for natural selection the way he did. When you try to do that you can't work it out.

Suzan Mazur: You think Darwin believed in Intelligent Design.

Jerry Fodor: I think, in a funny sense, he did. Intelligent Design people say there's intelligence in choosing this process. But Darwin didn't think that. What he thought was that the process of natural selection could be modeled on processes in which an intelligence—

Darwin says in the first chapter of the *Origin of Species*—it's really a good book and he's very smart. So, he says in the first chapter, look, let me tell you how breeding works. Features are produced at random, at random in the sense that some of their traits vary at random. So there are big pigs and smaller pigs and very small pigs and there are fat pigs and thin pigs, and so on. There's just random variation from generation-to-generation. And the way selection works is the guy stands there, the farmer stands there and actually selects.

Suzan Mazur: The farmer is a tyrant to his pigs.

Jerry Fodor: Yes. Right. He says, throw away the little ones and keep the big ones.

So, there's a model there. There's variation in the genome, or whatever. There's variation in the phenotypes. What matters is that the statistical distribution of properties, traits in a population, changes over time. Including heritable traits. It's not a case of learning. So now the question is: How does it work? Darwin says it works just like artificial selection except there isn't anyone selecting. Now it's not at all clear what that means. . . .

But it's clear that the selection model, the model that says natural selection is just like artificial selection only without an intelligence, that model is the standard picture. If you want to argue with biologists, that's what you have to argue with.

Okay, I want to argue with biologists, not for the fun of it but because I think the standard model is wrong. But that is the standard model. What is of interest is finding out whether the theory is true.

Suzan Mazur: What about evo-devo? The fellow from *The Economist* says development is not evolution.

Jerry Fodor: No, of course it's not. You've been talking to too many people.

A genotype changes from generation-to-generation for some reason or other. Selection says basically that. But now when the genotype gets expressed in phenotypic properties like having two arms, having one nose, and so forth and so on—we know that that expression relation is not one-to-one. So, something goes on between the genotype of the organism and the phenotype it produces, and whatever that story is, it's complicated. But it doesn't make any difference to the story about natural selection. Natural selection is looked at this way—it's about what genotypic changes do to phenotypes. Whatever the intervening mechanisms are, developmental or whatever. If you're interested in natural selection, you should throw all that stuff away. Not because it's wrong, it's not relevant. . . .

Given that the genotype is changing, and the phenotype is changing with it, how are the properties of phenotypes that are conducive to fitness as Darwin would put it—how does the selection of those properties work? Whatever the developmental sequence is like. Darwin thinks he knows. He thinks it's very like your coming along and saying I'm going to throw out all the goldfish and only let the short ones breed. Except there isn't anybody there literally doing the selecting. So, you need some mechanism for that. And the question is whether Darwin's got one. And I think he doesn't. I think he thinks he does. But I think he doesn't.

But at first cut, anyway, questions about how development works, questions about how you get from a genome to a phenotype are just irrelevant. Do you see that?

Suzan Mazur: I see the point you're making.

Jerry Fodor: Look suppose I'm shooting dice and the dice come up at random. And there's somebody who doesn't like odd numbers. Mr. Smith doesn't like odd numbers. So every time an odd number comes up he throws out the die. Sooner or later only even numbers are going to come up. Now there are two questions you could ask. One is what determines which number comes up when you roll the dice. That's one question. The other question, quite independent is, what is it that accounts for the shift in the relative sequencing of odd and even numbers over time? For the first question you have to have the mechanics of rolling dice, that's analogous to the mechanics of development. The second question is, it's clear in the case of dice Mr. Smith is standing there throwing out the bad ones. Now take that guy away. It's still comes out that the dice get more and more even numbers. So, we need a mechanism that's choosing even numbers in opposition to odd numbers. It can't be that guy. It can't be any other guy either. We need a mechanism that does that. And we need that, whatever the story is about how shaking the dice leads to the numbers.

Development has nothing to do with the question of selection. Maybe I can make it graphic. Here's the organization of the organism. Its genetic structure, its development. From a given organism, depending on what the internal organization of the organism is and what variables, you can get any number of phenotypes. If you boil the thing, you get one phenotype, if you freeze it, you get another phenotype, if you raise it on sodium, you get another phenotype. That's all about the question, how does an individual phenotype get expressed via the developmental process. That's not the question that evolutionary theory asks or purports to ask. Evolutionary theory is about the question of how the genomic structure varies and the consequent phenotype varies from generation-to-generation. It wouldn't matter to this if there were no developmental issues, if the one-to-one story were true. . . .

You could say that there are constraints on the number of genotypes that can be produced at a given time. If that's true, it's independent of selection anyway except that there are fewer possible genotypes for selection to choose among. . . .

Suzan Mazur: How long do you think it will take science to scrap the idea of natural selection?

Jerry Fodor: I have no idea. Who cares? The question is who's right. If I'm right, it should, and if I'm not right, it shouldn't. We'll see. But what's important at this stage is to get clear what the question is we're trying to answer. The question we're trying to answer is what is it that makes a statistical population of genotypes change over time. **The answer is, Darwin doesn't know the answer: Natural selection.**

Suzan Mazur: As you said earlier, some of the confusion has to do with a lack of communication among the various fields of science.

Jerry Fodor: Most people in my profession don't believe it either, which is essentially philosophy, don't believe my story either. That's okay. We'll see. I don't really care who believes what. Over time, as I said, in the long run we're all dead. It doesn't matter who believes what. The question is, who's got the story right. **I think the central story of the theory of evolution is wrong in a way that can't be repaired**, saving the properties of the evolutionary theory. So, if that's right, things have to change. Who's going to change it. Not me. I'm not even a biologist. But don't worry about sociology. Don't worry about who believes what. In the long run, as I say, everybody's dead so it doesn't matter who believes what.

Suzan Mazur: What about the way evolution is being presented to the public in the news?

Jerry Fodor: Why should it be discussed in the magazines? Nobody's going to understand it anyway. All that will change if it's discussed in magazines is cocktail party conversations. Who cares what's said at cocktail parties. I'm very dubious that it matters what people believe. It matters what scientists believe in the sense that it matters to what's true.

This is, as it were, a conceptual argument. It's an argument that says, certain concepts that are central to the theory of evolution can't, in fact, be coherently explicated.

Suzan Mazur: But not all scientists are tenured, so they may not want to accept the argument that the standard theory is wrong.

Jerry Fodor: Look, suppose you're an official in the National Science Foundation, and a guy comes to you and says: Listen I have this interesting idea, give me $100,000 and I'll work on it. And then 50 of the most respected people in the field come up to you and say: Look, the guy's crazy, that can't be true. Who are you going to believe? You're going to end up supporting a very conservative, middle brow scientific institution. It's hopeless.

Suzan Mazur: But the public does want to know what's going on. I think it's important to get it out to the public.

Jerry Fodor: People think they want to know. Actually, if you ask—how much would you pay to know, the answer is not much. . . . Do you care how your refrigerator works? No, as long as there's a repairman around when it breaks down. Nobody really cares.

Suzan Mazur: What's the point in sticking with an evolutionary theory that's not relevant anymore? Your articles appear in the *London Review of Books*. That's a high brow publication but the public can buy it on the newsstands.

Jerry Fodor: Sometimes I don't live up to my own principles. You're quite right. I thought it would be interesting to get this out to a broader audience than the journals. But it's not really important.

Suzan Mazur: It is.

Jerry Fodor: Why?

Suzan Mazur: Public funds are being wasted for one thing.

Jerry Fodor: NASA is spending billions of dollars. People like the idea of people going up into space.

Suzan Mazur: It should be reported in the press.

Jerry Fodor: You can't put this in the press because it's an attack on the theory of natural selection and 99.99% of the population have no idea what the theory of natural selection is. . . .

Chapter 2

Vincent Fleury on Origin of Form
(And PZ Myers)

6/26/2009

Vincent Fleury is a French scientist investigating origin of form with experiments involving cellular flow. He was recently featured in a PZ Myers *Pharyngula* blog—where his work first caught my eye.

Born in 1963, Vincent Fleury lived for eight years in Uruguay before returning to France with his family. He completed a PhD at the Ecole Polytechnique in pattern formation in electrochemical growth and then began to focus on biological systems, studying the development of blood vessels and the lungs. Fleury says he's long advocated the role of physical forces in development, apparent in blood vessels and in the lungs.

Fleury has proposed a biomechanical model of tetrapod formation by extending the concepts of cellular flow to the formation of the embryo as a whole. He says that "once the formation of the body of a tetrapod is boiled down to a simple physical field, different animals appear as different instances of a similar process, thus explaining obvious tendencies in evolution, and maybe the very origin of these animals."

Vincent Fleury is the author of four popular science books: *Arbres de pierres, Des pieds et des mains, De l'oeuf a l'eternite, La chose humaine*, and under a pseudonym, six detective novels (four for adults and two for children).

My recent phone conversation with Vincent Fleury follows:

Suzan Mazur: Would you say there's more than a language barrier when it comes to French and American thinking about evolution?

Vincent Fleury: That is a complex question. Yes. There is more than a language barrier regarding evolutionary science. American and British, i.e., Anglo-Saxon thinking is in terms of efficiency. The way Americans work, everything should work, everything is extremely pragmatic. Everybody on the team has a little bit of a job to do.

The consequence of that thinking is that Darwinism fits in very well. The animal works. It does the job it has to do. And it survives.

In general terms, French people are more Cartesian. We have a more philosophical way of thinking. We try to find deep concepts.

Suzan Mazur: What would you say the significance is of recent discussions at the Sorbonne on evolutionary mechanisms and of the Jean-Baptiste Lamarck conference in Israel?

Vincent Fleury: I was invited to such a conference at Versailles about two years ago.

Maybe there's some kind of nervous breakdown among scientists, especially with a significant number of biologists who are exhausted and truly don't understand what they are doing. Some of them wonder whether it's science at all. They keep piling up facts about genes and chemicals but don't have a satisfactory scheme.

Suzan Mazur: PZ Myers, the Howard Stern of science bloggers, recently reviewed your paper "Clarifying tetrapod embryogenesis, a physicist's point of view," which was published in *The European Physical Journal: Applied Physics*. It appears Myers is increasingly doing a *pas de deux* with the physical approach to evolutionary science, trying to reposition himself now that a paradigm shift is afoot. In essence, so he can maybe say, well I knew it all the time.

Last week he praised D'Arcy Thompson and Brian Goodwin, saying he found Goodwin's work "thought-provoking." What is your response to Myers tactics?

Vincent Fleury: I have mixed feelings. On the one hand he's trying to promote good science and bring back people who are lost in creationism. The problem is…

Suzan Mazur: Do you agree he's trying to reposition himself?

Vincent Fleury: Well that's fine. But I have a problem with this fellow. He uses a very rhetorical technique. He starts off with some smooth positive statement and then progressively trashes the paper. I'm not so sure it's sincere.

Suzan Mazur: It's his way of saying I love you. He knows he can't maintain his present ground, so he's increasingly introducing the newer evolutionary science, however he can. He projects himself as a bully so he won't look like a sissy when he has no choice but to go with the flow.

Vincent Fleury: There are several issues. First of all, it's the style of the man. When you read his blog, you read things like I'm a professor and if I had a student, I would have asked him to rewrite the paper in this and that way. *Who is this man?*

Suzan Mazur: Think *Animal House* and pimply adolescence. His audience, incidentally, includes some prominent evolutionary scientists—one of whom commented on your paper in the *Pharyngula* blog.

Vincent Fleury: Myers' blog is constructed in a certain way. He writes reviews that are not that bad but then he opens it up to his hounds, half of whom are mad. Crazed! They finish the job.

Freedom of speech is one thing, but it is extremely insane to open the microphone to crazy people.

Suzan Mazur: Why was your paper sent to *Pharyngula*?

Vincent Fleury: Someone else sent the paper in to harass me. Myers says implicitly that he despises all these self-organization ideas, but if you look at his blog, his web site is an example of self-organization.

Suzan Mazur: How have your colleagues at CNRS (French National Center for Scientific Research) responded to his attack?

Vincent Fleury: Who cares? The few who know of him in France understand it's rubbish.

Suzan Mazur: You've commented that PZ Myers doesn't know how the human body is established.

Vincent Fleury: Well that's true. He doesn't.

It's been known for almost 100 years that the initial spherical oocyte becomes a spherical blastula. When it starts to resemble an animal, that happens by the third day in a chicken, it's by a vortex motion. It's a pattern of eddies. Little swirling movements.

You have vortices, like wind turning around, that transform the spherical thing into an elongated thing with two bumps in the hip region and two bumps in the shoulder region. So these are vortices.

Suzan Mazur: You've said it is a hyperbolic flow that transforms a round blastula into an embryo.

Vincent Fleury: How do animals acquire their form? You have a reference for it, the sphere. Oocytes are more or less spherical.

A couple of days after, you have an animal which is roughly recognizable. In the third day of the development of a chicken you already recognize the typical shape. It's very rapid. It lasts about 15 hours. That specific movement transforms a sphere into something resembling an animal.

What is that? It's a vortex flow. It's composed of four vortices revolving around a stagnation point. And that's a hyperbolic flow.

Suzan Mazur: What about the criticism that this may be too simple an approach.

Vincent Fleury: It's not too simple. The problem is that for a century or so these vortices have escaped the attention of biologists. It's not something that you can address with the biology techniques and concepts. However, today we can watch this with time-lapse microscopy, etc. People have recorded these vortices. There are actual movies of this.

I first made the theory about this. It had never been done before. It contains a lot of physics.

Suzan Mazur: So the hyperbolic flow can in essence be the origin of all form.

Vincent Fleury: Yes it's the archetype. In Darwin's book, chapter 13, there is a description of archetypes. He states there are four archetypes of animals. One of the archetypes is the tetrapods. He says that for whatever purpose they have limbs, etc. and that I don't know what the origin of the first archetype is, but afterwards all the animals may be obtained simply from the same archetype by stretching or flattening. That's explicitly stated in Darwin's book.

Suzan Mazur: And does the torus concept have any bearing on this?

Vincent Fleury: Maybe there is some torus inside the oocyte or in the first cell before the first cleavage that could be at the root of the phenomenon I don't know. What I do know is that if you take the first two cleavages when it's basically crossed inside the first four blastomeres and you extrapolate the blastula and then you start the flow, it starts to move. With that initial big cross inside, you make a tetrapod. It's completely automatic. It's the attractor of the flow. It takes just a few hours.

Next, the only thing you can do is stretch the animal in six directions. The head, the tail and the limbs. All animals are obtained from the basic form by stretching the limbs, the neck or the tail.

Suzan Mazur: You talk about the deformation rate field. Can you explain what that is?

Vincent Fleury: When you start with a certain form, say spherical —10 hours later you have a little fish. You have to deform the thing during a certain time. And this is what is called in physics a deformation rate, or strain rate. The deformation rate for an inflated balloon, for instance, is the speed of inflation.

Suzan Mazur: And you said you had the equation to deform an embryo to make a mouse and various other animals. To go from a lizard to a snake, from ape to human. Would you address that?

Vincent Fleury: When you deal with a physics problem, you try to have a simple mechanism that explains it all, so to speak, but that you can refine to any specifics. So when you look at the blastula you realize that it's a hyperbolic flow. The hyperbolic flow has an extraordinary property. A major property. There is a point where the speed is zero in all directions. And this point represents the navel, the belly button.

So the very origin of our belly button is the fact that in the blastula, there is a zero point where the speed is zero in all directions. This is a fact. I'm not speaking of something hypothetical. You can observe it.

In mathematics when you have a point where the quantity that you are studying equals zero, then you can do a mathematical expansion of the problem around zero. And when you do that, you can show that with the hyperbolic flow—the first step is the hyperbolic flow—there is a contraction in the lateral direction and expansion in the head-tail direction. So the first tendency mathematically speaking of this flow is to transform a sphere into an elongated elipsoid. This is typically the transition of all animals which are more or less squarish.

In the direction of evolution you find more elongated animals. But it doesn't mean there is a gene of elongation. There is no gene of elongation. It means that within the dynamics of the system, it is wired. Whatever gene you change, you make an animal which is more squarish or more elongated. It's very simple. It's one dimension. One degree of freedom around the belly button. This is why animals tend to be squarish around the belly button as is da Vinci's "Vitruvian Man," which bears the caption: "The true center of the human being is the navel."

Or if you start to make more elongated animals, they will look like anguids or like snakes. In evolution, snakes result from a prolonged hyperbolic flow. It's automatic. That's the first order.

Now the second order is the twist of the tissue in each quadrant of the hyperbolic flow, which generates the position of the limbs. And depending on whether this twist is more or less twisted, you have an animal with a pelvis that is more or less warped and shoulders that are more or less warped. So you get an animal that is more like a kangaroo or more like a mouse.

Suzan Mazur: Your PhD is in physics pattern formation and crystal growth, is that correct?

Vincent Fleury: Electrochemical deposition and pattern formation.

Suzan Mazur: Would you explain how crystals come into the evolution picture? How do they come into the biology?

Vincent Fleury: It's very well understood how a crystal grows. A lot of very beautiful mathematics have been developed over 250 years. A French man, Hauy, is the one who first invented crystallography and discovered that atoms were regularly ordered in crystals. At that time they were not sure that atoms existed, but Hauy understood that crystals were made of ordered elements.

The beautiful thing about crystals is that you see in the global shapes the property of the microscopic texture. You can recognize in the global shape the property of microscopic organization. That suggests two things. **Forms appear by physics of moving boundaries and the fact that a small feature has an influence on the larger scale. And these two facts, I think, are really at the root of the development of the physics of evolution and of animal development right now.** [emphasis added]

Suzan Mazur: Antonio Lima-de-Faria, the University of Lund cytogeneticist, has been talking about things like this for many years as well. He says the biological and crystal levels are now found to have several common atomic parameters.

Vincent Fleury: In one of my papers regarding an equation for crystal growth I found a way of applying it to the growth of fruit and vegetables. You can show that lemons, for instance, or other fruit are some sort of crystals. They are not crystals of atoms, they are crystals of fibers.

Quartz, diamond, etc., their microscopic texture is made of organized atoms. The same physics with a slightly different input (fibers instead of atoms) gives you different shapes, and this is why biological shapes are not quite like crystal shapes but they share the same organizing principles. [emphasis added]

Suzan Mazur: Here's what Lima-de-Faria says: "The gene is only the bearer and the carrier, of the atomic order that already determined mineral symmetries. Moreover, due to the occurrence of molecular mimicry an organism may not even need to have the same genes to produce the same structural pattern."

Vincent Fleury: Absolutely. That's a central point in my paper. **In fact, the number of shapes which are produced by the physical laws are very limited.** [emphasis added] And in fact a huge quantity of genes will apply or project themselves on the same shapes.

If you look at dwarfism, there exists a hundred kinds of dwarfism associated with completely different genetic anomalies. But the consequence is the same thing. A condition, a morphology you call dwarfism. But it has a completely different origin. Because in fact you can change lots of genes, the consequence is basically the same. So in fact, it reduces considerably the number of outputs.

So, for example, you can make an elongated animal from a squarish one in a completely different way. You have fish that are somewhat squarish and fish that are very elongated. It's the same mechanism for lizards becoming snakes. There is not a gene for an elongated animal.

Suzan Mazur: Scientists in America tend to be conservative about these subjects.

Vincent Fleury: In America you have big scientific teams with a lot of money, so the principal investigator has a heavy responsibility. In France and other countries in Europe we have less money and more individuals working in very small groups

35

one or two people. So they do things which are newer or more original. They don't have the need to prove to their staff that what they are doing is safe.

Suzan Mazur: Here, to get funding from the government, scientists have to agree to ensure national security and the economic well-being of the country. You're a government funded scientist, you don't have similar constraints?

Vincent Fleury: A few years ago we had more freedom. Now they're looking more to the American model of efficiency. We fill out a file in which we more or less explain what will be the results of our experiments, ahead of doing them.

Suzan Mazur: The cost-effective approach.

Vincent Fleury: One last thing about PZ Myers. He made the following comment on his blog regarding my right of reply, instead of just publishing it: "I'm always happy to help a fellow hang himself."

Even if he's trying to make a joke, we all know people who've committed suicide, and I would never entrust my children to a babysitter who states he is always happy to help someone hang himself.

Chapter 3

Saga of the Extended Evolutionary Synthesis

"However, while the Altenberg 16 organizers noted that their July symposium 'could turn into a major stepping stone for the entire field of evolutionary biology,' this book is not an endorsement of any attempt to 'graft' novel ideas onto the Modern Synthesis—only of the decision to begin sorting out the mess. The real task is one of making a coherent theory of evolution, including pre-biotic evolution, where none previously existed. That will require casting a wide net for visionaries who have political courage."—**Suzan Mazur**, *The Altenberg 16, An Exposé of the Evolution Industry*

1/30/2018

A decade ago I published a ground-breaking story about an Extended Evolutionary Synthesis (EES), four months in advance of the first scientific symposium on that subject in Altenberg, Austria. The meeting in July 2008 at Konrad Lorenz Institute held great promise and featured then-lively themes like epigenetics, punctuated evolution, niche construction and theory of form. However, personal pettiness and political timidity on the part of event organizers took their toll on the scientific reach of the conference proceedings, despite a book being published by MIT two years later about the event.

In October 2015, there was an attempt by scientists to resuscitate EES in a Royal Society article with no attention to the biggest part of the biosphere—viruses and microbes. The following April they succeeded in securing $8 million in funding from the Templeton Foundation, a deep-pockets, non-transparent organization that has a soft spot for supporting projects that pursue a science & religion theme—which, unfortunately, taints scientific results. Then in November 2016 there was a public Royal Society evolution summit with almost half the presenters related to the EES project, where we heard about natural selection *ad nauseam* until Sir Patrick Bateson, an organizer of the event, cautioned from the stage that the term was a metaphor only and its use should be kept to a minimum.

A week or so ago an essay defending the EES project but offering no new science was featured in an online magazine called *Aeon*, written by Templeton-funded EES principal investigator Kevin Laland—an animal behavioralist at St Andrews University in Scotland.

Aeon, whose publisher has a Master's degree in the psychology of religion, accepts funding from Templeton World Charity Foundation, among other charities, so it is not surprising to see the Laland story appearing there.

In the unconvincing *Aeon* article, "Evolution unleashed," Laland asks the question: "If the extended evolutionary synthesis is not a call for a revolution in evolution, then what is it, and why do we need it?

Good point. To answer Laland's question—We don't need it. We don't need a graft onto Darwinism and neo-Darwinism.

What we do need is a coherent evolutionary theory, untainted by mystical influences and non-transparent funding. An evolutionary theory that reflects the world of microbes and viruses

38

that all animals, plants and fungi live in and that includes pre-biotic evolution as well.

Laland says further in his recent piece that he knows of no biologist who wants to "throw out natural selection." But Laland was a presenter at the Royal Society evolution conference where Pat Bateson said onstage that natural selection was merely a metaphor, cautioning about its use. And is it really possible that Laland has never heard of Eugene Koonin and Richard Lewontin, who had this to say about natural selection?:

> *"Perhaps making all these parallels between natural selection and artificial selection, the way Darwin does in his book, could be somewhat dangerous because in artificial selection there is someone who is selecting, even if unconsciously. In that respect, the evolutionary process is very different in nature where nothing is there to actually select. . . . No one in the mainstream scientific community now takes selection literally."*—**Eugene Koonin** in conversation with me in 2017

> *"The circulation of the proof copy of* What Darwin Got Wrong, *the product of a noted philosopher and a prominent student of linguistics and cognitive science, has resulted in a volume of critical comment from biologists and philosophers that has not been seen since 1859. . . . Not to be misunderstood, perhaps biologists should stop referring to "natural selection," and instead talk about differential rates of survival and reproduction."*—**Richard Lewontin**, *New York Review of Books*, 2010

Lewontin was, of course, referring to Jerry Fodor's compelling philosophical argument:

> *"Sometimes when I'm in a mildly bitter mood I think, look the trouble with Darwin is he believes in Intelligent Design. He never really got it clear to himself that there*

really isn't a designer. So it's questionable whether you can take artificial selection as a model for natural selection the way he did. When you try to do that you can't work it out."—**Jerry Fodor** talking to me in 2008

Finally, Laland makes the point that "the vast majority of researchers working towards an extended evolutionary synthesis are simply ordinary, hardworking evolutionary biologists."

"Simply ordinary"? Science is all about bold discovery and hopefully evolutionary biologists are in it for that reason. If not, science is not being served, neither is the public that funds science.

I recently traveled to St Andrews, home of St Andrews University (founded in 1413). It's a trek getting there from New York as well as a trip back in time. Named for Scotland's patron saint who was crucified on an X-shaped cross in Greece in 60 AD, St Andrews is a seaside town (population 14,000) set against a countryside of misty fields, potato farms, and roads designed by sheep. But EES being rehashed from St Andrews is not a reflection of the quaintness and remoteness of the region, although EES is clearly mired in the bog.

Chapter 4

Does the "Extended Synthesis" Replace or Not Replace Neo-Darwinism?—What Has Templeton Funded?

**GERD MÜLLER—Extended Synthesis Founding Father:
ES REPLACES NEO-DARWINISM**

**KEVIN LALAND—Extended Synthesis Project Leader:
ES DOES NOT REPLACE NEO-DARWINISM**

The Big Questions are these: What exactly is the extended evolutionary synthesis ("ES") that the John Templeton Foundation has recently funded with $8M (and $3M more going to ES from institutional contributions)? [https://evolution-institute.org/article/empowering-the-extended-evolutionary-synthesis/]

What good is an extended synthesis without the largest part of the biosphere—viruses—factored in?

Why fund now, when ES has been kicking around ever since it was born at Altenberg! eight years ago?

Paul Wason, Science and Religion chief at Templeton simply won't say, declining my request for an interview and emailing that he "would prefer not to be involved in the debates."

Of the above Big Questions that Wason won't answer, the really sticky one is: What exactly is the extended synthesis?

Kevin Laland, an animal behavioralist serving as ES Project Leader for Templeton, and one of the organizers of the November Royal Society meeting on evolution, has described ES like this:

> *"The extended evolutionary synthesis does not replace traditional thinking [he means neo-Darwinism], but rather can be deployed alongside it to stimulate research within evolutionary biology. The new perspective retains the fundaments of evolutionary theory—genes and natural selection remain central, for instance—but there are differences in how causation in biology is understood."*

Hmmm. . . "The extended evolutionary synthesis DOES NOT REPLACE [emphasis added] traditional thinking [neo-Darwinism], but rather can be deployed alongside it to stimulate research".

I recently asked Gerd Müller, one of the founding fathers of the extended synthesis, to clarify the meaning of the term. A little background: Müller barred me from attending the Altenberg!

42

meeting for getting out in front of the story with a series of reports and an ebook prior to the event and for branding conference participants as "the Altenberg 16" in print.

Contrary to Kevin Laland—Gerd Müller sees ES as a new synthesis that will replace the modern synthesis (neo-Darwinism). In an email exchange with Müller a few weeks ago I reminded him of statements made to me for an *Archaeology* magazine story [http://archive.archaeology.org/online/interviews/newman.html] in 2008 by Stuart Newman, another Altenberg 16 scientist, characterizing ES as a graft onto or a major departure from the modern synthesis depending on who was describing it. Müller, an Austrian whose first language is German, informed me of this:

> *"The term "Extended Synthesis" was never meant to refer to an "extension of" the Modern Synthesis but to a new and different kind of synthesis that includes many more components—hence "extended." The inclusion of the new concepts completely alters the structure and "logic" of the evolutionary model, and hence (as a theory) can only replace the Modern Synthesis, not merely improve it. This is not a change in opinion. Denis (Noble) originally also thought that our term "extension" referred to an "add on," but now we are in agreement that this is not the case."*

[Note: Denis Noble advises he's addressed the matter in his latest book**]**.

Hmmm. . . "hence (as a theory) [ES] CAN ONLY REPLACE [emphasis added] the Modern Synthesis [neo-Darwinism], not merely improve it".

Müller then noted, "Stuart [Newman] knows about this."

Several hours later, Müller followed up:

> *"I wrote to let you know what the scientific meaning of "Extended Synthesis" is. Many terms in science have a different meaning from the public usage, because they depend on particular definitions of the phenomena to which they apply."*

He then concluded:

> *"there is no dilemma. I quick check with your Word thesaurus will show you that synonyms of "extended" include "comprehensive", "extensive", "broad" etc. This is the meaning in our case. As in "Extended Family", referring to the wider family and not to an extension of the family."*

Gerd Müller and Kevin Laland are both part of the Templeton-funded ES project. But while Müller is adamant that ES replaces neo-Darwinism, Laland is firm that ES does not replace neo-Darwinism.

What then has Templeton just funded?

Chapter 5

Kurland & Harish Rethink Deep Evolution

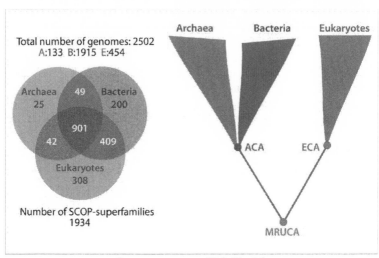

Image, courtesy Ajith Harish

2/26/2017

I recently had a three-way phone conversation with Swedish deep evolution investigators Charles Kurland and Ajith Harish about their phylogenomic Tree of Life (ToL) based on protein structure, which shows that we are descended from a "complex" ancestor—MRUCA (most recent universal common ancestor)—not a simple bacteria. Kurland and Harish think a ToL paradigm shift may be in order. What's more, Kurland and Harish figure that MRUCA was not the first ancestor, but represents complex survivors of a now-extinct biosphere.

The findings of Kurland and Harish challenge not only mainstream ToL perspectives, but also those of endosymbiosis hypothesis fans, as well as the "HGT industry"—as Kurland describes the inflated role he sees assigned to lateral gene transfer in evolution.

Kurland and Harish have published several scientific papers showing MRUCA shares three-quarters of its proteome with eukaryotes, bacteria and archaea (**see Venn diagram above**). They have another paper forthcoming, which they say reconfirms their results. Part of the investigation in recent years has been supported by the Nobel Committee for Chemistry of the Royal Swedish Academy of Sciences.

The Kurland-Harish research is computational but starts with experiments, i.e., x-ray crystallography of proteins, which are then translated to statistical models used to assign genome sequences to the experimentally determined structures.

Says Harish:

> *"Our data contradicts the mainstream scenario(s) for origins of life as we know it, based on gene trees. Such hypotheses are based on analyses that are about two decades old and were artifact prone."*

Charles Kurland and Ajith Harish first developed a professional rapport at the University of Illinois, Urbana-Champaign more than a dozen years ago and were initially both very influenced by the work there of Carl Woese, the discoverer of archaea. Harish says he took a class at UIUC taught by Woese: "which got me into evolution." But neither of them agrees now with the Woese Tree.

Kurland, a native New Yorker, loves Scandinavia and settled in Sweden decades ago, where he is now Professor Emeritus of Molecular Biology at both Lund University and Uppsala University and a member of the Royal Swedish Academy of Sciences, Stockholm. He is also a member of the Royal Science Society, Uppsala; the Royal Academy of Sciences, Copenhagen; the Estonian Academy of Science, Tallin; the Royal Physiographical Society, Lund; and the European Molecular Biology Organization.

Kurland's PhD is in biochemistry from Harvard, where he was part of James Watson's team in the early 1960s. He is known for his study of the *E. coli* ribosome. But also for his talent as a lively and highly effective communicator of science.

Ajith Harish, is a native of Bangalore, India, where he received his BS (St. Joseph's College—microbiology, chemistry and botany) and MS (Bangalore University—biotechnology). Harish says his roots are in experimental science, studying plant molecular biology and physiology, "in vitro" and "in vivo," but that his analyses are now "in silico," computational.

After receiving his PhD (2010) from UIUC in biology (bioinformatics and molecular evolution), Harish headed north, to Sweden, for postdoc research at Lund University and to continue his collaboration with Charles Kurland. Harish has also been a researcher at Uppsala University in recent years, working in the lab of molecular biologist Måns Ehrenberg. He is currently a Guest Researcher at Uppsala.

Our interview follows.

Suzan Mazur: Charles, are you a native New Yorker? I detect some accent.

Charles Kurland: Yes, I was born in the Bronx.

Suzan Mazur: Are you a graduate of Bronx High School of Science?

Charles Kurland: No, I went to Great Neck High School because by that time my parents had moved to Long Island.

Suzan Mazur: You're a member of the Royal Swedish Academy of Sciences now, no longer a Foreign Member—does that mean you are a citizen of Sweden?

Photo, courtesy Charles Kurland

Charles Kurland: I'm a dual citizen of Sweden and the United States.

Suzan Mazur: Ajith, I know you are a native of Bangalore and that you received your BS and MS from schools in Bangalore, but for many years you've been working in Sweden, sometimes in Måns Ehrenberg's lab at Uppsala. Do you also have dual citizenship?

Photo, courtesy Ajith Harish

Ajith Harish: I'm a citizen of India and a permanent resident of Sweden with something like a US green card.

Suzan Mazur: Charles, would you establish yours and Ajith's central position regarding the Tree of Life?

Charles Kurland: The basic idea is—and I think Ajith and I are rather convinced of this now—something like the Tree of Life that Ernst Mayr was talking about in his argument with Carl Woese. In 1998, there were two perspective papers published in *PNAS*. One was an attack by Mayr on what he considered a very "unbiological" Tree of Life, which was the Woese Tree of Life, and Woese's counterattack.

As it turns out, all this was for technical reasons that were wrong. That was very well established by French investigators like Forterre and Philippe, who did a great Yeoman's service in cleaning up the effects of biased mutation rates on gene trees.

Both Mayr and Woese were kind of talking from different points of view. Carl was defending—and he always was a champion—

genotypic views of evolution, sequence-based. Sequence for him was the whole business.

Mayr all he wanted, being really a biologist —you can say more a naturalist than an evolutionary biologist. Maybe that's unfair, I don't know. But Mayr was very much a biologist and very much into using phenotypes of organisms for his understanding of phylogeny.

Those, unfortunately, were two very opposed points of view.

Suzan Mazur: When you say the French work on TOL, are you referring to early or more recent?

Charles Kurland: The French started on this in the 1980s. Carl just ignored them. Everybody just ignored them.

There is a tendency—and this is nothing special to the United States—but the scientific community in the United States is a community and it tends to insulate itself from other scientific communities.

Woese did tremendous work establishing the genotypic or sequence-based way of doing phylogeny. Tremendously important. He was certainly a major pioneer in this. The problem was that he did not himself realize that he was skating on thin ice because there was an artifact (a bias) buried in his work that completely ruined his phylogenies.

That artifact was the one that was very well worked out by Forterre and his people and by Philippe in the 1980s and 1990s and then into the first few years of this century. They and their collaborators—names like Delsuc and Brinkmann and so on, really did a bang-up job showing that gene trees are very susceptible to biased mutation rates.

In a gene tree you're counting mutants and then you're trying to plot some kind of rate of mutant accumulation as a rate of

50

evolution. But if that rate is uneven, then you're in lots of trouble. And, unfortunately, with the genes used in the Woese model it was vastly uneven.

The reason why people didn't appreciate it early in the 70s or 80s was that everybody was very taken up by the view of neutrality, especially in the United States, where Jukes and King and certainly Kimura were the leading figures and had an enormous influence on population genetics.

Suzan Mazur: Neutrality is something Eugene Koonin has been talking about recently.

Charles Kurland: Unfortunately, a lot of people waited too long to look at it.

We are looking at phylogeny through the eyes of protein-domains, superfamilies, which have very well conserved structures that are selected structures. Therefore, the sequences that encode them are selected. This has been illustrated by studies of coding sequence variation by Dan Hartl's group; they've illustrated that proteins that are under selection for structure and functions can change their sequences in a process they call "sequence meandering." This is sequence drift, but to avoid confusion with neutral drift it is called meandering. In nature the superfamilies, which have a fixed structure, are represented by multiple coding sequences in the genome, and these sequences specify the same structures. They are intensely selected structures.

Suzan Mazur: Ajith, do you know if the University of Illinois, Urbana-Champaign—where you received your PhD in molecular evolution and bioinformatics and took a class with Carl Woese — is UIUC adhering to the Woese model?

Ajith Harish: I don't know if anybody at UIUC has specifically moved from the Woese model. Probably not, but I'm not in touch with people there.

Suzan Mazur: Charles, can we go back to discussing the essence of yours and Ajith's idea about the Tree of Life?

Charles Kurland: What Ajith and I believe, and I can assure you that neither one of us started out with this perspective, it's something we learned from the data, which I'm now very proud of. That is because both of us had to change our ideas about things. I was friendly off and on with Carl Woese. He was a difficult fellow, but there were times that we were very close. And I was very much under his influence. And Ajith was very much under his influence by being a graduate student at UIUC.

Suzan Mazur: I did a feature interview with Carl Woese shortly before he died.

Charles Kurland: He was tough, but he could be a lot of fun. There were a lot of very good people at UIUC. Both Ajith and I were very much under the influence of Carl. Our view emerged from the data after a lot of very painful experiments trying to make a sensible phylogeny. We found that there were three superkingdoms, but they were not arranged as Carl had said. They were arranged the way Ernst Mayr said they were arranged.

Ernst Mayr was very impressed with the cellular phenotype of eukaryotes as opposed to the cellular phenotypes of archaea and bacteria, which for him were just dots, very undeveloped images. The nucleus, the endoplasmic reticulum, the membranous systems—all of that for Ernst Mayr was a coherent phenotype for eukaryotes. It was clearly different from archaea and bacteria. And what struck Mayr was that archaea and bacteria are so similar to each other and different from eukaryotes. So Woese's phylogeny with archaea and eukaryotes as sister clades made no sense to Mayr. That was the basis of his phenotypic argument. Of course, he made it in a much more sophisticated way.

What Ajith and I discovered was that yes, indeed, the phylogeny that we can see from a very, very thorough examination of genomic data, rather than a gene tree, is a common ancestor out of which two empires grow. One of them contains four or six major eukaryotic groups and the other one contains two major—what they used to call "prokaryotes." We prefer to call them "akaryotes" following Forterre because this notion of "pro"— that they came first—is definitely contradicted by the phylogeny we see. They seem to be "parallel" rather than "pro." So we call them akaryotes, non-nuclear as opposed to the nucleated eukaryotes.

We've gone through test after test and this phylogeny holds.

Suzan Mazur: You discovered that of these three groups, there's a commonality.

Charles Kurland: There's a commonality between archaea, bacteria and eukaryotes. The universal common ancestor is the root of eukaryote and akaryote lineages and it contains more than a thousand superfamilies!

The other really remarkable thing, the thing that really stunned us is that there were people before us who had seen this also and at the time were totally ignored. The people I have in mind are Christos Ouzounis and his collaborators from Cambridge. They recognized that the universal common ancestor was a very complex ancestor. It is apparently a very big genome. But, now I have to qualify that. We cannot say more than that the universal common ancestor is a population. We don't know how it is structured. We have no idea how many species/populations are in that ancestor.

Suzan Mazur: Ajith, can you explain a bit about your methods at arriving at the results and tell me how much commonality you found to the three groups?

Ajith Harish: We were looking at genomes and also we were looking at the Superfamilies, which are based on the three-dimensional structure. We have four nucleotides, 20 amino acids, 2,000 Superfamilies. These are the building blocks of both genes and genomes.

Suzan Mazur: What I've read in your papers is this. You're saying eukaryotes and bacteria and archaea all descended from a most recent universal common ancestor that shared three-quarters of the Superfamilies of all three of these domains. That the Superfamilies are "homologous to those of modern mitochondria, chloroplasts, nuclei, spliceosomes, cytoskeletons and the like" and that this was "evident in the proteome of the most recent universal common ancestor as well as thinly dispersed among the eukaryotes." That this ancestor represents complex survivors from a now extinct biosphere.

Ajith Harish: Correct. This is from phylogenetic reconstruction. When we do a phylogenetic reconstruction, we can trace back three quarters to a common ancestor. This is basically the genetic toolkit of that ancestral population.

Suzan Mazur: But how did you do this, what were your materials and methods? You say you used the Superfamily database. What is that?

Ajith Harish: There is something called the SCOP database, which is a structural classification of proteins. That's where things start. In that hierarchy we have what are called Superfamilies, members of which can be inferred to be homologous. If you have many sequences in that Superfamily, all of them have a common ancestor.

Suzan Mazur: Where do you get the database?

Ajith Harish: SUPERFAMILY database takes these structural quantifications and annotates complete genomes.

Suzan Mazur: Who put together the database?

Ajith Harish: Julian Gough [British bioinformaticist].

Suzan Mazur: This is something that many researchers use?

Ajith Harish: Yes, this is publicly available.

Suzan Mazur: You also identified recurrent protein domains based on the Hidden Markov Models.

Ajith Harish: We have the Protein Data Bank (PDB), which has all the three-dimensional crystal structures. Starting from there you can assemble a sequence profile. You can use that sequence profile to identify all the homologs. This is done by the SUPERFAMILY database.

Suzan Mazur: This is based on x-ray crystallography.

Ajith Harish: **You start with protein sequences for which the structure is known and then you use that information to build. You can find related sequences and build a probabilistic model. That's what the Hidden Markov Model is. It's a probabilistic model that can identify the protein structure in any given sequence that is related.**

Suzan Mazur: **What you're doing, isn't everyone doing that? What makes your approach unique?**

Charles Kurland: **No one is doing it.**

Ajith Harish: **Not many people use Superfamilies and genomes to build phylogenies. Most people use just gene sequences. Mainstream papers are based on 30 or 40 genes that we call the genealogy-defining core of genes. A majority of people construct gene trees based on gene sequences and what we are doing is comparing genomes. We are presenting as much of the genome as possible using a statistical protein structure model—Hidden Markov Model.** [emphasis added]

Charles Kurland: This notion of using the Superfamilies as an operational phylogenetic character. It comes out of a fantastic paper that was published in 1992 by Cyrus Chothia. He's a bioinformaticist who's been working at the MRC (Medical

Research Council) in Cambridge. What he did was recognize that these folds made up a kind of alphabet of all the proteins on the planet. And he realized that there weren't so many of them: Maybe a thousand. It turns out there are between two and three thousand, by present estimates.

What was very special about what Ajith and I did was to take this up very seriously and say, yes, let's use this alphabet to do our phylogeny instead of nucleotides or amino acids. And it worked very, very well. We got the kinks out of it.

Suzan Mazur: Key geologists I've interviewed—particularly, Roger Buick, Bob Hazen and Mark McMenamin recognize the Snowball Earth scenario, i.e., global ice age, that is central to your thinking on deep evolution. There were several Snowball Earths, according to Bob Hazen. Some scientists think these global ice ages were precipitated by bacteria producing oxygen that destroyed the methane layer in the atmosphere. Buick's research shows eukaryotes survived Snowball Earth, apparently. And McMenamin, who's an expert on ediacara, also thinks eukaryotes survived Snowball Earth.

You're saying something more. You're saying eukaryotes and bacteria and archaea all descended from a common ancestor that shared three-quarters of the Superfamilies of all three of these domains. Charles, would you say more about the Snowball Earth scenario and the most recent universal common ancestor as you and Ajith see it?

Charles Kurland: It's not simply Snowball Earth. It's Snowball Earth that recovers in a volcanic period where temperatures go off-scale. It's not clear what the crunch is, whether it's the Snowball ice, per se, or what some people say is a Slushball. It's not necessarily the low temperatures that are killing off the preexisting organisms. It can be the recovery. The volcanism can drive the temperatures up so high that much on this surface cannot survive.

The other thing is this. If you look at the fossil remains, at the micrographs that the paleontologists can produce — it's very interesting. They have by microscopic examination what they very tentatively identify as bacterial groups. But actually identifying bacteria in rocks as fossils is a tough game, and I think that none of those identifications are worth the paper they're printed on.

Suzan Mazur: That's fascinating.

Charles Kurland: All paleontologists have are some kind of little spherical, little microscopic something or others—the identity of which they don't know. But they can find organic matter associated with these, so there is evidence of masses of very small, microscopic something or others and I wouldn't call them bacteria. I wouldn't call them archaea. We don't know what they are.

We have to be very serious about this because a lot of early phylogenetic theory about archaea together with bacteria make eukaryotes, etc., is based on this language that presupposes we know what came first. And we don't know what came first. All we know is that there are these little dots in micrographs. [emphasis added]

The other thing that we know and this is really very interesting, particularly because of the results that Ajith and I got for the ancestor. There's a history and it's a very well documented history of big, round something or others, a thousand times larger than any bacteria. From the cellular point of view these are gigantic. And they have been seen as far back as 2.9 billion years ago, I read, perhaps 3.4 billion years ago.

Ajith Harish: 3.2 billion.

Charles Kurland: Okay, 3.2 billion years ago. And they're called acritarchs. What they look like is something that we actually would identify with our big, fat common ancestor.

Suzan Mazur: How amazing.

Charles Kurland: Really intriguing. There's not much science to go on it, it's more aesthetic identification.

Suzan Mazur: Where have the acritarchs been found?

Charles Kurland: Everywhere. They were found in lots of different places and in lots of different ages and suddenly they disappear just before the Cambrian Explosion. And that's when we expect the most recent universal common ancestor to take off —in the Cambrian Explosion. Because we think that our phylogeny is essentially a description of the Cambrian Explosion.

Ajith Harish: Going back to Snowball Earth, the big issue is that we cannot really date the age of MRUCA (most recent universal common ancestor) because we don't have any particular events to pinpoint it. Ours is a best case scenario. That is the limitation of all phylogenetic analysis. So we don't really understand how other scientists can date the ancestor to 4 billion or 3 billion years.

Suzan Mazur: Your Tree of Life analysis challenges not only the work of Carl Woese and Lynn Margulis but John Maynard Smith, Ford Doolittle and Eugene Koonin, among others. You see endosymbiosis as wrong, and rampant horizontal gene transfer as a reflection of the "HGT Industry." You think HGT was a negligible factor in evolution. Charles, would you address these two points, endosymbiosis and HGT?

Charles Kurland: Sure. They're separate.

Suzan Mazur: I'd like to add one more point. I did an interview recently with Jeff Errington who's investigating wall-less organisms called L-forms. In our conversation I referred to what you and Ajith are doing and your position on HGT and Jeff Errington said this:

58

"I think it's likely HGT was fairly rampant in the primordial L-form-like cells. However, my feeling is that invention of the cell wall (perhaps separately in archaea and bacteria—which have completely distinct cell wall structure) could have brought an abrupt halt to the primordial HGT."

Charles Kurland: Yes, absolutely. I agree with that.

Suzan Mazur: Errington said further:

"Once the wall was in place, new mechanisms of HGT may need to have emerged to enable DNA transfer across the barrier wall."

Charles Kurland: We have to remember there's only a little background of horizontal gene transfer in bacterial populations. The simple reason is that bacteria eat DNA. So sequences are going in all the time. Most of them get chopped up.

Suzan Mazur: Did you say bacteria eat DNA—that's an interesting way of putting it.

Charles Kurland: Yes, of course. You're not going to see a lot of DNA left hanging around uneaten. It's an excellent food. But I agree completely with what Jeff Errington said. We think that the most recent universal common ancestor was the product of a lot of HGT and Carl Woese described the reasons for this.

You see, Ford Doolittle was a postdoc with Carl Woese and he came away with this idea of HGT that Carl in his 1970s papers had described for the progenote—this very primitive thing. Carl was right on the money there.

We identify MRUCA (most recent universal common ancestor) with the progenote. And I think Jeff Errington is right on the money in that quote you just read about HGT.

If you read Ford Doolittle's paper of 1999, that paper, which was a very powerful statement of a hypothesis—but in the middle of the paper we are led to forget that it was just a hypothesis. The most important source of data at the time was that gene trees or the evolution of gene sequences was very, very erratic and variable between different genes.

Ford grabbed on that variability as evidence for HGT, and all it is is evidence for variability. The point being that at that time—or at least in Ford's mind—neutral evolution was a big thing. It was supposed to be based on the assumption of constant rates of mutation. So that variability could not have been—in Ford's mind —due to mutation variability because that was by hypothesis excluded by Kimura and by King and Jukes. So it had to be something else. Ford thought that something else was HGT. It's all a mirage. We think it's variable mutation rates.

Suzan Mazur: You also see endosymbiosis as wrong. Would you touch on that a little?

Charles Kurland: Ajith and I are just writing up a paper devoted to that issue. The thing is once you see the phylogeny of the sort that we have, that Ernst Mayr predicted, where the akaryotes are separated in their descent from the eukaryotes, the obvious possibilities for akaryotes to make eukaryotes are just not there. But that's the essence of the symbiosis hypothesis—the bacteria gets together with an archaea and it makes a eukaryote, the bacteria becomes the mitochondria and the archaea becomes the nucleus cytoplasmic host. That's the theory. It's very, very clearly specified that way.

It's interesting because it was Lynn's [Margulis] attempt to explain why DNA was found in the cytoplasm of eukaryotes, and it turned out to be DNA located in mitochondria. It turned out to be DNA located in chloroplasts. Her idea was that: Ah, the mitochondria, the chloroplast, certain kinds of flagella, were actually originally bacteria. Her idea was that if you look at mitochondria, the DNA that was there was the whole genome of that bacteria.

It turns out that it's nothing like that. And we should have been much more suspicious of the hypothesis as soon as it was discovered that a minor fraction of information for mitochondria is coded in the mitochondria. We should have been very suspicious of that.

Suzan Mazur: She was an amazing presence in science.

Charles Kurland: Yes, she was. When I went for my second postdoc at Berkeley, Lynn was at the Life Sciences laboratory doing her PhD. We got to know one another. We were very friendly. She and her husband at that time, Carl Sagan, who was a tremendous scientist, visited me in Copenhagen when I was a postdoc there. When I went to Berkeley, I kind of hooked up with Lynn. By that time she and Carl Sagan had split up. My wife and I knew her very, very well. She was a force of nature.

Suzan Mazur: I interviewed her at length when she was at Oxford. We had both written for *Omni* and knew some of the same people going way back. She was, indeed, a force.

But it's important that science not become dogma. I read some statements you've made to that effect, that there's too much of that going on. I think it's wonderful that you're speaking out.

Charles Kurland: It's definitely a problem. It gets embedded in the education system. There's no one who takes a biology course that does not believe archaea plus bacteria make eukaryotes. It's a rule now. It's beyond criticism now. Well, let's see if we can change that.

Suzan Mazur: Ajith, you say you were very careful with methods and materials in laying out the ToL. Still things are missing from your analysis, which you and Charles acknowledge in one of your papers. You note linkers that constitute one third to one half of the

61

sequence length of proteins were left out of your computations. Also viruses that move consortially and non-linearly and affect the ToL from bottom to top were left out. So these are two significant missing ingredients. What are your further thoughts, Ajith?

Ajith Harish: Compared to any other ToL, we cover almost 70% of the genome so it is a substantially large amount of data compared to mainstream analysis. Because the technology is not there at the moment, we could not include linkers in our analysis but we plan to do so as the technology improves. Right now we don't have good analytical methods to find homologous features corresponding to linkers.

Suzan Mazur: The same goes for viruses?

Ajith Harish: Yes, because the annotations are very patchy. Also, because viruses are so small, you cannot really compare them with cellular genomes.

Suzan Mazur: So you've gotten as close as you can get for the moment.

Ajith Harish: Yes.

Suzan Mazur: What is some of the resistance you're encountering to your ToL analysis?

Ajith Harish: First, people were not used to this kind of data, the Superfamily data. The second thing is that we used different kinds of models.

Most models of evolution used to infer the ToL assume that the underlying evolutionary process is stationary and reversible. This implies that the frequencies of characters (traits) do not change during the evolutionary time period and that the changes are unpolarized. As a result they produce unrooted (unpolarized) trees. An unrooted tree has no evolutionary direction: that is from ancestors to descendants.

The standard assumptions of stationary and reversible processes are contradicted by empirical data. That is, the frequencies of characters change during evolution: the process is non-stationary. So when we implement non-stationary models, we cannot only find the root of a tree but can estimate what the ancestral frequencies of different characters are, from the same model. In a way, we can say what the root or starting condition was. We can infer the root using non-stationary models, but not stationary models.

The non-stationary model was not very common, mainly because it's a bit more sophisticated computationally, mathematically. People didn't often use these kinds of models before. Now these are available. And in our papers we've shown that non-stationary models are better fitting models for the data we have.

Suzan Mazur: Does the discovery of Lokiarchaeaota affect your model?

Charles Kurland: No. The thing that is wonderful about the Loki is that they are big archaea in terms of proteome size and that is attractive for people who want to have an archaea and bacteria becoming a eukaryote. But there's nothing really substantial by way of phylogeny to support the relationship of that archaea to eukaryotes. In our phylogeny, it's just one of the archaea.

Suzan Mazur: What are your thoughts about the distinction in cell wall composition in terms of the ToL? Archaea usually have a paracrystalline proteinaceous shell, and bacteria have peptidoglycan walls, either one thick one, or one thin one *plus* an outer membrane. Eukaryotes have neither.

Charles Kurland: That's right. They're all somewhat different.

Suzan Mazur: I was talking to Jeff Errington about this and he said:

"I think it's curious, really curious that the archaea and the bacteria have a fundamental difference in terms of their cell development structure. It reflects also the very fundamental differences in the way they replicate, transcribe and translate DNA."

Charles Kurland: Absolutely. There is a split there and in our phylogeny, the split occurs very early. But if you look at the eukaryotes, there are even more early splits. So the plants and the protists and the fungi and the animals—they split out from one another very early in the eukaryotic branch. This business of splitting is something very early. And I agree with Errington that it's very interesting—what is the basis of this archaeal bacterial split? We can philosophize about it but we have no clear evidence to support any particular way of looking at that. It's a mystery.

Suzan Mazur: Jeff Errington says the cutting edge is the extent to which bacteria live in the L-form state in a wall-less state. In that state they would proliferate by way of HGT. So how would this affect your ToL?

Charles Kurland: No much at all. Also, I'd like to make a general comment. **The cutting edge is in the eye of the beholder.** [emphasis added]

Suzan Mazur: Jeff was actually referring to the cutting edge of research regarding L-forms.

Ajith Harish: It's one feature out of so many different features, L-forms. We build a ToL using genomic features, so then it remains to be seen how we can get all these other phenotypic features to correspond to this ToL.

Suzan Mazur: Ajith, did you say the ToL model and methods were part of your PhD—your doctoral dissertation at the University of Illinois, Urbana-Champaign?

Ajith Harish: Partly, yes.

Suzan Mazur: Charles, you say the standard model reflects Aristotelian simple to complex thinking. Your model starts with a complex ancestor and reflects reductive evolution. Would you say more?

Charles Kurland: It gets simpler. This is something that gets very troublesome for people.

Suzan Mazur: In my conversation with Jeff Errington the other day, for instance, he talked about *Mycoplasma* now being wall-less but it's related to bacteria that have a wall, so at some point it lost the ability to form a wall. So this is one case of reductive evolution.

Charles Kurland: Yes, of course it is. And there are lots of such examples. The thing that may be behind all of this, the reductive evolution to some degree of simplicity, is that it may be that in the period of time that we're looking at the environments become simplified and stable. Loss is encouraged by a stable environment.

If you have a toolkit for all kinds of environmental eventualities, and you're living in an environment that turns out over evolutionary time to be very, very stable—you're going to start simplifying your toolkit.

Suzan Mazur: That's right. That's why as a New Yorker I don't drive anymore. I've lost the ability to drive.

[Laughter]

Charles Kurland: That's interesting. I don't drive either. So I think it's hard to say, but this could be a very direct environmental influence on the evolution of organisms. Environments have become stable and so the organisms can become simpler.

Suzan Mazur: You talked earlier about the problem of science becoming dogma. Can you say a bit more about that?

Charles Kurland: I'm certainly not immune to this because both Ajith and I had to go through some really serious soul searching as the data developed and as our story developed, because both of us entered this game actually quite law abiding citizens of the molecular evolution community and we were essentially trying to solve a technical problem and had no idea that we were getting involved in developing a really different view of evolution.

Suzan Mazur: You've gotten some serious support there from the Royal Swedish Science Academy, from the Nobel Committee.

Charles Kurland: Yes. But I think if it were up to most molecular evolutionists, we would be starved to death.

Suzan Mazur: You've said that if your thinking about the most recent universal common ancestor being part of an extinct Earthly biosphere is wrong, then the other option is that the origin is extraterrestrial. In light of that thinking, NASA has joined with the Templeton Foundation and the Center of Theological Inquiry to canvas the religious community as to how it would respond to the discovery of extraterrestrial life. Do you have any thoughts about that?

Charles Kurland: Most people would arm to the teeth. As a species we're very aggressive and very territorial. We are easily frightened. Imagine a monkey colony that has been startled. It would be a very, very scary moment for us to have a spaceship land at Rockefeller Center and—"We come in peace." We would be shooting at them immediately. And who knows what kind of beings evolved in the Trappist system. They might be nuttier than we are.

Suzan Mazur: NASA and Templeton have thrown almost $3M to this project.

Charles Kurland: I know. I just hope it takes a long time before anyone makes that contact because we have a certain amount of maturation that we have to do before we can handle it. You see what happens with ethnic or racial conflict and migration. Now think what would happen if something really different showed up.

. . .

Chapter 6

DEEP EVOLUTION and its discontents

Ajith Harish (left), Charles Kurland (right)

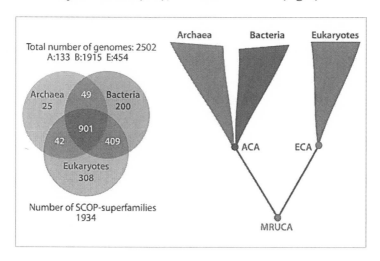

"In the field of studying ancient evolution, it's very hard to falsify or verify. As such people tend to attach unreasonable weight to their beliefs of one possibility or another."—**Julian Gough**, father and principal architect of the open-access database SUPERFAMILY

3/17/2017

There has been a vigorous and somewhat sharp response to the Charles Kurland and Ajith Harish Tree of Life interview, reminiscent of the email chain circulated by theoretical biologist Stan Salthe following Jerry Fodor's article in the *London Review of Books*, "Why Pigs Don't Have Wings." I thought it important to share some of the responses to the Kurland and Harish interview.

I received an email via L-form investigator and Leeuwenhoek Medalist Jeff Errington at Newcastle University with comments from his colleague Martin Embley at Newcastle's Institute for Cell and Molecular Biosciences. Embley has his own Tree of Life.

In my interview with Jeff Errington (see Chapter 18), Errington refers to Embley's Tree:

> *"I have a colleague here at Newcastle University named Martin Embley who's been very prominent in this TOL discussion. Martin and his team have done incisive work that I think supports the idea that there are only two domains and that the eukaryotes are derived from a group within the archaea rather than being an out group and separate from the archaea. The latest textbooks are starting to show the two-domain tree instead of the Woese three-domain tree."*

Martin Embley had this to say in the email Errington forwarded to me:

> *"As of today a root on the bacterial stem or within bacteria still seems to be the best supported hypothesis*

69

and is consistent with other forms of evidence. Kurland and Harish should publish their evidence/analyses in a decent journal like we did and let the community decide how convincing it all is."

I don't think Embley was referring to my Kurland & Harish interview, but to Kurland and Harish not publishing their ToL in such scientific journals as *Science* and *Nature*, *PNAS*, etc., as opposed to *Biochimie*, an Elsevier publication, or to *Genome Biology and Evolution*, an Oxford University Press journal— where Kurland and Harish have published their deep evolution papers.

Charles Kurland emailed me as follows regarding Embley's remarks:

> *"Embley doesn't seem to realize that with all of his clubby English self assurance that he and his mates have turned Nature into an indecent journal for subjects such as molecular evolution. It is interesting, but he will learn soon that we subjected his phylogenetic model to a statistical test of reliability (Bayesian), and it turns out to be the least probable of the four we tested. . . ."*

I once interviewed science and technology historian David F. Noble at length about peer review—which Noble saw as censorship—and also covered the now infamous *PNAS* publishing maneuvers with respect to paper submissions by Lynn Margulis, who at the time (2010) was a member of the National Academy of Sciences.

Kurland said more about the *PNAS* publishing process:

> *"Ford [Doolittle] once rejected a manuscript we sent into PNAS because we had not published more papers previously on our data but he had no criticism of what we said in our paper. Peer review is a many splendored thing!"*

70

Speaking of Ford Doolittle—because Chuck Kurland during our interview said that Doolittle in a 1999 *Science* magazine article exaggerated the extent to which horizontal gene transfer is a factor in evolution, and then identified Doolitte as a former postdoc of Carl Woese—Doolittle responded with a slur in an email to me, calling Kurland the "Donald Trump of molecular evolution." (That, by the way, was prior to Trump's speech to Congress and the Dow surging over 21,000.)

Here are Ford Doolittle's comments:

> *"what can I say to that. I was not a postdoc with carl woese and I challenge you to find anything about, or depending on the notion of molecular clocks in my 1999 Science paper. Chuck is the Donald Trump of molecular evolution."*

It's interesting that Doolittle responded to me regarding Kurland, but did not reply to my request for an interview a couple of years ago when I was putting together my book, *The Paradigm Shifters: Overthrowing 'the Hegemony of the Culture of Darwin'*.

Kurland replied directly to Doolittle, copying me on the email:

> *"Dear Ford;*
>
> *I am sorry that I identified you as a postdoc with Carl. That mistake arose as my misinterpretation of comments Carl often made to me about your relation to him. Those and your use of the rampant HGT idea in modern organisms, a randomizing principle that he proposed for the progenote, confused me. No dishonor was intended."*

Kurland then excerpted Doolittle's 1999 *Science* article:

> *"After Zuckerkandl and Pauling (4), biologists came to think that the universal tree could be reduced to a tree based on sequences of orthologous genes, any of which*

71

(practical considerations aside) could serve as a marker for an entire genome, organism, or species."

He noted further:

> *"I think that you will find this a very concise summary of what you would reasonably call a 'molecular clock.' It is introduced I suppose to provide contrast to what you say next as a description of rampant HGT:*
>
>> *"If, however, different genes give different trees, and there is no fair way to suppress this disagreement, then a species (or phylum) can 'belong' to many genera (or kingdoms) at the same time: There really can be no universal phylogenetic tree of organisms based on such a reduction to genes." "*

Kurland wrapped up:

> *"I take those two excerpts as the essence of your article, which concludes that there are rampant departures from the constant molecular clock mode of mutations. I say this because I interpret the first situation as requiring constant rates of mutation.*
>
> *Who is trumping whom?*
>
> *Cheers/chuck"*

Ford Doolittle replied directly to Kurland, copying me on the correspondence:

> *"Hi Chuck,*
>
> *Good to hear from you.*
>
> *Really, of course, I was a sort of spiritual postdoc of Carl's, and am happy to be so considered. As to Z[uckerkandl] and P[auling], indeed they endorse a clock, but that was not what I had in mind in 1999.*

It was the widespread (at that time) assumption, not formally articulated by them as I recall, that all orthologous genes would give the same topology. I also think that we, or at least those of us not actually doing the math, thought at the time that even if different genes evolved at different rates, this would affect branch length but not tree topology.

I find it amazing and somehow satisfying that us old geezers are still engaged in debate.

Regards,

Ford"

SUPERFAMILY father Julian Gough, a bioinformaticist at MRC Laboratory for Molecular Biology, Cambridge whose database Kurland and Harish relied on to build their ToL agrees that HGT is overblown. **Gough wrote to me**:

"I agree strongly with some of their [Kurland & Harish] assertions, such as that horizontal gene transfer has been overblown by some segments of the scientific community (because it's an engaging story and a good excuse for our shortcomings in untangling evolution). . . . I think you capture in your interview something very important, that 'it's important that science not become dogma' and these guys are calling everyone out on some stuff that really has been insufficiently challenged. So I am really pleased that as a journalist you are helping to air the views."

Since publishing the Kurland & Harish deep evolution conversation, I've interviewed Julian Gough. When I asked Gough what he thought about evolution scientists appearing to find the Kurland & Harish model unsettling and being more comfortable with gene sequence analysis, **Gough said the following**:

"A lot of the objections I see are not so much to the approach but to the conclusions. But often the devil is in the details—i.e., whatever data you use as your starting

73

point for whatever philosophical or technical approach you take."

The Kurland and Harish ToL challenges the Woese ToL, but there were no defenders of the Woese model, per se, who stepped forward following publication of my interview with Kurland and Harish.

I phoned one high profile scientist who I know is a Woese fan for his reaction to the story, but he didn't mention the Woese Tree either. He did, however, characterize the Kurland & Harish ToL as "Flat Earth" science, saying it didn't matter how sophisticated the methods or evidence, the Kurland & Harish conclusions were wrong. He added that I'd made a mistake by doing the interview, and that I shouldn't have done it.

Bruce Fouke, co-author of the book, *The Art of Yellowstone Science* and a former colleague of Carl Woese at University of Illinois, Urbana-Champaign did email me but said nothing about Woese or about the science. Fouke was an investigator on the five-year $8M NASA Astrobiology Institute-funded project with Woese seeking the principles of the origin and evolution of life. **Fouke said simply**:

> *"Thank you Suzan . . . I am following with great interest!!!"*

Uppsala University molecular biologist Måns Ehrenberg, an ally of Charles Kurland and Ajith Harish, initially commented: *"Dear Suzan, thanks a lot! Great stuff."*

Ehrenberg later emailed:

> *"Dear Suzan, there are some remarkable responses among these, e.g., that only Nature published manuscripts or their equivalents can be read and commented upon. In a world where status is the only measure of scientific quality, science is obviously dead. We are not there, yet, but working on in. Take care, Måns"*

Mark McMenamin, a paleontologist at Mount Holyoke and former colleague of Lynn Margulis, wrote to me saying he thinks the Kurland and Harish deep evolution scenario "has merit." Apparently his friend Simon Conway Morris does too, according to Ajith Harish, who spoke with Simon Conway Morris about it at the recent ELSI conference in Tokyo on the emergence of the biosphere.

But McMenamin envisions certain mergers taking place, which he describes as "Margulis writ large" and referred me to the "Pandora's Pithos" chapter in his book: *Dynamic Paleontology* for specifics.

However, Kurland and Harish dismiss the Margulis hypothesis of endosymbiosis—which inspired more comments from Margulis's allies, among them **University of Chicago microbiologist James Shapiro**:

> *"I think Kurland and Harish are mistaken about symbiogenesis and eukaryotic origins. There are too many similarities between eukaryotes and archaea in core information transfer and transcriptional regulation functions for them not to be ancestrally related, and mitochondria are clearly alphaproteobacteria endosymbionts. Then there are the many photosynthetic eukaryotic groups that originated either in a cyanobacterial or algal endosymbiosis. Those cases cannot be explained in any other way."*

Kurland responded to the Shapiro comment:

> *"The bathos of the note from Jim Shapiro makes me want to cry. Why do people who have not the slightest notion of phylogeny feel compelled to make judgements about things that they simply do not understand.*
>
> *Please tell your respondent, Shapiro that there are at least two ways to account for the structural similarities of mitochondrial and bacterial and archaeal proteins.*

One is by normal vertical inheritance. The other is by a transfer say from a bacterial genome to the mitochondrial genome (nuclear or organellar). We do phylogeny rather than stare into tea leaves to distinguish these two. The phylogeny is unambiguous so far. There is no evidence of transfer of eukaryote genes from bacteria—NONE. There is strong evidence for vertical inheritance from the common ancestor of more than 90% of the mitochondrial protein determinants.

Of course this has required that we identify the proteome of the last common ancestor. We have done this. But the gene sequence people have not. There is no real evidence that any eukaryote genes had originated in a cyanobacterial genome. Similarity of protein structures does not by itself constitute proof of transfer!!

The 60s was a time when many were discovering drugs and the endosymbiosis model is a fitting product of that period. It is a pipe dream. I have nice feelings about both that period of discovery and that pipe dream. But that does not qualify as a demonstration of the validity of the endosymbiosis model."

Jim Shapiro was not satisfied with Kurland's explanation and argued further:

"Neither Kurland nor Harish addresses the photosynthetic lineages, where plastid origins by endosymbiosis are undisputed. The use of emotive terms (as Kurland does) is generally a tip-off that more than a dispassionate analysis of the data is in play."

Ajith Harish then picked up the thread:

"The data we have so far shows that many photosynthesis-associated superfamilies (SFs)—whether from cyanobacteria or plants or unicellular photosynthetic organisms—can all be traced back to MRUCA [most recent universal common ancestor].

76

There is a large overlap between mitochondria-associated SFs and plastid-related SFs. But, we need a larger data set to confirm these results. Note that we started out our studies to find the root of the ToL using an objective and rigorous analysis to locate the root despite the common prejudice of where the root "should be." [W]e sampled a broad range of eukaryotes and bacteria (and archaea). Photosynthetic organisms make up about 25% of the sampling. [W]e want to check with a larger data set. It is on the to-do list.

Phylogenetic analysis is a test of hypothesis, but there have been decades of biased or misguided analyses/interpretations using gene trees where rather than finding an answer, presumptions are simply confirmed. . . . See Keeling's perspective: "The impact of History on Our Perception of Evolutionary Events: Endosymbiosis and the Origin of Eukaryotic Complexity". . . .

It has taken decades and armies of gene jockeys to paint the picture we have today. And we [Kurland & Harish] have just started to straighten things out and we are only two of us. It gets very tiring sometimes to answer the same (blind) criticisms, which are raised without reading our papers. Why should anybody read new analyses? Everybody knows what the answer is.

To our knowledge no one has done a rigorous and objective analysis of all the different tree of life proposals (i.e., rootings) and compared them head to head. We've done just that."

Plant physiologist František Baluška at the University of Bonn, who also likes the Margulis endosymbiosis hypothesis, wrote:

"Hi Suzan,

Thank you very much for sending me these links. I am little bit puzzled by the Kurland sentence:

'. . . the bacteria gets together with an archaea and it makes a eukaryote, the bacteria becomes the mitochondria and the archaea becomes the nucleus cytoplasmic host. That's the theory. It's very, very clearly specified that way.'

Especially, of:

'. . . the archaea becomes the nucleus cytoplasmic host. . .'"

[Note: Kurland's full sentence was this: "But that's the essence of the symbiosis hypothesis—the bacteria gets together with an archaea and it makes a eukaryote, the bacteria becomes the mitochondria and the archaea becomes the nucleus cytoplasmic host. That's the theory. It's very, very clearly specified that way.]

František Baluška continued:

"This is somehow perplexing—is the archaea leading to both: the nucleus and cytoplasmic host?"

Ajith Harish commented on Baluška's comments:

"As for František Baluška's opinions, all I can say is that everything conveyed there is wishful thinking and unsupported speculation. Again, hand-waving arguments are of no help."

Baluška then said:

"Only time will show how this problem can be solved. I am looking forward to read their new papers when they will be out. From those they have published, I am not convinced."

Margulis archivist James MacAllister, sent me this message:

> *"Woese and Fox's discovery of archaebacterial was certainly fabulously important. When new technology is used, discoveries are made. But Woese's 3 Domains only make sense when you ignore (as Woese admitted doing) the symbiogenesis that created eukaryotes, eukaryote's bacteria-derived organelles and the obligate relationship of the holobiont to its microbiomes."*

Virologist Luis Villarreal thought it was "curious" that Kurland and Harish in our interview referred to microbiologist Patrick Forterre at Institut Pasteur but did not speak to "virogenesis."

But **Patrick Forterre** in a *Frontiers in Microbiology article* in July 2015, in which he proposed an updated version of the Woese Tree with several rootings, said he was not indicating viruses in his ToL either, saying further:

> *"Viruses (capsid encoding organisms) are polyphyletic, therefore their evolution can be neither illustrated by a single tree nor included in the universal tree as additional domains. However, this should not be viewed as neglecting the role of viruses in biological evolution because "the tree of life is infected by viruses from the root to the leaves."*

Forterre, incidentally, regards the ToL as a metaphor, "illustrating the history of life on our planet."

Villarreal said more:

> *"Also they [Kurland & Harish] seem unaware of the giant viruses that can infect single cell eukaryotes. I'm attaching two links that might interest you. One on RNA stem-loop cooperation and the other on phage making nucleus-like structures. FYI, the giant DNA viruses also make nucleus-like 'factories.'"*

However, Kurland, Harish *et al.* did publish an open-access virus article in August 2016 in the Oxford University Press journal *Genome Biology and Evolution*, titled: "Did Viruses Evolve As a Distinct Supergroup from Common Ancestors of Cells?" in which they write:

> *"The debate on the ancestry of viruses is still undecided: In particular, it is still unclear whether viruses evolved before their host cells or if they evolved more recently from the host cells. . . .*
>
> *The recent discovery of the so-called giant viruses . . . revived the reductive evolution hypothesis. . . [E]xamples of common viral components that are analogous to the ribosomal RNA and ribosomal protein genes, which are common to cellular genomes, are not found. This is one compelling reason that phylogenetic tests of the 'common viral ancestor' hypotheses seem so far inconclusive."*

Harish has told me he and Kurland hope to include more about viruses in their research as the technology improves.

Brig Klyce at Panspermia.org was excited to see the Kurland & Harish analysis of complexity early:

> *"The SCOP analysis and plenty of others point to "complexity early." This does not work at all for Darwinism. But what does work?"*

Klyce will be happy to know that as part of "an aspirational training exercise" on directed evolution, Julian Gough's former students at University of Bristol in the UK are sending extremophile bacteria into space in a CubeSat to "learn how organisms may have evolved ancient pathways to deal with space travel."

Meanwhile, **Binghamton University theoretical biologist Stan Salthe awaits answers for the origin of the gene**:

"Thanks Suzan! BTW, what's the latest on the origin of the nucleic acid gene system?"

Chapter 7

Julian Gough on SUPERFAMILY & Open Science

Photo, courtesy Julian Gough

3/13/2017

Julian Gough, a bioinformaticist at Medical Research Council Laboratory for Molecular Biology (MRC), Cambridge, UK believes in the tradition of open science—the free-gift-to-the-world kind of science that first brought us the World Wide Web developed at CERN. Gough's gift to the world is SUPERFAMILY, a database all about proteins in genomes, which he created as part of his PhD a dozen or so years ago.

Plug certain information into SUPERFAMILY and it can analyze a vast assortment of genomes and assist you in building a Tree of Life using superfamilies—i.e., domains with an evolutionary relationship — and the conserved part of thousands and thousands of protein structures called protein domains. Everyone can access this robust repository online, and it looks like everyone is. Gough says the site currently gets one hit per second.

Julian John Thurstan Gough (not to be confused with Julian Gough, the Irish novelist and former singer with the band "Toasted Heretic") received his PhD at the University of Cambridge in Theoretical and Computational Biology ("Hidden Markov models and their application to the genome analysis in the context of protein structure"). His doctoral advisor at Cambridge was Cyrus Chothia, and Gough says SUPERFAMILY grew in part from Chothia's work and influence. Gough's undergraduate degree is in Mathematics and Physics (joint honors) from the University of Bristol. His postdoctoral research was with Nobel laureate Michael Levitt at Stanford University and at LMB.

He's been a research scientist at the RIKEN Genomic Sciences Centre, Japan and at the Pasteur Institute in Paris, a professor at Tokyo Medical and Dental University, and until his move to MRC Laboratory for Molecular Biology earlier this year, a professor at the University of Bristol in the UK.

Julian Gough is currently on the editorial board of BioEssays, and is Director and Co-founder of Genetrainer, a company that offers personalized workouts that include DNA analysis.

I spoke recently by phone with Julian Gough at his lab at LMB, Cambridge about the wonders of SUPERFAMILY.

Suzan Mazur: What is your role there at MRC? You made the move from the University of Bristol fairly recently?

Julian Gough: Yes. I started in January. My job title is program leader. So I'm currently recruiting postdocs. I didn't move any of my group from Bristol. They're all finishing up. My role here is to run a scientific program.

Suzan Mazur: Program leader in what area?

Julian Gough: My two main chosen research directions at the moment are cell reprogramming, that is, computational prediction of cell reprogramming, and phenotype prediction. Those are my two main projects, but underlying that in everything I do, I have a history of developing algorithms and resources, and of course, that has to continue to support all the rest of the research that I do.

Suzan Mazur: So it's bioinformatics.

Julian Gough: Yes, bioinformatics. I make these resources public and people around the world can use them for their research too.

Suzan Mazur: That's wonderful. You're the father of and principal architect of the SUPERFAMILY database.

Julian Gough: Yes. I think that's fair to say. It was conceived while I was doing a PhD with Cyrus Chothia, and it's highly dependent on the SCOP database [Structural Classification of Proteins], and the architect of that or the main person for the intellectual content, was Alexey Murzin. SUPERFAMILY grew from their influence and their work.

Suzan Mazur: SUPERFAMILY 1.75 was part of your doctoral dissertation at Cambridge.

Julian Gough: The original one was one of my outputs for my PhD — not 1.75. I can't remember which number it was on then. It's since been updated many times and its current version is 1.75.

Suzan Mazur: Would you say essentially what the database is?

Julian Gough: Three-dimensional atomic resolution protein structures are solved using experimental techniques, such as crystallography, NMR [nuclear magnetic resonance] and cryo-electron microscopy and the coordinates of these structures get deposited in the Protein Data Bank (PDB).

The SCOP database that I alluded to before takes those structures and it breaks them into domains, which are globular units of evolution. It classifies them into evolutionary-related groups called Superfamilies. There's actually a whole hierarchy in the classification, but the relevant level for the SUPERFAMILY database is unsurprisingly the Superfamily level.

What the SUPERFAMILY database does, using hidden Markov models and a couple of other techniques, is attempt to take those domains of known structure, as classified in the SCOP database and map them to genome sequences.

There are about 100,000 protein structures, probably more—getting on to 150,000 protein structures in the PDB.

Suzan Mazur: Who has actually done the protein x-ray crystallography in your database?

Julian Gough: The whole world has been working on it since the first protein structure by Max Perutz of myoglobin. Many, many labs—all structural biology labs around the world have been solving these structures and depositing them in the PDB.

Suzan Mazur: How can you be sure that the protein x-ray crystallography is solid? That the work previously done is accurate that you've got in your database?

Julian Gough: Some protein structures may be of low quality. They have to go through a great deal of validation steps to make it into the Protein Data Bank. Some of them may still contain errors. But I think it's very rare and there are probably very few Superfamilies in the database that are due to errors in the solution of the structures.

A Superfamily will often have many structures representing it. So even if there is a mistake in one structure, once you accumulate a whole group of structures, it should be very clear that they are not all going to have the same mistake.

Suzan Mazur: Do protein Superfamilies represent the current limits of our ability to identify common ancestry?

Julian Gough: Yes. That is exactly what their definition is. So if you want to group two protein structural domains into the same Superfamily, the question that you ask is whether there is structural sequence and functional evidence for common evolutionary ancestry. So they're classified based on that.

The most powerful part of that classification comes from the structure. Structure is far more conserved than sequence and so the knowledge of the structure allows you to classify very distantly related things that have no apparent or detectable similarity in sequence.

Suzan Mazur: This is what Charles Kurland and Ajith Harish have done with their Tree of Life.

Julian Gough: Several people investigating evolution use the data, as they have. And you have, I think, in the Superfamily database the most—via the SCOP classification and structures—you have the most distant evolutionary classification that you can have at the moment mapped to all genomes.

Suzan Mazur: I see you are interested in viral evolution. Can you track viruses for a Tree of Life through your database? I understand the virus genome may be too small compared to that of a cellular organism to effectively include them at this point in a ToL.

Julian Gough: Viruses can be sequenced.

Suzan Mazur: But they move nonlinearly and consortially.

Julian Gough: That's not my area of expertise. Some viruses are very large, larger even than small bacteria. The majority of viruses are very small and some of them don't even contain any protein or they contain one protein. So using this approach is insufficient.

Viruses also evolve orders of magnitude more quickly. Because they evolve so rapidly, within a population of viruses you have a diversity that is not comparable to the diversity you'd get within a population of cellular organisms.

Suzan Mazur: So their presence could really affect the Tree of Life, considering how they evolve? The recent Ebola and Zika epidemics, for instance. The way the viruses spread was off the chart.

Julian Gough: I'm not aware of many people who have attempted to reconstruct an evolutionary tree of viruses.

To put the evolution of viruses in context, you have different categories of viruses. You have double-stranded DNA, single-stranded DNA, double-stranded RNA, single-stranded RNA. They're not even using the same way of storing genetic code. So to try to make an evolutionary tree of viruses, bringing these together, I think it goes too far back.

Suzan Mazur: But the viral content of the human genome is 10%, as well as the genome content of other animals, for example.

Julian Gough: Yes. So this crosstalk, I guess it can lead to horizontal gene transfer from cellular organisms to viruses and then transported back into cellular organisms. If you're trying to look at resolving a new evolutionary tree of cellular organisms, viral transfers may add some noise to that. But I don't think that they're responsible for completely rewriting it.

Suzan Mazur: The SUPERFAMILY database is free. That's great. How widespread is its use?

Julian Gough: There are various ways of looking at how widespread the use of SUPERFAMIY is. If you look at metrics, if you like that kind of thing, then the original paper has just passed 1,000 citations. But it also forms part of the InterPro database. So if you add up all the InterPro papers and SUPERFAMILY papers, it's many thousands of citations. If you look at it in terms of how often the web site is accessed—on average it's about once per second. Thousands of different Internet addresses visit SUPERFAMILY every month.

Suzan Mazur: How does SUPERFAMILY 1.75 enable researchers? They go to your site and plug in what information to get results?

Julian Gough: The site has many different kinds of users. Someone may be using it for many different things. Some people are interested in a specific gene and they might go in and type in the code for that gene and see what the predicted domains are. Somebody else might be interested in families, so they might want to look at the list of proteins that contain a globin domain in the mouse genome. Or you get people who want to look at whole genomes. They may want to look at all kinds of domains. What is the most common domain in a particular bacterium. And there are lots of tools there for cross-comparing between organisms.

Power users, or people who are investigating evolution, can download the whole database or parts of it. For example, you might download all of the domains, all the Superfamilies and their arrangement into domain architectures in all of the genomes and try to do a huge mass comparison across all of this. You can download in computer-readable files.

Suzan Mazur: Who else is building a ToL using SUPERFAMILY besides Kurland and Harish?

Julian Gough: We have a paper on doing exactly that, although maybe not in the same way. But I think the first person to publish using the SUPERFAMILY database to attempt to build a tree was a student with Phil Bourne. That was more than 10 years ago.

Suzan Mazur: Do you see this as cutting edge, because most scientists still rely on gene sequence analysis for ToL.

Julian Gough: What defines cutting edge? I think if cutting edge is the best possible technique that you can apply to the problem—

88

in that sense it is. But, if you're saying that because this hasn't been used for more than 10 years, then it's not cutting edge. Also, people were making gene sequence trees 10 years before that, so that's even older.

Gene trees and trees derived from domain architectures give quite a different picture and they both have valid applications. But if you want to look at deep evolution, then using domain architectures will give you more information content on reaching deeper parts of the tree than you'd get from sequence alignments or gene trees.

Suzan Mazur: What do you say to those who say numbers are meaningless because we're dealing with life regarding evolution?

Julian Gough: You could say that the whole field of evolution is not quantifiable and to think it's not measurable because we were not there and so we really don't know what happened. Putting numbers to things and including ranges of numbers and errors is required in science though, so you have to try.

Suzan Mazur: What are your thoughts about directed evolution? I see it's one of your areas of research.

Julian Gough: Yes. We did some directed evolution experiments with yeast, but we've finished those experiments now.

Suzan Mazur: What are your thoughts about directed evolution?

Julian Gough: The way in which we were using it was to try to discover mechanisms by which multicellularity can evolve. I think for that and for other things too, it was a useful approach.

We also have a directed evolution project ongoing at the University of Bristol, but I've now left the project with the move to MRC. That project looks at directed evolution with some extremophile bacteria we will launch into space. We will allow the bacteria to evolve in space before sequencing them up there and beaming their evolved genomes back down to Earth to compare with parallel bacteria that have evolved on Earth.

It's not beyond the reach of a university now to launch its own satellites. There are things called CubeSats and they're about 30 centimeters by 10 centimeters by 10 centimeters. You can pay to piggyback on launches to put your experiments in orbit.

Suzan Mazur: Fascinating.

Julian Gough: The idea is to learn how organisms may have evolved ancient pathways to deal with space travel, if life did not originate on Earth. It's a very far-fetched project really. It's a teaching project—more of an aspirational training exercise for students. It's not a research project.

Suzan Mazur: What is your reaction to the scientific community regarding the Superfamilies protein database approach to mapping the Tree of Life? Investigators appear to be largely more comfortable with gene sequence analysis than with this more sophisticated approach. It seems to upset their scientific models, etc.

Julian Gough: In the field of studying ancient evolution, it's very hard to falsify or verify. As such people tend to attach unreasonable weight to their beliefs of one possibility or another.

A lot of the objections I see are not so much to the approach but to the conclusions. But often the devil is in the details—i.e., whatever data you use as your starting point for whatever philosophical or technical approach you take.

However, if somebody comes up to you and says, I observe the Earth to be flat, and this is the experiment I did to test it—to reject the measurement without looking at the evidence is not scientific. It's taking a belief almost at face, as in religion, that because it goes against your belief that the Earth is round, it should not be examined. That's not a scientific approach. Ironically, people in the past with this attitude would have been unable to discover that the Earth is round.

The scientific approach is to look at the evidence and the work that was done and try to come up with a better interpretation of it.

Chapter 8

Eugene Koonin:
"The New Evolutionary Biology"

Photos, courtesy Eugene Koonin

2/3/2017

"They should have invited Eugene Koonin," Canadian biochemist Larry Moran told me in the hallway during a break at the November Royal Society "new trends" in evolution conference in London —somewhat exasperated by the proceedings. And I agreed. But Eugene Koonin doesn't quite see it that way, as he revealed during our recent conversation.

Eugene Koonin is a consummate scientist, Leader of the Evolutionary Genomics Group at the National Center for Biotechnology Information, NIH, who sees science scandals and controversy as unproductive. He prefers the lab to the battlefield and is regarded as one of the most qualitative and prolific thinkers in science today (H-index 196; author of more than 600 scientific papers).

But his numbers as a road runner are not bad either, per his Chevy Chase Turkey Chasestats.

In our interview that follows, Koonin sorts out any confusion over his recent statements about the importance of population genetics—part of the Modern Synthesis—and his 2009 statement: "Not to mince words the Modern Synthesis is gone." He agrees with Richard Lewontin that the term natural selection is metaphorical and goes further noting, "No one in the mainstream community now takes selection literally." And he also agrees with the Woese-Goldenfeld perspective about biology as "the new condensed matter physics," although Koonin thinks biology is still en route there.

Eugene Koonin is the author of several books, among them *The Logic of Chance*: *The Nature and Origin of Biological Evolution*; and *Sequence—Evolution—Function:Computational Approaches in Comparative Genomics* (with Michael Galperin). He is also founder and editor-in-chief of the journal *Biology Direct*. In 2002, Koonin and NCBI colleague Kira Makarova identified the genetic region now known as CRISPR-Cas.

I spoke by phone with Eugene Koonin at his lab in Bethesda, Maryland.

Suzan Mazur: Do you have any thoughts about the recent Royal Society meeting on new trends in evolutionary biology?

Eugene Koonin: Yes. Perhaps there is a need to make some comment. I was quite unhappy reading at and around this public evolutionary meeting at the Royal Society. Frankly, I think that the less sensationalism, the less controversy brought into these discussions the better. It's really important that we try at all costs to do normal science rather than some sort of scandalous activity. I was happy about one thing, though—that I was not there and was not directly involved.

Suzan Mazur: Why is it so difficult to pull together the most compelling ideas in evolutionary biology and come up with an approximate understanding of how it all works? Michael Lynch once told me it was because reaching out to other fields is a "daunting task." But if scientists across the board won't come together to give us a coherent understanding of how it all works —however approximate—the public will lose confidence in the science establishment's ability to deliver. This is already beginning to happen. Would you comment?

Eugene Koonin: First of all, I think the public may not have much to lose in terms of confidence in the scientific establishment in this case because the public is already extremely skeptical about the value and the scientific nature of evolutionary biology. It's not quite that way about science in general but I think largely so when it comes to the study of evolution. Much of the public is poorly informed about it, poorly understands it and is highly skeptical for various reasons. So I would frame the discussion a little differently, in the sense that evolutionary science may not be doing the best possible job to convince the public of the true importance of evolutionary biology. That said, I do believe that a coherent understanding of "how it works" is slowly but steadily emerging in evolutionary biology. However, one has to face the facts: first, it is a slow process, and we are still far from the goal; second, the emerging picture is highly complex and, furthermore, makes little sense without mathematical theory. Thus, communicating modern evolutionary biology (as opposed to deceptively simple antiquated ideas) is indeed a daunting task.

Suzan Mazur: If you were organizing a public evolution summit, what discoveries in biology would you showcase?

Eugene Koonin: I would try to focus on two aspects. One is genomics, and in particular, comparative genomics and metagenomics discoveries—all this comes under the wide umbrella of genomics. That's one. The other is the existence of solid theory in evolutionary biology. I'll elaborate on both aspects.

The first aspect, genomics, has in roughly the last 25 years completely transformed the ability to investigate, assess and measure evolutionary processes. All our conclusions on the course of evolution until the advent of genomics had been indirect. **It's remarkable how many of these conclusions and findings remain relevant, but the fact is that all our ways to peer into the evolutionary process and evolutionary past had previously been indirect.** [emphasis added]

Genomics now provides us windows into the evolutionary past by which we can compare directly the DNA and protein sequences from a rapidly widening range of organisms and thereby make solid conclusions about evolution.

Suzan Mazur: Are you saying this is the top discovery in evolutionary biology in the last 50 years?

Eugene Koonin: The word "discovery" may not apply quite directly here. It's a transformation of the whole science, which is based on a variety of discoveries. The very approach to evolutionary studies has changed completely. Not only the fact of evolution itself but the existence of deep evolutionary connections between different domains of life—to be concrete—evolutionary connections between, let us say, mammals, such as humans, and prokaryotes, bacteria and archaea, have become indisputable. **These findings make questioning not only the reality of evolution but the evolutionary unity of all life on earth completely ridiculous and outside of the field of rational discourse.** [emphasis added]

Then to be more specific, I would probably showcase the advances of metagenomics—you know, the genomic revolution continues in the sense that now through metagenomics scientists are able to obtain a less and less biased picture of the diversity and evolution of life on Earth. It's becoming not so unrealistic to think about

95

something approaching a complete picture of the evolutionary history of life.

And then I would showcase something very specific. That is, the latest discovery of the particular group of archaea that was the direct ancestor of eukaryotes. And in this case, "discovery" is the right word.

There is a necessity to bring to the broader audience of biologists and lay public Mike Lynch's reformulation of the principles of genomics in terms of population genetics. Paraphrasing the famous pronouncement of Theodosius Dobzhansky, one of the founding fathers of the Modern Synthesis ["Nothing in biology makes sense except in the light of evolution."], Lynch wrote in one of his papers: "Nothing in evolution makes sense except in the sense of population genetics." That is absolutely true. The details of population genetics theory are difficult to explain even to biologists who are not specially trained, yet we have to communicate these ideas to a broader audience, including the lay public, and in qualitative terms.

Suzan Mazur: How much of the research in your lab is bench experiments and how much is computer modeling?

Eugene Koonin: That's easy, 100% of the research in my lab is computational, not necessarily modeling, but 100% is done by computer and 0% is done experimentally. Of course, we constantly collaborate with experimental laboratories.

Suzan Mazur: In a 2009 paper of yours commenting on the 150th anniversary of the *Origin of Species* you make the following statement: "So, not to mince words, the Modern Synthesis is gone."

Yet in your recent *BioMed Central* paper you write that it's time for biologists to start paying attention to population genetics because of advances in functional genomes. But population biology IS part of the Modern Synthesis. So your current position has some in the science community confused. Would you talk about the evolution of your thinking about evolution and begin by how you define "gene" and "genome"?

Eugene Koonin: Such confusion makes one wish, at least for a moment, they never made such general statements aimed at a mass audience, yet I think such generalizations are necessary. There isn't really much change in my thinking. There isn't any dramatic change let alone a turn-around in my thinking. Population genetics is a mathematical framework that is essential for building evolutionary theory but it is not the theory itself. The Modern Synthesis does employ that framework and is a correct theory but only for a narrow range of evolutionary processes in certain groups of organisms. It is quite a typical situation in science, actually.

Suzan Mazur: There's also a lot of confusion in the evolutionary biology community about what a gene is. For instance, Jim Shapiro says he doesn't think in terms of genes as entities. He thinks in terms of systems all the way down.

Eugene Koonin: This is a completely different level of discussion. Let's try to separate it, whatever. I know exactly what Jim Shapiro said and a lot of people say. It's just a translation into a different language, from a somewhat different viewpoint. I do not disagree, genomes are dynamic systems evolving in space and time not static collections of genes. But it is also OK to view them as entities, information storage devices. These viewpoints are complementary.

Coming back to the evolution of my thinking from 2009 to 2016, which really hasn't been much. Quite frankly, if I were writing what I wrote back in 2009, I would have been even more cautious and non-combative than I was then. I don't think I was ever really bombastic. But I would have been even less demonstrative and maybe I would not have written that the Modern Synthesis is gone.

Suzan Mazur: I think your paper in 2009 does sort of leave the door open for the paper that you just published in *BioMed Central*.

Eugene Koonin: Absolutely, all the doors were open. I would not say that it's [Modern Synthesis] gone just like that. It has to be understood in context. I think now any actively working scientist in evolutionary biology probably realizes that the Modern Synthesis or neo-Darwinism, or whatever the name is, is insufficient in the post-genomic era. This is a set of concepts that is insufficient for understanding the entirety of evolution. It doesn't mean it's wrong. It's only becoming wrong if someone claims that they need nothing past the concepts in the Modern Synthesis.

Suzan Mazur: Again, there are complaints in the evolution science community that nothing ever seems to get solved. You've commented in the *BMC* paper that there continues to be a parade of just-so narratives and that "if biology is to evolve into a "hard" science with a solid theoretical core, it must be based on null models, no other path is known." You note further that null models are standard in physics but not in biology. Would you say more, beginning with your definition of "null model"?

Eugene Koonin: Sure. In any field, null model is the simplest explanation of the available data that does not violate physical laws. Good and sensible scientific practice in physics but also in other sciences. Scientists first come up with the simplest rational explanation of the available data and then see if anything in the data refutes that explanation and requires a more complex model. And so on and so forth.

Suzan Mazur: Nigel Goldenfeld in recent years referred to biology as the "new condensed matter physics."

Eugene Koonin: Yes. He wrote a paper with the late Carl Woese where they expressed this, and I agree. Maybe with a caveat. I would rather say biology *has to become* the new condensed matter physics.

98

Suzan Mazur: At the November Royal Society public evolution meeting mentioned above, Sir Pat Bateson cautioned about the overuse of the metaphor of natural selection. And Richard Lewontin has famously said in the *New York Review of Books* that Darwin never meant the metaphorical term to be taken literally by generations of scientists. You keep natural selection in your most recent *BMC* paper and identify a family of selection terms: "weak selection," "purifying selection," "positive selection," "local selection," and "global selection." Aren't these all metaphorical as well and contrary to your interest in seeing biology "evolve into a 'hard' science"?

Eugene Koonin: Well. Yes, these are metaphorical. From Darwin to this day. I also agree with Lewontin, Darwin did not mean natural selection to be taken literally. But we have to be, I guess, a little more specific about what it means to take natural selection or any kind of selection literally. It means, one would assume, the existence of a selecting agent. Perhaps making all these parallels between natural selection and artificial selection, the way Darwin does in his book, could be somewhat dangerous because in artificial selection there is someone who is selecting, even if unconsciously. In that respect, the evolutionary process is very different in nature where nothing is there to actually select. Darwin certainly realized this and wrote more precisely of "survival of the fittest." In modern evolutionary biology, it is sometimes "random survival" but the key point remains the same: organisms survive and leave progeny differentially. I think it is quite alright to denote some forms of differential survival selection, metaphorically. And there is no confusion here, within mainstream thinking. No one in the mainstream scientific community now takes selection literally.

Suzan Mazur: You also say in the *BMC* paper: "Counterintuitive as this might seem, evolutionary reconstruction in my laboratory clearly indicates that the ancestral state in most major groups of eukaryotes and apparently the last common eukaryotic ancestor had an intron density close to that in extant animals." You note that introns persist in eukaryotes because introns invaded their genomes as mobile elements early on and that selection was too weak to get rid of them. You also say "the substantial majority" of introns harbor no detectable gene.

What is the significance of this observation? And would you define, in this case, what you mean by intron because you cite two groups of introns in your October table of defined virus terms. Thank you for that paper, by the way—it's very useful—the paper in *Studies in History and Philosophy of Science Part C*.

Eugene Koonin: Thank you. I appreciate that. What was said there in the virus paper?

Suzan Mazur: You provide an extensive table of defined virus terms, and you identify two groups of introns: Group I and Group II.

Eugene Koonin: We are going into technicalities here, so just very briefly. Prokaryotes also have genetic elements that are called introns but they're very, very different from eukaryotic introns. Prokaryotic introns are more like mobile elements, self-splicing introns, unlike the eukaryotic introns that just sit there and wait to be excised by the spliceosome.

Prokaryotic introns are active. They have the machinery to excise themselves and even to move to a different location. There are two classes of such self-splicing introns, Group I and Group II, but the distinctions between these groups are important only for those who study these things.

The point for the general reader is that the eukaryotic introns evolved from the Group II self-splicing introns, which invaded the genomes of early eukaryotes and then lost their mobility.

Suzan Mazur: Would you touch on the possible importance of stem-loop RNA in origin and evolution of life?

Eugene Koonin: It's a bit of an unexpected turn. All RNAs contain stems and loops, all RNAs that exist in life forms, in organisms are stem and loop structures.

Suzan Mazur: Luis Villarreal is very keen on this idea.

Eugene Koonin: I cannot right now comment on the specific statements of Luis. I simply don't remember them. Sounds very generic as long as one believes in the primordial RNA world, in some form. Yes, within the RNA world model, stem and loop structures are essential. But random stems and loops do not form the right structure, they cannot have ribozyme activity let alone complex ribozyme activity. So they are only starting material for pre-biological evolution, they do not solve any problems by themselves

Suzan Mazur: In a presentation last year in Tokyo at ELSI (Earth-Life Science Institute) on the emergence of the biosphere, Uppsala University scientist Ajith Harish pointed out that "advances in our understanding of protein evolution indicate that tertiary structures of proteins are the molecular fossils of evolution while coding sequences are transients."

Harish also says the Universal Common Ancestor of the contemporary Tree of Life (ToL) "is distinct from any specific modern descendant," that the Universal Common Ancestor was not the first cell lineage and that the modern ToL is the crown of a "recently" rerooted tree, that "bottlenecked survivors of an environmental collapse, which preceded the flourishing of the modern crown, seeded the current phylogenetic tree."

Harish concludes that the "new data raises questions about traditional hypotheses based on sequence-based gene trees as well as divergence time estimates based on limited information in gene sequences," noting further that "there are so far no identifiable 'universal' viral genes that are common to viruses such as the ubiquitous cellular genes."

Would you like to comment on this?

Eugene Koonin: The short answer is no, I do not want to comment on that, because it's impossible to make any responsible comment on a long and complex quote like this unless I've heard the lecture (or much better yet, read the paper). There are a variety of things on which I would agree (for example, that protein structures are more conserved than sequences which is common knowledge) and a variety of things on which I cannot immediately agree. But the bottom line is I did not hear the lecture.

Suzan Mazur: At the same ELSI meeting, Hiromi Saito from Osaka University questioned whether the common ancestor of bacteria had a cell wall noting, "many bacteria can transform themselves to a cell-wall-deficient state" called an L-form. Do you have any thoughts about that?

Eugene Koonin: I know very well what L-forms are, in particular, with respect to their simple cell division mechanism. And this is an interesting possibility when we think about early evolution of cells. The modern L-forms obviously are derived, and comparative genomics tells us that the last common ancestor of bacteria probably did have a cell wall. Wall-less forms might have been important in evolution of cells but at an even earlier stage.

Suzan Mazur: Would you like to make a final point?

Eugene Koonin: Yes. I would like to come back to this issue of the Modern Synthesis, population genetics theory and the like because it is true that population genetics theory is part of the Modern Synthesis. And that is great. That is part of the power of the concept and why it remains quite relevant in explanations of microevolution but also an important part of the new evolutionary biology. That's what I wanted to convey in the *BMC* paper, that population genetics theory (in its modernized form because it too has not remained static over 50 years) has to be systematically applied in evolutionary genomics, which is the new mainstream of evolutionary biology. Indeed, it's changed dramatically over the last 25 years, and as previously mentioned, has completely transformed the ability to investigate, assess and measure evolutionary processes. The modern version of population genetics theory (it too has not remained static over 50 years) has to be actively, constantly and systematically applied to our understanding of genome evolution. That is too often not the case.

The whole of Mike Lynch's work on this, his talks, papers and books are of paramount importance, even if I sometimes disagree with Mike on specific issues. The foundation Mike Lynch laid for modern evolutionary genomics cannot be reasonably disputed and is of huge importance.

Part 2

Hello Mechanobiology

Chapter 9

Mechanobiology—Tour de Force

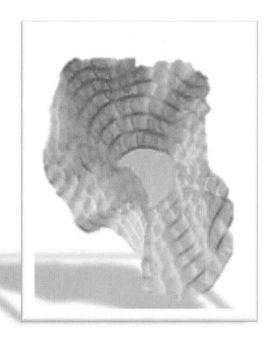

"**Suzan Mazur**: *Nigel Goldenfeld in recent years referred to biology as the 'new condensed matter physics.'*

Eugene Koonin: *Yes. He wrote a paper with the late Carl Woese where they expressed this, and I agree. Maybe with a caveat. I would rather say biology has to become the new condensed matter physics.—**Eugene Koonin: 'The New Evolutionary Biology'**"*

6/12/2018

Not since the biomath genius of D'Arcy Thompson, the Osaka structuralists, and the curve of Manolo Blahnik has the science of shape been so in the spotlight as now. From the Americas to the UK and Europe to Singapore and Down Under

Australia, events are in evidence drawing attention to the dynamics of mechanobiology and to the mechanome.

What do I mean by mechanobiology and the mechanome? Wikipedia defines mechanobiology as the "field of science at the interface of biology and engineering that focuses on how physical forces and changes in the mechanical properties of cells and tissues contribute to development, cell differentiation, physiology, and disease."

And the mechanome? Think systems-level "omics," regarding the role of force, mechanics, and machinery in biology.

[*See also* University of California-Irvine meeting, "The Mechanome in Action," in the conference list that follows.]

The mechanobiology field actually goes by assorted names, among them: soft matter, the new condensed matter physics, morphomechanics, morphometrics, biomechanics, biophysics, mathematical biology (partial list), and importantly integrates life across the board: animals, plants, fungi, microbes—which has to include viruses. It also encompasses materials science. So you can put active matter under the mechanobiology umbrella (but without Lee Cronin's "Alien chemist").

When I say mechanobiology is all the rage, I'm not simply referring to lab research and scientific conferences on the subject, although they are, of course, central. But also to: (1) mechanobiology university courses based on current scientific papers (not textbooks); (2) academic bootcamp to train high school teachers about mechanobiology; (3) university fellowships tied to the mentoring of students K-12 on mechanobiology; (4) various museum installations, including a permanent, full scale exhibit on shape designed to interactively educate kids as young as toddlers (1)—to cite a few examples.

Private foundations such as the Simons Foundation; government organizations—in particular, the National Science Foundation and National Institutes of Health in the US, European Research

Council, and Singapore's National Research Foundation *plus* industry are all keen on supporting the science, with industry recognizing extensive possibilities for applications.

For example, the Center for Engineering and MechanoBiology (CEMB) at the University of Pennsylvania has a robust mechanobiology program, describing its mission as follows:

> *"CEMB, with its focus on the interactions between structure, mechanics, and function in both the plant and animal kingdoms, will have a major impact on the ability to construct engineered tissues and organs, create new scaffolds for tissue repair and regeneration, integrate implants in reconstructive surgery, provide therapy for tissue inflammation and fibrosis, develop designer cellulose fibers, manage crops that are resistant to stresses and require fewer resources, and understand the positive and negative effects of exercise, activity, and trauma."*

And Washington University in St. Louis, a CEMB partner, cites this as its aim in mechanobiology training:

> *"The overarching goal of the MBnc Training Program is to provide pre-doctoral students at Washington University with the insight and skills needed to elucidate the role of mechanical forces in biological systems across many length scales. . . . We aim to provide pre-doctoral students in basic biological science with enhanced training in mechanics and to train pre-doctoral engineering and physics students to apply advanced mechanics to biological problems. These ambitious paired objectives will enhance interactions among students and provide trainees with skill sets tailored to address questions involving mechanics in biology."*

So, after decades of being derailed by selfish gene dogma, biology appears to be back on course and mechanobiology flourishing.

Following is a country-by-country sampling of recent and future mechanobiology conferences:

Austria:

(1)   InCem, "International Symposium Measuring and Modelling Cell Migration," Vienna, Austria, February 22-25, 2018

(2)   ATMCS8 ("Algebraic Topology, Methods, Computation and Science"), Institute of Science and Technology, Klosterneuburg, Austria, June 25-29, 2018

(3)   8th Summer School on Biomechanics, from Tissue to Organ: Modeling and Computation, Graz University of Technology, Graz, Austria, September 3-7, 2018

(4)   Joint Meeting of the German and Israeli Societies of Developmental Biology, University of Vienna, Vienna, Austria, February 17-20, 2019

Australia:

1st "Mechanobiology Down Under" meeting, Sydney, New South Wales, Australia, May 3-4, 2018

Brazil:

"Geometry of Soft Matter," International Institute of Physics, Federal University of Rio Grande do Norte, Lagoa Nova, Brazil, May 21-25, 2018

Canada:

(1)   ICMCM 2018: 20th International Conference on Mathematics and Computational Mechanobiology, Montreal, Canada, May 24-25, 2018

(2)   Japan-Toronto Morphogenesis Symposium, University of Toronto, Canada, July 16-17, 2018

(3)   9th International Plant Biomechanics Conference, Montreal, Canada, August 9-14, 2018

(4)   MechanoChemBio2019: Multiscale Mechanochemistry & Mechanobiology from molecular mechanisms to smart materials, McGill University, Montreal Canada, July 29-31, 2019

Chile:

EMBO Workshop: Bridging cell and tissue mechanics to fate specification in development, Santiago, Chile, April 2-5, 2019

Cuba:

Statistical Physics Approaches to Systems Biology, University of Havana, Havana, Cuba, February 4-15, 2019

Czech Republic:

International Conference of Vertebrate Morphology, Grandior Hotel, Prague, Czech Republic, July 21-25, 2019

France:

(1)   BIOPOL Summer School on Mechanobiology of Polarized Cells, Les Houches, France, April 8-13, 2018

(2)   First International School on Hemophysics, Monpellier, France, May 15-18, 2018

(3)   "Physical Approaches to Understanding Microbial Life," Summer School PALM (Laboratoire d'Excellence Physique: Atomes Lumiere Matiere), Paris, France, August 28-September 6, 2018

(4)   Physics of Living Matter, Marseille, France, September 11-12, 2018

(5)   Summer Course on Physical Biology of Morphogenesis, EMBO workshop, Cargese, Corsica, France, September 11-21, 2018

(6)   3rd International Meeting on Building the Cell, Institut Pasteur, Paris, France, September 26-28, 2018

(7)   "Modeling Cell Fate," Conferences Jacques Monod/CNRS, Roscoff (Brittany), France, November 19-23, 2018

(8)   Fifth International Oocyte Meeting, Institut de la Mer de Villefranche (IMEV), CNRS – Sorbonne University, Villefranche-sur-mer, France, January 16-19, 2019

(9)   4th Workshop in Mechanobiology and Physics of Life in Lyon, Amphi Merieux, Lyon, France, January 28, 2019

(10)   Developmental and Cell Biology of the Future, Biopark Auditorium, Paris, France, March 27-28, 2019

(11)   Biology and Physics Confront Cell-Cell Adhesion, Biophysics Society, Aussois, France, October 14-17, 2019

Germany:

(1)   SoftComp Topical Workshop on Filaments, Membranes, Cells and their Interactions, Research Center, Juelich, Germany, January 28-31, 2018

(2)   "Tissue Self-Organisation: Challenging the Systems," EMBO/EMBL symposia, EMBL, Heidelberg, Germany, March 11-14, 2018

(3) International Titisee Conference: "117th From Oocyte to Embryo—Illuminating the Origins of Life," Black Forest, Germany, April 11-15, 2018

(4) "Key Challenges in Biophysics," Munich, Germany, July 31-August 2, 2018

(5) Biennial Meeting of the German Biophysical Society, Duesseldorf, Germany, September 16-19, 2018

(6) International Symposium on Mechanobiology: Measuring and Modeling Cell Migration, Aachen, Germany, September 27-28, 2018

(7) BIOMS Symposium 2018, University of Heidelberg, Germany, October 1-2, 2018

(8) Juelich Soft Matter Days 2018, Institute for Complex Systems, Juelich, Germany, November 20-23, 2018

(9) Synthetic Morphogenesis, EMBO/EMBL Symposia, Heidelberg, Germany, March 17-20, 2019
(10) Mechanical Forces in Development, EMBO/EMBL Symposia, Heidelberg, Germany, July 3-6, 2019

India:

(1) EMBO Lecture Course: Experimental and Theoretical Approaches to Cell Mechanics, Bangalore, India, April 23-May 6, 2017

(2) Q-Mat, a cross section of new condensed matter physics research, Mohali, India, July 25-27, 2018

(3) Indo-French Research Workshop on Theory and Simulation of Hyperbolic PDEs arising in Mathematical Biology and Fluid Flow, BITS-Pilani University, Pilani, India, January 5-11, 2019

Ireland:

8th World Congress of Biomechanics, Dublin, Ireland, July 8-12, 2018

Italy:

(1) "Nanoengineering for Mechanobiology," Camogli, Genova, Italy, March 25-28, 2018

(2) Wivace Conference highlighting the "quantum nature of biology and life," etc., Parma, Italy, September 10-12, 2018

(3) CISM-AIMETA Advanced School on Cell Mechanobiology: Theory and Experiments on the Mechanics of Life, Udine, Italy, September 24-28, 2018

Japan:

(1) 20th International Conference on Mechanobiology and Biomechanics, September 13-14, 2018, Osaka, Japan
(2) 3rd International Symposium on Nanoarchitectonics for Mechanobiology, National Institute for Materials Science, Tsukuba, Japan, March 7-8, 2019

(3) BDR Symposium 2019: Control and Design of Biosystems, RIKEN Center for Biosystems Dynamic Research (BDR), Kobe, Japan, March 25-27, 2019

Montenegro:

Regional Biophysics School on Mechanobiology ("From Ion Channels to Biomaterials, Animal and Plant Systems, Biophysical Techniques of Analysis"), Kotor, Montenegro, October 6-8, 2018

Portugal:

CMBBE 2018: 15th International Symposium Computer Methods in Biomechanics and Biomedical Engineering and 3rd Conference on Imaging and Visualization, Instituto Superior Technico, Lisbon, Portugal, March 26-29, 2018

Russia:

(1) "Physics of Cancer," Institute of Strength Physics and Materials Science, Siberian Branch of Russian Academy of Sciences, Tomsk, Russia, May 23-26, 2017

(2) 13th Russian German Conference on Biomedical Engineering, Aachen, Germany, May 23-25, 2018

Singapore:

(1) "Mechanobiology in Health and Disease," Mechanobiology Institute (MBI), National University of Singapore (NUS) and Institute of Medical Biology, Singapore, May 31, 2018

(2) 2018 Bootcamp on Mechanobiology: "An Integrative Approach to Understand Cell Function," MBI, NUS, Singapore, August 2-11, 2018

Slovenia:

"Mechanobiology of Cells and Tissues in Health and Disease," Slovenia, June 13-15, 2018

Spain:

"Mechanobiology Across Networks," Spanish Network of Excellence in Mechanobiology and the European Innovative Training Network BIOPOL, Institute for Bioengineering of Catalonia, October 6-7, 2016

Switzerland:

EMBO Workshop on Cell and Developmental Systems, Arolla, Switzerland, August 20-24, 2018

The Netherlands:

(1) "On Growth and Form 2017" Workshop, Lorentz Center (Leiden) and Institute for Advanced Studies, University of Amsterdam, The Netherlands, October 23-27, 2017

(2) 1st International Symposium on Building a Synthetic Cell (BaSyC), Delft, The Netherlands, August 28-29, 2018

United Kingdom:

(1) "On Growth and Form 100," University of Dundee and University of St Andrews, Scotland, October 13-15, 2017

(2) "Mechanics of Development," Royal Society, Buckinghamshire, UK, February 5-7, 2018

(3) British Biophysical Society (BBS) Biennial Meeting, University of Southampton, UK, July 11-13, 2018

(4) Physics of Life Summer School, Grey College, Durham University, UK, July 16-20, 2018

(5) EMBO Conference—Physics of Cells: From Biochemical to Mechanical, The Majestic Hotel, Harrogate, UK, September 3-7, 2018

(6) The Physics of Microorganisms II, Institute of Physics, London, UK, April 8, 2019

(7) Contemporary Morphogenesis, The Royal Society, London, UK, October 7-8, 2019

United States:

(1) "Mechanics in Morphogenesis," Princeton Center for Theoretical Science, Princeton University, Princeton, February 21-23, 2018

(2) Synthetic and Artificial Cells Workshop/Physics of Living Systems (Talk Videos), The Westin Alexandria, Alexandria, Virginia, May 13-15, 2018 (event sponsored by National Science Foundation)

(3) 20th International Conference on Computation and Mathematical Mechanobiology, World Academy of Engineering, New York, June 3-4, 2018

(4) The Physics of Life Summer School, Princeton University, Princeton, June 11-22, 2018

(5) International Physics of Living Systems (iPoLS) Annual Meeting, Rice University, Houston, Texas, June 22-26, 2018

(6) "Mechbio Conference 2018: The Mechanome in Action," University of California, Irvine, July 26-27, 2018

(7) "Mechanobiology Symposium," CEMB (Center for Engineering MechanoBiology with support from NSF), University of Pennsylvania, Philadelphia, September 13-14, 2018 "will cover emerging issues in forces that control living systems in both plant and animal cells."

(8) "Morphometrics, Morphogenesis and Mathematics" workshop, Center of Mathematical Sciences and Applications (CMSA), Harvard University, October 22-26, 2018

(9) "Morphogenesis: Geometry and Physics" workshop, CMSA, Harvard University, December 3-6, 2018

(10) American Society for Cell Biology/European Molecular Biology Organization meeting, San Diego, California, December 8-12, 2018

(11) Keystone Symposia: Single Cell Biology, Beaver Run Resort, Breckenridge, Colorado, January 13-17, 2019

(12) Gordon Research Seminar: Directed Cell Migration, Galveston, Texas, January 19-20, 2019; Gordon Research Conference: Directed Cell Migration, Galveston, Texas, January 20-25, 2019

(13) Gordon Research Conference on Physical Virology, Ventura, California, January 20-25, 2019

(14) Gordon Research Seminar—Plant Lipids: Structure, Metabolism and Function, Galveston, Texas, January 26-27, 2019; Gordon Research Conference—Plant Lipids: Structure, Metabolism and Function, Galveston, Texas, January 27-February 1, 2019

(15) "Winter Q-Bio," Quantitative Biology on the Hawaiian Islands, February 2019

(16) Janelia Conferences: Frontiers in Imaging Science II, Janelia Research Campus, Ashburn, Virginia, May 5-8, 2019

(17) Gordon Research Seminar, Emergence of Complex Tissues from Single Cell Behavior and Cooperation, Mount Holyoke College, South Hadley, Massachusetts, June 15-16, 2019

(18) Gordon Research Conference—Identity and Diversity: Developmental Biology from Molecules to Cells to Organisms, Mount Holyoke College, South Hadley, Massachusetts, June 16-21, 2019

(19) Morphogenesis in Animals and Plants: Search for Principles, Kavli Institute for Theoretical Physics, University of

California-Santa Barbara, Santa Barbara, California, July 22-August 23, 2019

(20) 2nd National Mechanobiology Annual Symposium, Washington University, St. Louis, Missouri, October 13-15, 2019

Vietnam:

(1) "Mechanobiology from Molecules to Tissue," Recontres du Vietnam, Quy Nhon, Vietnam, June 26-July 2, 2016

(2) 2nd Mechanobiology Meeting in Vietnam: When Physics meets Biology, International Center for Interdisciplinary Science and Education in Vietnam, Quy Nhon, Vietnam, July 7-13, 2019

Labs of Special Note (in no particular order):

Wolfram Research (Stephen Wolfram)

Hernandez Research Group (Christopher Hernandez)

Nelson Group (Celeste Nelson)

MechMorpho Lab (Lance Davidson)

Manning Group (M. Lisa Manning)

Hiiragi Group (Takashi Hiiragi)

Leptin Group (Maria Leptin)

Mechanics of Mammalian Development (Jean-Léon Maître)

Vincent Fleury Lab

Emmanuel Farge Lab

Braun Lab (Dieter Braun)

Liu Lab (Allen Liu)

Pathak Lab (Medha Pathak)

The He Lab (Bing He)

MBI Laboratories

EMBL - Barcelona

Institute of Mechanics, Chinese Academy of Sciences

Center for the Physics of Living Cells, University of Illinois at Urbana-Champaign

Center for Biological Physics, Arizona State University

Center for Biological Physics, University of California-Los Angeles

Center for Biological Physics, University of Massachusetts-Amherst

Center for Soft Matter and Biological Physics, Virginia Tech

University of Washington: Biological Physics, Structure & Design

University of California-San Diego: The Biological Physics Group

Center for Quantitative Biology, University of Peking

Institute of Cell Biophysics—Russia

University Courses:

Caltech:

> *"We will use current literature to explore concepts in signal transduction and mechanics in the context of morphogenesis. This is an area of active research, so it can be argued that the best way to learn about it is to dive into the literature. . . . **The course consists almost entirely of reading current literature.**"* [emphasis added]

Washington University in St. Louis: Among the requirements for $24,324 fellowships for graduate students in mechanobiology at Washington University, St. Louis is assurance that the grad student will participate in "outreach to K-12 students or community." The WUSTL program looks across animal, plant and fungi kingdoms.

University of Pennsylvania: Fall 2018, "Integrative Plant and Animal Mechanobiology," as CEMB describes it:

> *"This novel course aims to provide students with an understanding of biomechanics that spans the plant and animal kingdoms, with the goal of emphasizing principles common to both. . . . Modules include (1) Plant and Animal Cell Biology; (2) Solid, Fluid, and Transport Mechanics; and (3) Integrating Biology and Mechanics."*

CEMB also supports:

> *"a summer professional development initiative for high school science teachers around the interdisciplinary research across the broad themes of mechanobiology. The goal is for teachers to (1) participate in a CEMB research project during the summer, (2) develop a personal curriculum plan with specific lessons and activities to use in their teaching practice the following academic year, and (3) participate*

119

in academic year workshops with the project team and other teachers."

Books and Journals:

Emerging Topics in Physical Virology (eds. Peter G. Stockley, Reidun Twarock)

Mechanobiology Handbook (Jiro Nagatomi)

Morphomechanics of Development (Lev Beloussov)

Plant Biomechanics: From Structure to Function at Multiple Scales (eds. Anja Geitmann, Joseph Gril)

Scale (Geoffrey West)

The Physics of Life (Adrian Bejan)

Acta Biomaterialia

ACS Biomaterials Science & Engineering

Biomaterials

Biomechanics and Modeling in Mechanobiology

Biophysical Journal

Journal of Biomechanics

Journal of the Mechanical Behavior of Biomedical Materials

Nature ("Mechanobiology Focus," December 2017)

Physics of Life Reviews

Chapter 10

Neuroscientist Medha Pathak and the "Mechanome in Action"

Photo, courtesy Medha Pathak

11/16/2018

She loves Southern California's beaches and whenever possible exploring their tide pools, coves and hiking trails. But University of California-Irvine's Medha Pathak is foremost a committed scientist—a biophysicist and neurobiologist at the crest of the wave of research into the mechanome, which she defines as: "the collection of molecules in the cell or in the body that participate in generating, detecting and transducing mechanical forces relevant to biological systems."

Pathak is currently a professor of physiology and biophysics at UCI and heads the Pathak Lab's investigation there into "how mechanical forces modulate neural stem cell fate in development and repair."

Earlier this year Pathak was the recipient of the NIH director's New Innovator Award ($1.5M) for her research: "Building the brain: How mechanical forces shape human neural development."

Medha Pathak is also affiliated with UCI's Sue and Bill Gross Stem Cell Research Center as well as the university's Center for Complex Biological Systems.

She is a native of India. Her BS degree is in biochemistry from St. Xavier's College in Ahmedabad and her MS in neuroscience from the National Centre for Biological Sciences in Bangalore. Pathak's PhD is from the University of California-Berkeley in biophysics. Pathak was a postdoctoral fellow in neurobiology at Harvard Medical School.

I managed to catch Medha Pathak recently for a brief telephone interview on her return from Europe and in between her lab and beach investigations. Our conversation follows.

Suzan Mazur: Were you encouraged in India as a young woman interested in science?

Medha Pathak: Yes. I had a lot of support from my family as well as from my teachers and professors to follow this route. With their strong backing, I never felt like I was lacking in ability or opportunities.

Suzan Mazur: Are your parents scientists?

Medha Pathak: My father was an engineer, and my mother taught child psychology at the university level and later as a school teacher. While they were not scientists professionally, they had the highest regard for scientific research and encouraged all the kids to pursue STEM education.

Suzan Mazur: Congratulations on the recent "Mechanome in Action" symposium you chaired there at University of California-Irvine. Would you tell me what you mean by mechanome?

Medha Pathak: The mechanome is the collection of molecules in the cell or in the body that participate in generating, detecting and transducing mechanical forces relevant to biological systems.

Suzan Mazur: Is sequencing the mechanome feasible?

Medha Pathak: By sequencing the mechanome, I assume you mean building a "parts list" using an "omics" approach, of all the molecules involved in generating, detecting and transducing force. . . . It is difficult to control and visualize mechanical force in biological systems. . . . That said, new technology and identification of novel cellular mechanotransducers are making this feasible.

Suzan Mazur: Do you see neutron scattering as a useful tool in this regard?

Medha Pathak: I haven't actually used the neutron scattering technique so I can't say how feasible it would be to retain the native cellular mechanical conditions, to visualize dynamic changes or to determine the magnitude of forces involved.

Suzan Mazur: I don't hear much about Darwinian natural selection these days. Has a deeper understanding of biology's dynamic physical mechanisms largely replaced the old dogma?

Medha Pathak: This is only tangentially related to my work so I wouldn't want to go into it in an interview!

Suzan Mazur: I don't blame you.

Would you tell me about the Pathak Lab's research involving the mechanome?

Medha Pathak: The Pathak Lab studies ion channels—molecular gates found in the cell membrane—that convert mechanical signals to chemical and electrical signals. We examine, from a multiscale perspective, how mechanical forces modulate neural processes—from embryonic development of the brain to neurodegenerative diseases later in life. Our focus is mainly on processes that involve neural stem cells, whose differentiation we found to be regulated by the mechanically activated ion channel Piezo1. We examine the role of Piezo1 in neural stem cell fate at the molecular, cellular, and organismal levels.

Mechanotransduction events occurring at a molecular level can have effects that manifest at the organ level, and we try to understand how that happens. My group is composed of cell biologists, bioengineers, microscopists, stem cell biologists, and developmental biologists who work together, bringing different technical expertise and conceptual perspectives to solve these complex problems.

Suzan Mazur: Your direct outreach to the public for research funding for your lab on neural stem cell transplant therapy is a bit unusual, isn't it?

Medha Pethak: With the growth of social media, researchers can now go beyond the traditional system of applying to federal agencies and private foundations for grant funding. Researchers can interact directly with the public to generate funding and share research results and knowledge.

We did a crowdfunding project in 2015 in partnership with an organization called Benefunder. There are a few similar platforms like Kickstarter and experiment.com.

Suzan Mazur: How successful have you been in receiving funding?

Medha Pathak: Through Benefunder we generated a few thousand dollars. This seed money was helpful in kickstarting a new line of research that at the time was not yet mature enough for a federal-funding application. We now have two NIH grants, which grew out of the crowdfunded research and are very grateful to everyone who responded to our outreach for support.

Suzan Mazur: Are you familiar with Matthew Lang's article on the mechanome from 2008? It was published in the National Academy of Engineering journal *Expanding Frontiers of Engineering*. He described the mechanome this way:

> *"The design of biological motors can be classified by cataloging the motor's general structural features fuel type, stepping distance, stall force, and other mechanical parameters. Detailed measurements of the motility cycles and underlying mechanisms for motility also provide information about how these mechanisms work. Ultimately "sequencing" the mechanome will lead to the discovery of the design features of biological motors in general, enabling us to catalogue them and outline the rules that govern their behavior."*

Is that along the lines of what you're thinking?

Medha Pathak: The focus in mechanobiology when Lang wrote that article was largely on molecular motors, which are the molecules that burn ATP to generate mechanical force. But, 10 years later, the field appreciates that the mechanome is much more than molecular motors. There are also molecules that detect force and molecules that transduce force into electrical and/or chemical signals. Cataloging is certainly important. But ultimately you have to know how a cell uses mechanical information and how it integrates that information with genetic and chemical information. And to do that you have to go beyond a "parts list" to an understanding of how the parts actually function, individually as well as in concert.

Suzan Mazur: If you google "mechanome," you don't see that many references to it.

Medha Pathak: The term is catching on. The first Mechbio conference, organized by colleagues Padmini Rangamani, Juan Carlos del Alamo and Debanjan Mukherjee in 2016 at UC-San Diego, was called "Putting Together the Cell Mechanome: Finding the pieces, building the puzzle."

When organizing the 2018 conference, the second one in the series, we—Jun Allard, Albert Siryaporn, Timothy Downing and I—wanted to go beyond putting the components together to function and decided to call the meeting: "The Mechanome In Action."

Suzan Mazur: Is there a final point you'd like to make? Is there anything more you'd like to say about the mechanome?

Medha Pathak: Traditionally the focus in biology has been on genetic and chemical cues. Mechanical cues have largely been understudied because until now we haven't had a good way of working with them.

It isn't easy to measure or manipulate mechanical forces in squishy cells, organs and tissues. Moreover, we have lacked an understanding of the molecules that transduce mechanical forces in cells.

Over the last decade or so, these bottlenecks have started to clear, largely because of collaborative efforts between engineers and biologists and physicists and computational scientists and chemists. It is an exciting time for the field of mechanobiology, and I believe we are on the brink of making several paradigm-shifting discoveries.

Chapter 11

Center Stage: Lisa Manning & Mechanics in Morphogenesis

Photo, courtesy Lisa Manning

3/6/2018

A half dozen or so years ago, Carl Woese and Nigel Goldenfeld characterized biology as the new condensed matter physics. More recently, Eugene Koonin advised "biology *has to become* the new condensed matter physics." It's an area of scientific research that is indeed ramping up, and not a moment too soon, after decades of puffery about a so-called selfish gene. But what exactly is meant by "the new condensed matter physics"? I decided to contact Syracuse University physicist Lisa Manning to help sort it all out in a conversation that follows.

Lisa Manning is on a meteoric rise as a young scientist. She's a distinguished educator, leader of her own research group, talented speaker, as well as a Simons Foundation investigator on two fronts—the glass problem and the mathematical modeling of living systems.

She's also got a furious schedule to go with all that. Over the last couple of weeks I've been lucky to catch Manning for comment in her office in between bits of microwaved lunch, briefly while on the road, and post-quality-time with her husband and two children before boarding a plane for the West Coast.

We first communicated during a break in the proceedings of a Princeton symposium she co-organized in February having to do with the new condensed matter physics, titled: "Mechanics in Morphogenesis," which organizers of the event thoughtfully streamed to the public over the Internet. One of the Princeton speakers described the meeting as "revisit[ing] D'Arcy Thompson with the power of 21st century developmental biology."

"What took them so long? It's been 100 years since D'Arcy Thompson's *On Growth and Form*"—embryo geometry investigator Stuart Pivar remarked after viewing the Princeton presentations, otherwise completely delighted to see "Mechanics in Morphogenesis" take center stage.

Following Princeton, Manning flew to Los Angeles for the annual American Physical Society meeting where she gave the 2018 Maria Goeppert Mayer Award Talk: "Surface Tension Is Weird in Confluent Biological Tissues" and accepted the APS 2018 Maria Goeppert Mayer Award.

This week Manning is guest lecturer in Manhattan at a Simons Foundation public gathering. The talk, "A Body Made of Glass," takes place in the foundation's "state-of-the-art" auditorium following high tea.

128

Glass (silica, SiO2) is an amorphous material—mechanically solid but microscopically disordered. And as it turns out, roughly 90% of all solid matter around us is amorphous material. Furthermore, because of mechanical interactions between cells, the tissues of our body behave like glass and influence pattern formation. Figuring out how it all works is the focus of the Simons glass collaboration.

Manning's Simons lecture on March 7 essentially kicks off the 2nd annual meeting of the Simons glass collaboration—a three-day pow-wow at the foundation's Flatiron headquarters.

The Simons glass group—its director is University of Chicago physicist Sidney Nagel—notes the following strategy for tackling the glass problem:

> *"The collaboration has developed a numerical scheme that takes advantage of the flexibility offered by computer simulations for sampling configuration space to bypass and overtake experimental dynamics. We are now in a position to study glass configurations that would have taken thousands or more years to prepare in standard experiments. These systems will allow us to gain unprecedented insight into the structure and dynamics of amorphous materials."*

At Lisa Manning's university home base in Upstate New York, she serves as both leader of the Manning research lab and as a professor of physics (departmental teaching awards 2014, 2013). The Manning Group's research focus is the modeling and computer simulation of mechanical properties of biological tissues and non-biological materials—working in collaboration with experimentalists in various parts of the world.

Manning's professional distinction comes as little surprise since she's been thinking about scientific problems most of her life. Her roots are in an engineering family in Kentucky, and she was an international science prize-winner as early as high school.

However, Manning does recognizes that women continue to be underrepresented in physics, and so two years ago she co-organized a conference at Syracuse University in support of undergraduate women in physics. It was sponsored by the American Physical Society, National Science Foundation and the Department of Energy.

Some of Lisa Manning's honors include: American Physical Society's Maria Goeppert Mayer Award (2018, for "her use of computational and analytical tools to develop microscopic understanding of flow in disordered materials, from metallic glasses to biological tissues"); International Union of Pure and Applied Physics Young Investigator Prize (2016, Statistical Physics); Simons Investigator MMLS (2016); Physics Department Teaching Award (2014, 2013, Syracuse University); Department Chair's Service Award (2007, Physics, University of California, Santa Barbara); Physics Circus Outreach Award, Department of Physics (2004-2006, University of California, Santa Barbara) (partial list).

Lisa Manning received her BS degree in physics—*summa cum laude*—and her BA degree in mathematics from the University of Virginia. Her MA and PhD (2008) are in physics from the University of California, Santa Barbara. She was a postdoctoral fellow at Princeton University.

Our conversation follows.

Suzan Mazur: Are you from a science family? I would guess that you're not related to Peyton and Eli.

Lisa Manning: I wish. Maybe I'd get better football tickets. I grew up in Kentucky, outside of Cincinnati, Ohio. My family was, indeed, very interested in science.

Both my parents are engineers. My mom is a civil engineer. She got her degree in civil engineering when it was rare for a woman to do so. She stopped working for a while when her kids were young, but both she and my dad always made it clear that they really value scientific inquiry. As a kid, I'd ask lots of questions and my parents were always eager to help me figure it all out. Athough I do think they wanted me to become an engineer, not a physicist.

Suzan Mazur: Studying physics at school you also found yourself in a place where women were underrepresented?

Lisa Manning: I went to Notre Dame Academy, an all-girls high school in Covington, Kentucky. I actually had a great physics teacher there—Sister Mary Ethel Parrott. I entered projects in a bunch of science fairs during those years and won an international competition in the engineering category. I bought a car with some of the prize-winnings, since my family didn't have a lot of money. That allowed me to go away to college—to the University of Virginia—and to be able to drive home from school.

So I did get a lot of support in high school. It was when I got to college and to graduate school that I began to recognize that there were a lot fewer women in my classes and a dearth of role models and people to talk to.

Suzan Mazur: You began your research career in the physics of glasses then moved on into morphogenesis. What is the tie-in?

Lisa Manning: I was interested in how physical forces generate patterns in embryos because the cells inside embryos are quite often disordered, although not all the time. It seemed there wasn't a lot of theory or framework for thinking about global mechanics. I did my PhD on how a disordered material responds if you push on it. It seemed no one had answered that question for disordered material that makes up embryos. I thought the subject was interesting. Because if you want to know how signaling changes an embryo into an adult, then you have to understand how material responds when physical forces are applied.

Suzan Mazur: One of the presenters at the recent Princeton University conference "Mechanics in Morphogenesis" you co-organized characterized the meeting as "revisit[ing] D'Arcy Thompson with the power of 21st century developmental biology." Thompson was, of course, fascinated by physical forces. Eugene Koonin has told me "biology *has to become* the new condensed matter physics." Others have said physics is actually moving toward biology. Is soft matter physics the new condensed matter physics Eugene Koonin is referring to? What is your perspective on all this?

Lisa Manning: There are several exciting frontiers for condensed matter physics. Exactly as you said, soft matter and its applications in biophysics is one of them, but not the only one. Metamaterials is another.

I view soft matter physics as the study of things that occur at a scale where objects are soft. That's typically on the scale of microns, which is the same scale as cells. Also, the focus is typically on systems where quantum mechanics does not play an important role. Fluctuations are introduced by things like changes in temperature rather than quantum fluctuations. That makes soft matter physics a great toolkit for approaching biology. Because it's at the right scale and it considers fluctuations that are not quantum mechanical but could be induced by cells moving or, say, ruffling their membranes, etc.

Also, in the work that we do in the Manning Group here at Syracuse and in other groups like ours, there's an exciting interplay where physics provides new information about how to understand biology. Models we're studying just to mimic biology actually introduce totally new physics.

I'm part of the Simons glass collaboration. Some of the models we developed initially to think about morphogenesis we're now using to probe deep fundamental mysteries of the glass transition in ways we did not think of before.

Suzan Mazur: I have a couple of questions about the Simons glass collaboration coming up. I'd like to first ask you about something Jack Szostak told me about making a protocell. Szostak said the self-organization aspect is really not understood, "how you get molecules to work together and act like a cell." Thoughts about that?

Lisa Manning: From my limited understanding of protocells, that makes sense. My focus is more on understanding the first multicellular structures. I'm a scale up from that question. But at that level the same exact analysis applies.

As you know, single cells have been around for billions of years, almost as long as the Earth has been in existence, while multicelluarity is a very late evolutionary phenomenon. Happening roughly 600 million years ago. The question is: What is the self-organization that allows cells to group to form functional structures?

Suzan Mazur: At the Princeton conference the point was made that there was a problem with 2D modeling attempting to predict morphogenetic flow because cells are 3D balloons not 2D. Your lab focuses on modeling and computer simulation of the mechanical properties of biological tissues and disordered non-biological materials like granular materials and glass. How closely do you work with experimentalists?

Lisa Manning: Extremely closely. All of our work in biology essentially has an experimental collaborator. I work very closely with Josef Käs at Leipzig University who studies cancer, especially breast and cervical cancer. He has direct mechanical measurements of tumors from human patients. I also work closely with Jeff Amack's lab across the street at SUNY Upstate Medical University. Jeff uses zebrafish as a model to understand organ formation.

We've developed three-dimensional models, for example, for tissues in our group specifically because of that question: What is the difference between two-dimensional and three-dimensional models?

Suzan Mazur: But you need to work with experimentalists. You can't just do it through computer simulation. Right?

Lisa Manning: I would have a nuanced answer to that. I'd say that I always work with an experimentalist because cells are already complicated enough. If you're going to make a simple model for a cell, if you're not working closely with an experimentalist, then your model is almost certainly wrong.

On the other hand, working closely with developmental biologists there's a lot to learn from a null model, a model that doesn't actually have too many assumptions. Because then you discover what is universal about groups of cells. We've found that you can do computer simulations and use those to help drive hypotheses of biology.

Suzan Mazur: Antonio Lima-de-Faria once said in a book called *Evolution without Selection*—

Lisa Manning: I know this book.

Suzan Mazur: Lima-de-Faria said we need to understand minerals before we can understand biology and he saw four routes from minerals to living organisms: solid crystalline, liquid crystalline, quasi-crystalline and amorphous. He also said that minerals and other pure chemicals have no genes, yet they display the constancy of pattern and the ability to change pattern by forming a large number of forms. Do you have any thoughts about this?

Lisa Manning: From my perspective, it's certainly true and there's a lot of growing interest—one of the most exciting fields is the behavior of self-replicating materials. As you say, you don't need genes or genomes to get self-replication. When you're thinking about the ingredients of life and the pieces that you need, there's an exciting interplay of structural order. As you mentioned, crystalline, quasi-crystalline, liquid crystalline and amorphous are different ways of categorizing structural order in a system.

So when you have objects that can self-replicate, it turns out that there's an interesting question of what structures facilitate self-replication. Some exciting work is being done on this, for example, by Michael Brenner. He's one of the people at Harvard researching how structure limits the ability for self-replicating objects without going into the details of genetics.

Suzan Mazur: You've been looking at the glass problem in your collaborative research funded by the Simons Foundation. Why is Simons interested in your work?

Lisa Manning: That's a good question. You could ask him. I'm funded both through the glass collaboration and as a mathematical modeler for living systems.

Suzan Mazur: That's wonderful.

Lisa Manning: Let me focus on the glass collaboration because that's what you asked about. There's a really deep, deep fundamental question. Phil Anderson once said that the glass problem is possibly the most important unsolved problem in condensed matter physics.

Suzan Mazur: I spoke with Phil Anderson at the 2013 Princeton meeting on origins of life. He was concerned at the time about origins and energetics, thermodynamics.

Lisa Manning: I think what Phil Anderson means by the glass problem possibly being the most important unsolved problem in condensed matter physics is that if you have something that goes from a fluid to a solid, you have an associated broken symmetry. There are deep reasons in physics why that is true.

With glasses you go from being a fluid to a solid without breaking an obvious symmetry and there are a lot of tools condensed matter physicists have developed to understand how phase transitions work. When things are disordered, transitions are not well understood. Also, you may say it's specific to granular material and glasses but actually the same phenomenon is evident in machine learning problems that are important for artificial intelligence. It's apparent in protein folding, which is important for biology.

In our case, what we're thinking about is also extremely important for understanding properties of groups of cells and multicellular organisms. Morphogenesis. It also shows up in neuroscience, in trying to understand complex networks in the brain.

So there's a deep, fundamental phenomenon we don't understand that's relevant to a lot of modern science. We do have a strategy in the Simons collaboration about how to make a breakthrough on that problem. So that's why Simons is excited.

Suzan Mazur: Regarding the glass problem—glass-formers differ from crystal-formers in their bonding. Recently researchers at the University of Tokyo reported that when water and silica cool, atoms assemble into patterns with a series of concentric shells forming around each O or Si atom. But while the first shell to form is tetrahedral in both water and silica, the second structure in the case of silica is no longer ordered. There's a lack of order in supercooled silica. Do you know the study I'm referring to?

Lisa Manning: I saw the paper reported but have not looked closely at it.

Suzan Mazur: You're probably aware of Ked Stedman's work with viruses and silica.

Lisa Manning: Yes, and I saw your interview with him on the subject.

Suzan Mazur: The promo for your upcoming Simons Foundation lecture titled: "A Body Made of Glass" notes "self-organization is governed not only by biochemical signaling but also by collective mechanical interactions between cells" and that "such interactions cause biological material to behave as glassy 'living materials' near a fluid-solid transition." Can you give me a sneak preview of your upcoming Simons talk about how cells "tune their stickiness" to get the job done?

Lisa Manning: As it turns out, many living tissues are confluent, meaning their cells are touching one another with no space between them. That means cell stickiness—how many adhesive molecules cells stick onto their surfaces, how sticky they are—determines cell shape. There's a bonus for cells having more area and contact with their neighbors, which is all adhesion is.

With elongated cell shapes, ones that look like pancakes basically, there is lots more area and contact with neighboring cells.

It was a real surprise to us to find that the parameter that governs the shape of cells inside tissues also triggers the fluid-to-solid transition. Meaning you can change the global properties of an entire tissue just by tuning how sticky a cell is.

Suzan Mazur: It's fascinating that you're turning a corner on this with your research. There's been an interest in stickiness of cells going way back, maybe 50, 60 years.

Lisa Manning: Yes. A developmental biologist named Malcolm Steinberg in the 1960s came up with this really cool idea, which was that organization during embryogenesis was driven by the stickiness of cells. In that case, he really was thinking about tissues behaving like fluids all the time.

We're now realizing that a bunch of things happen in between fluid-like and solid-like behavior. Why do we care if a tissue behaves like a solid or a fluid? Because if a tissue behaves like a fluid, cells can migrate.

During early embryonic development, it makes a lot of sense for cells to cover large distances—to migrate to new places for gastrulation and to form new structures. Later on in development you need things to buckle.

Also, adult organisms need to be able to support weight to do things like move and walk. You can only really do that if you're a solid. So the change from fluid-like behavior to solid-like behavior at other times, understanding that can be a useful guide for biologists.

During wound healing and cancer metastasis—the opposite happens, which is there is a fluid-like invasion of tissues. Something that should be solid behaves like a fluid.

Suzan Mazur: Is there a final point you'd like to make?

Lisa Manning: I think there are two areas of importance: How can you get a single cell to form and replicate in the first place. A second, related problem is the origin of groups of cells working together as well as the breakdown of groups of cells working together. This is where some of the most cutting-edge science is happening now and where condensed matter physics or soft matter physics can be easily and effectively applied.

Chapter 12

On the Frontline—Allen Liu:
The Mechanome & Synthetic Cell Development

Photo, courtesy Allen Liu

11/6/2018

I spoke last week with mechanical and biomedical engineer Allen Liu, who's now on sabbatical at Max Planck Institute of Biochemistry in Martinsried just outside Munich— one of Europe's research centers on synthetic cell development. His own lab is at the University of Michigan, so he called me from Germany for our scheduled interview. We were first in touch regarding my coverage of the Dutch Synthetic Cell Symposium at Delft where he was a keynote speaker this past summer.

Allen Liu is originally from Taiwan and his cultural roots are clearly evident in his gracious professional communications. Not surprisingly, he's received a National Science Foundation grant for his synthetic (artificial) cell project and is currently in the swirl of some of Europe's most cutting edge science. Liu was also one of the speakers—and perhaps the youngest—at the NSF meeting in Alexandria, Virginia on synthetic and artificial cell development earlier this year.

Allen Liu heads the Liu Lab at the University of Michigan—where the focus is on the mechanobiology of biological membranes—and he is a professor in the university's departments of mechanical and biomedical engineering.

Liu also serves as associate editor of *RSC Advances* and is an advisory editorial board member of *WIREs Nanomedicine and Nanobiology* as well as an editorial board member of *Heliyon*.

Awards include: Emerging Investigator (*Chemical Communications*, 2017); Rising Star Award (BMES-Cellular and Molecular Bioengineering, 2017); Young Innovator in Cellular and Molecular Bioengineering (2014); NIH Director's New Innovator Award (2012), among others.

Allen Liu's BSc is in biochemistry, *with honors*, from the University of British Columbia and his PhD from the University of California, Berkeley (working with Daniel Fletcher). He was a postdoctoral fellow in cell biology at Scripps Research Institute (working with Gaudenz Danuser and Sandra Schmid).

Our interview follows.

Suzan Mazur: I detect a faint Canadian accent in your NSF video presentation on the artificial cell. Are you a native of Canada?

Allen Liu: I was born in Taiwan actually and moved to Canada as a teenager. I lived in Canada for eight years and did my undergrad studies there. I've been living and working in the US since then, except for my current sabbatical here in Germany at the Max Planck Institute of Biochemistry. I did my PhD, my postdoc and started my lab all in the US.

Suzan Mazur: Do you come from a science family?

Allen Liu: My dad has a Master's degree in chemical engineering. Mom specialized in pharmacy in medical school. Both of my parents trained in Taiwan. So, as a kid I had a keen interest in science.

Suzan Mazur: Do you have time for other interests outside the lab? Hobbies?

Allen Liu: I find that I have less and less free time outside the lab. Work as a scientist is pretty intense and I do work a lot. But I like sports, particularly tennis. And I very much enjoy spending time with my family. I have two daughters now.

Suzan Mazur: Is your wife a scientist?

Allen Liu: My wife trained as a biologist and educator. Before we had our daughters she taught at a Montessori school—kids age zero to six. She is now taking care of our two young daughters.

Suzan Mazur: You seem to be the one scientist who has presented at all the pivotal meetings in the last six months: (1) the National Science Foundation workshop on synthetic and artificial cells, (2) the Dutch Synthetic Cell Symposium, (3) "The Mechanome in Action" meeting. You also attended the Munich "Molecular Origins of Life" conference in October. Let's start with what you understand by the term "mechanome."

Allen Liu: Mechanome refers to the set of proteins or molecular entities that sense or respond to forces. How cells respond to mechanical cues, etc.

Suzan Mazur: A decade ago, then-MIT bioengineer Matthew Lang writing in the National Academy of Engineering journal *Expanding Frontiers of Engineering* spoke of sequencing the mechanome, i.e., "the role of force, mechanics and machinery in biology," and expressed the following:

"The design of biological motors can be classified by cataloging the motor's general structural features, fuel type, stepping distance, stall force, and other mechanical parameters. Detailed measurements of the motility cycles and underlying mechanisms for motility also provide information about how these mechanisms work. Ultimately 'sequencing' the mechanome will lead to the discovery of the design features of biological motors in general, enabling us to catalogue them and outline the rules that govern their behavior."

Lang concluded:

"Once we understand the physical rules that govern biological systems and can measure nature's machinery, we should eventually be able to 'sequence' the mechanome."

My question is—how far along are we in sequencing the mechanome?

Allen Liu: I don't see it as something that can be 'sequenced' as we do with the genome. I think Matt had an important insight that if we measure the forces and displacements of proteins under forces, we may be able to decipher the design principle of molecular machines.

If you think about all the proteins that sense or respond to forces, one can argue that in principle all proteins are sensitive to forces. This is because proteins are folded into three-dimensional structures by non-covalent interactions. And if you apply a force by grabbing onto a single molecule and extend it, the protein will unfold. So by their nature, all proteins are sensitive to forces.

The key thing the field is trying to understand now is that if a force is applied, how does it change the energy landscape of the molecular interactions. How does that force facilitate binding or unbinding to other molecular entities? We still don't know which proteins have cryptic sites that open upon physiological force applications. To a certain extent, we have not identified all the key molecular players in force transduction.

We learned only about eight years ago [in 2010], for example, of the existence of mammalian ion channels that are mechanically activated and are involved in touch and pain sensation. They are called Piezo1 and Piezo2.

[piezo, from the Greek word, *piesi*—meaning pressure]

Suzan Mazur: That's quite interesting. I didn't know about Piezo1 and 2.

Can you separate the mechanome from the genome?

Allen Liu: I see the mechanome in a way as a subset of the proteome—sensitive mechanical forces as a subset. In describing the mechanome, it's not an individual protein that does the job. A set of proteins is required to orchestrate mechanotransduction.

One example is force applied to focal adhesion. When you stretch the N-terminal region of talin, it reveals cryptic binding site to vinculin. For the protein to be sensitive to mechanical force, the action is often orchestrated not by one single protein but by a set of proteins.

Then, of course, there's the cytoskeleton, which is involved in contractility. A sort of chain reaction happens—cells exert force on the substrate and neighboring cells as part of the mechanotransduction process.

Suzan Mazur: Eberhard Bodenschatz said—at that same NSF meeting in May where you presented—that scientists at Max Planck are trying to see how far they can go in developing a synthetic cell WITHOUT introducing a genome. Unlike the Dutch who have added a genome to the equation. What are your thoughts?

Allen Liu: I do remember Eberhard making that statement. What I gather from that is, it depends on what you want to do with a synthetic cell. It may not need to divide. It can be an entity that can perform certain functions. To do that you can reconstitute everything from the bottom up, by including purified proteins and encapsulate all of that in a lipid bilayer vesicle.

That is essentially what the PIs [Principal Investigators] in the MaxSynBio groups are doing, although the MaxSynBio groups, to my knowledge, are targeting multiple areas (energy supply, metabolism, growth, division, etc.) as well as developing platform technology (microfluidics and cell-free expression).

Suzan Mazur: You're now doing research in one of these groups, in Petra Schwille's lab. So, would you say the MaxSynBio groups are making an artificial or synthethic cell?

Allen Liu: An artificial cell that does not have any encoded components. It can still come from purifying a protein out of a host cell like *E. coli*. A major approach is based on protein reconstitution.

The way that this could work is—if you think about the cells in our bodies that do not have a nucleus, like red blood cells and platelets. Although these cells do not have a nucleus, they perform very sophisticated functions. For instance, a platelet is just ~2-3 microns in size, yet it has all the protein machinery enclosed within its own cell membrane and can function in blood coagulation without having any genetically encoded components.

Petra's lab encompasses several areas, but with the major focus on dynamic pattern formation of cell division machineries.

Suzan Mazur: Can you tell me about the patent you hold regarding an artificial cell?

Allen Liu: That was part of my PhD work with Dan Fletcher at Berkeley. The basic idea is to use a vesicle and purified proteins as a platform for an artificial cell with controlled membrane compositions and asymmetry. At the time we developed a strategy to encapsulate using a liquid jet.

Suzan Mazur: The Liu Lab at the University of Michigan is particularly interested in the mechanobiology of the cell lipid membrane. Would you briefly describe your hypothesis about cell tension and membrane trafficking and the significance of this in building an artificial cell?

Allen Liu: The hypothesis is currently more relevant to living cells. At the moment it would be a bit difficult to extrapolate that for synthetic or artificial cells.

We are building mechanosensitive cells—artificial cells that will basically respond to mechanical forces. In this case, we are mimicking the basic process that cells can sense and respond to forces. This is work we've done on our own as well as in collaboration with Vincent Noireaux at the University of Minnesota.

Basically, we are incorporating channel proteins that are known to respond to membrane tension in the bilayer. If we incorporate this successfully, the artificial cell senses elevated membrane tension and will open. A pore, like a little door, enables molecules to go in and out. We're writing this paper up now.

Suzan Mazur: Are you looking at neutron scattering for information in designing your artificial cell? It's fascinating what can be seen with neutron scattering. I've had recent conversations about this with John Katsaras who's at Oak Ridge National Laboratory and Tommy Nylander at Lund University/ESS. They're both membrane specialists.

Allen Liu: I am not working with neutron scattering, but I'm aware of some of the classic work that's been done. That you can see the structure of membranes precisely with neutron scattering.

Suzan Mazur: And motion.

Allen Liu: That's right. We're mostly using fluorescence light microscopy as our main tool coupled with careful image analysis. But just to finish my comment about membrane trafficking—this has very little to do with the synthetic cell at the moment.

In my lab I have also been very interested in understanding the dynamics of membranes from the perspective of plasma membrane in living cells.

As a postdoc I studied endocytosis. This is a process where cells internalize plasma membrane into endocytic vesicles.

The classic paradigm that was set up before by Columbia University biologist Michael Sheetz [a founding director of Singapore's Mechanobiology Institute] was that if you had a tense membrane, it becomes very difficult to endocytose. Because the cells like a membrane at a certain tension.

So it has to do with the homeostasis of the membrane. The tension of the membrane is at a relative set point, When the tension is high, you exocytose, and when the tension is low, you endocytose.

To me this is relevant regarding communication with the external environment. If you want to cross information in and out—you know the cell uses receptors in binding, uses light but also uses force. So, if you just consider receptor-ligand binding in signal transduction pathways, one of the key players is the receptor. The receptor can be internalized.

There's an intersection between mechanobiology and endocytosis. This is an intersection that has not been looked at very much. People I meet in the mechanobiology world focus on focal adhesion, cell-cell tension, and cytoskeletal tension, but rarely look at the effect on membrane trafficking. It's something my lab is actively working on right now.

Suzan Mazur: Can you say what you're working on there in Petra Schwille's lab in Germany?

Allen Liu: If you look at natural cells—there are compartments, there's a nucleus, mitochondria, etc. I'm looking at the engineering inside the cell.

I'm thinking about an artificial cell. My perspective on the distinction between synthetic and artificial is this. If I'm making something, say naturally extracted glucose, using a synthetic as opposed to a natural approach—then that is synthetic. If I'm making something that does not exist in nature—it's artificial.

But artificial cells are now also being referred to as synthetic cells. Funding agencies, like NSF, seem to have settled on the term synthetic cell to describe both artificial and synthetic cells. I too switched to NSF's preferred use of synthetic cell terminology in my recent project proposal that NSF funded.

Suzan Mazur: Can you tell me a bit more about your current research?

Allen Liu: One area that I'm happy to share involves liquid-liquid phase separation in organizing reactions within an artificial cell.

A decade or so ago there was a big discovery in cell biology: Compartments in cells that are not lipid bound— membrane-less organelles of liquid-nature that can fuse with one another, dissolve and grow. This discovery inspired scientists doing synthetic cell research to investigate the phenomenon. It has now been looked at quite a bit.

Christine Keating, at Penn State, has actually been studying liquid-liquid phase separation for 15-20 years—primarily using polymers of dextran and PEG [polyethylene glycol]. But short polymers, coacervates can also be used.

I'm experimenting with these systems to see if there's a way to form droplets within a cell-free expression system that can alter protein expression. The idea is to create an artificial cell with an internal organelle. A sort of internal organelle that then specializes in one function. I'm experimenting with liquid-liquid

147

phase separation to see how this can be used in making artificial cells.

Suzan Mazur: Thank you. You raised several questions at the NSF meeting: Can we build an artificial cell that couples mechanical input to a biochemical output? Can we assemble biological components? Can we insert membrane protein to build an artificial nucleus? Are we closer to answering these questions six months later?

Allen Liu: The first one and second one my lab has worked on extensively. So I think we can say yes. The third point about building an artificial nucleus—no, that has not been done. I have just submitted a proposal on this but it has not been funded yet.

Suzan Mazur: Were any of these origins of life and synthetic cell conferences in Europe video recorded?

Allen Liu: No, I don't think so.

Suzan Mazur: It would be good if the Europeans publicly streamed these meetings.

Allen Liu: I'll speak to Petra to see what she thinks about it.

Suzan Mazur: Thank you, Allen.

Chapter 13

Kim Sneppen, Simons Center Talk:
"We Are Basically All Doughnuts"

Photo of Kim Sneppen, Niels Bohr Institute

12/7/2018

Over the last several days (December 3-7) the Simons Center for Geometry and Physics at Stony Brook University has been hosting a series of lectures on Nonequilibrium Physics in Biology and streaming the video talks over the Internet.

Stony Brook is where philanthropist Jim Simons taught math for a decade before starting his enormously successful hedge fund—and with his wife Marilyn, the Simons Foundation, which is now at the forefront of a revolution in science.

This week's Simons Center talks on nonequilibrium physics in biology are also permanently linked as videos. It helps to know some fancy math in viewing them, but many of the presentations rely more on speaker charisma and images to drive home the salient points.

Among the more interesting presenters is Kim Sneppen, a professor of complex systems and biophysics at Niels Bohr Institute in Copenhagen, who addresses the diversity of shapes in the biological world.

Sneppen says, "We are basically all doughnuts" and describes how we go from a sphere to a torus in his talk titled: "Theoretical Tool Bridging Cell Polarities with Development of Morphologies."

I once asked physicist Leonard Susskind about this concept since he'd co-authored a paper on "the incredibly shrinking torus," but Susskind told me he had "NO IDEA how the torus enters biology" and that everything he knew about evolution he'd learned from reading Richard Dawkins' book.

The concept is one Stuart Pivar's been thinking about for quite some time.

Here's a link to the Sneppen Simons Center video: **http://scgp.stonybrook.edu/video_portal/video.php?id=3864**

Last year Sneppen was awarded DKK 16.5M (US$2.5M) by the European Research Council to "explore the diverse and complex world within and between cells." In relation to his ERC grant, Sneppen said the following:

> *"I want to initiate a new research direction at the research frontier between biology and physics. By its diversity of molecules, interactions and cells, biology expresses its universality in different forms than found in systems conventionally explored by statistical physics. . . .I describe biological systems with focus on the rules of interactions and their consequences rather than dig down into the smallest details."*

In discussing the diversity of shapes in his Simons Center talk, Sneppen emphasizes that it's most effective to "work close to the scale of the phenomenon."

I had the pleasure of meeting Kim Sneppen several years ago in Copenhagen during ICSB2013, the International Conference on Systems Biology. It was September and Sneppen was wearing bermuda shorts and an oxford shirt—sleeves rolled up. He's an attractive man with Nordic blue eyes dramatically framed by unruly brows.

At one point in his Simons Center talk he informs the audience about the way hair grows perpendicular to skin, although Sneppen's own brows are very clearly in defiance!

In much of the lecture Sneppen discusses how cells make sheets and tubes. He notes that cells have proteins on the outside that enable them to stick together. But that by putting an organizing force on the polarity vectors, shape can change.

Sneppen identifies several rules for embryonic development: (1) polarity, (2) signaling, (3) differential adhesion, (4) apoptosis.

The strength of planar cell polarity (PCP) he says is associated with tube formation and that the strength of PCP controls tube length and width. He also says PCP drives gastrulation and neurulation.

Sneppen announced recent publication of his paper: "Theoretical tool bridging cell polarities with development of robust morphologies."

Other talks of interest include Joe Howard's on what's responsible for cell oscillations: "Oscillatory enthalpic changes during early embryogenesis driven by the cell cycle." And Jacques Prost's "Tissues as Active Systems" (serious math involved).

December 7 is the last day of the workshop but, again, the Simons Center video talks remain posted for future viewing.

Chapter 14

David Edelman: Origin "3D Organismal Form"

Photo, courtesy David Edelman

8/27/2015

Neuroscientist David Edelman, who's currently on the adjunct faculties of the University of San Diego and the University of California, San Diego, and is the son of late Nobel laureate Gerald Edelman—like his father has an interest in "how 3D organismal form comes about." In the interview that follows, we discuss origin of morphology, paradigm shift, as well as Edelman's fascination with the octopus.

David Edelman has been a professor of neuroscience at Bennington College, an associate fellow in experimental neurobiology at The Neurosciences Institute (NSI) and assistant professor of neurobiology at The Scripps Research Institute. His PhD is in paleoanthropology from the University of Pennsylvania and his BA in sociology and anthropology from Swarthmore. His postdoctoral work was done at Scripps and NSI.

He is currently on the advisory board of the Society for Mind Brain Science and has served on the editorial board of *Frontiers in Psychology: Theoretical and Philosophical Psychology.*

Suzan Mazur: You're continuing along the lines of some of your father's research in neuroscience. I'm sorry you lost your father, Gerald Edelman, last year. What an inspiration he must have been and must continue to be. What was it like growing up in that kind of science environment?

David Edelman: I'd say more normal than you might think. For instance, both of my parents insisted that I learn, and that my siblings learn, a musical instrument. My father was a violinist. My mother played flute and piano. My parents didn't care which instruments we chose, as long as we learned to play an instrument. They were very wise in their insistence because the violin has always been something I could lean on in the absence of anything else in my life.

Music, was, of course, central to my father's life. His professional aspirations as a violinist were interrupted by his mother's insistence that he pursue something with which he could actually make a living. My father steered clear of imposing science on us. He was eager for us to be interested in science, but he wasn't activist about it.

Suzan Mazur: Of course you didn't steer clear of science. From your perspective as a neuroscientist, is there a paradigm shift underway in evolutionary thinking?

David Edelman: I think there should be a shift. . . . The Modern Synthesis was a scientific reckoning—or coming to terms— among great thinkers: George Gaylord Simpson, Ernst Mayr, JBS Haldane, Theodosius Dobzhansky, to mention some of the key players. They had noble aspirations, but there was a problem in that a very determinist point of view reigned among geneticists, and genetics was an important part of the argument being made by the neo-Darwinians. They had what they thought was the basis for heritability. They thought that essentially it was all going to be gravy at that point, that they could merge the fields of natural science and genetics, using genetics to explain both heritability of individual traits and the appearance of higher taxa—new species, families, genera, etc. They were way off base at the time. I don't think they knew just how far off base they were.

One of the problems, and we're still confronting these problems in modern genetics, is that we do not have the ability to discern from a 1D code, which is basically what a given genome is, a 3D organism. We don't yet have any way to explain how 3D organismal form comes about.

One of my father's scientific legacies that remains underappreciated is—he pointed this out 26, 27 years ago in his book *Topobiology* —that just understanding the order and identity of bases, however many there are, was not going to give us the basis for understanding the origin of morphology whether during development or in the course of evolution.

Suzan Mazur: So it is still somewhat mind-boggling to consider how body form arises because we don't even understand yet how a cell works?

David Edelman: I do think there are some really poignant clues.

I am in admiration, for instance, of Stuart Pivar's description of what I believe are very large scale physical and mechanical forces— or constraints that influence what happens when populations of cells reach a certain size and density. In a sense, Stuart has described the top end of things.

Photo, courtesy Stuart Pivar

154

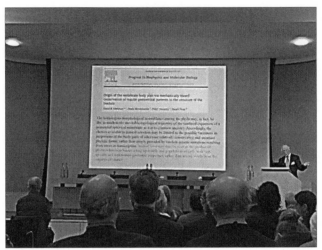

Edelman, Pivar paper, 2016 Royal Society Evolution Summit

My father, when he was doing his work on CAMs, was describing the bottom end of things—the local cellular "neighborhood." So there's this interaction between the two scales of development and evolution, between what Stuart Pivar is talking about and what my dad talked about. I think the explanation actually lies in the interaction. I think it would be most fruitful if someone were to take the bull by the horns and try to find out what's going on [in that interaction].

Suzan Mazur: It's interesting that Fermilab is exploring whether we actually live in a 3D world. They think it may be 2D and we're living in a hologram.

David Edelman: There's an intellectual crisis in modern biology. A hyper-determinist streak runs through the thinking, particularly in molecular biology and genetics. Even if researchers can't get directly from DNA code to a 3D organism, they believe essentially that it's simply a coding problem.

It's actually more complex. The problem is that we cannot observe a lot of processes in sufficient detail and at all the necessary levels of interaction—either during individual development or across evolutionary time. And these processes are messier than we believe. Right now, we can't infer processes in a systematic way regarding the relevant levels of morphological change. We don't have the capacity to do that yet.

Suzan Mazur: What would you say about the following driving biological evolution toward increasing complexity? (1) adhesive interactions among cells, which your father was studying, (2) infection of cellular organisms by viruses, bacteria or fungi plus symbiosis, (3) the constructal law of flow systems—

David Edelman: It's a combination.

The real problem is that what we're after is a moving target.

One of the unfortunate aspects of Western science is that it's hyper-reductionist. There's nothing wrong with that to a certain extent. You can certainly pull things apart to study them and look at the constituent elements; at a certain level of organization they look like a highly mechanical system and to some extent you can discern from your dissections what each element does. When you look at certain molecular biological problems, for example, that's what you see. But the critical issue is that we're talking about much larger systems, systems nested within other systems. It's the interactions across those different levels of organization that need to also be considered.

Suzan Mazur: That's one of the reasons why your father went on from CAMs (cell adhesion molecules) to neuroscience?

David Edelman: Right. . . .

Suzan Mazur: There's now a growing interest in viruses and viroids. Scientists report that roughly 10% of the human genome is inhabited by viruses, and a viroid-like entity is considered a "very good candidate" for the first replicon on Earth.

František Baluška, a European cell biologist and plant physiologist has described cell-cell adhesion that happens as viruses enter cell membranes of other organisms and start manipulating their protein receptors on the way deeper into the cell to make copies. Here's what Baluška thinks:

> *"Infection, especially the viral one, but also bacterial and fungal infections, followed by symbiosis, is proposed to act as the major force that drives biological evolution toward higher complexity."*

He says, "Without infection no evolution."

What are your thoughts about the virosphere?

David Edelman: I don't bristle at this. I embrace any new ideas; it's important for science to be creative. But I'm always circumspect when a concept comes along and claims are made that it is THE motive force.

My own scientific career, which is very checkered—I trained as a human paleontologist, I did a postdoc in gene transcriptional regulation, and then I moved on to cellular neurobiology and eventually to problems of higher brain functions—specifically the evolutionary origins of consciousness and its nature in non-human animals. What I'm saying here is that a lot of things have exerted influence on the trajectory of life.

I also think it's in the nature of trained Western scientists to look for a big breakthrough answer. We scientists tend to admire the mechanistic reduction of classical physics. What my dad used to call a case of "physics envy." We'd love the biological world to cooperate in the same way that the atom and everything else scaled up to the atom behaved prior to Einstein, prior to 20th century physics. For the world to be reducible in a very mechanistic way. I am leery of this conception because biology defies it at every turn.

Suzan Mazur: Are you looking at signaling?

David Edelman: I've been particularly interested in the visual system of the octopus, this beautifully convergent visual system relative to that of the vertebrates. The octopus eye has a focusing lens. It has six or seven ocular muscles. The octopus has incredible distance vision as invertebrates go. It's seldom that you come across an invertebrate that can actually look you in the eye and even track you with its eyes. We don't see that in insects (arthropods such as spiders are a different story). The eye in the octopus is a perfect entrée to the notion of a sophisticated suite of neural function and behaviors that in many ways seem to converge in nature and complexity on those of vertebrates.

If you look at the neurons of an octopus, they don't strike you as very unusual. You see similar-looking nerve cells in much more primitive mollusks, such as mussels and clams. But if you look at the density of their brain nuclei and you look at their sensory and motor adaptations—their eyes, their tactile sense, the way they connect with the world—it's an amazing degree of complexity, especially for an invertebrate.

Suzan Mazur: What are your thoughts about epigenetics?

David Edelman: I think epigenetics is critically important.

Suzan Mazur: Do you define epigenetics as development or as acquired traits?

David Edelman: Both. DNA methylation suggests a somatic mechanism for heritability, which is somewhat far afield of neo-Darwinism.

Suzan Mazur: The criticism is that the change that happens only appears for a few generations. On the other hand, experimental evidence exists that the Weismann barrier is being crossed, leading scientists to question whether the Weismann barrier exists.

David Edelman: It's a ripe area for further exploration. There are years to go before we have an inkling about what's actually going on. What we have found, as you say, is pretty constrained. It's very suggestive.

We really don't know the rules of the game, and one of the reasons why we don't know the rules of the game is that we don't yet have an experimental paradigm to track these things at myriad levels in real time.

Chapter 15

D'Arcy and the Dutch Anatomists

"In other words, what we call Form is a ratio of magnitudes, referred to direction in space. . . . When in dealing with magnitude we refer its variations to successive intervals of time (or when, as it is said, we equate it with time), we are then dealing with the phenomenon of growth."—D'Arcy Thompson

11/16/17 (above photo and following anatomy images by Suzan Mazur)

A mini-exhibit in Amsterdam of D'Arcy Thompson themes set up for the public to view by Dutch academics who recently held a private meeting on these subjects, seems clearly anticlimactic to the rich display offered the public at the centenary celebration of Thompson's On Growth and Form book last month in Scotland. Indeed, the Dutch exhibit at Allard Pierson Museum (through January 8) appears largely a promotion for University of Exeter research fellow Gemma Anderson's text on drawing research.

It could have been a livelier exhibit in Amsterdam if other science art had been showcased as well. I'm thinking of the color plates by Peter Sheesley for embryo geometry investigator Stuart Pivar, for example. And a page or two from Matthew Jarron's D'Arcy comic book (left) would clearly have cheered up the room.

160

With the exception of an invagination display (top photo)—on loan from the Museum Vrolik—the Allard Pierson mini-exhibit was a bit of a bore.

On the other hand, Vrolik—an anatomy museum 45 minutes by train outside Amsterdam's city center—IS an astonishing place to visit for any serious researcher of human growth and form.

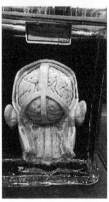

Set inside the Academic Medical Center (AMC), the museum
houses 1,100 specimens, most dating from the 19th century. The

present museum grew out of the private collection of two Amsterdam professors of anatomy—Gerard Vrolik (1775-1859) and his son Willem Vrolik (1801-1863). The tie-in to Thompson is obvious in the Vrolik displays of every part of the human structure. The collection also chronicles human development from earliest embryo to full-term fetus. In his 1,136 page masterpiece, *On Growth and Form*, D'Arcy Thompson shares these relevant insights:

> *"The action of the molecular forces has been variously explained. But one simple explanation (or mode of statement) is that the molecules of the surface-layer are being constantly attracted into the interior by such as are just a little more deeply situated; the surface shrinks as molecules keep quitting it for the interior and this surface-shrinkage exhibits itself as surface-tension. The process continues till it can go no further, that is to say until the surface itself becomes a 'minimal area.'"*

> *"We have little reason to doubt, and no just cause to disbelieve, that the whole configuration, for instance, of an egg in the advanced stages of segmentation is accurately determined by simple physical laws, just as much as in the early stages of two or four cells, during which early stages we are able to recognize and demonstrate the forces and their resultant effects."*

> *"It will be seen at once that there is a 'point of inflection' somewhere about the fifth month of intra-uterine life; up to that date growth proceeds with a continually increasing velocity. After that date, though growth is still rapid, its velocity tends to fall away; the curve, while still ascending is becoming an S-shaped curve."*

But Gerard and Willem Vrolik were not only fascinated by form, as biologist/mathematician D'Arcy Thompson was. They were also intrigued by malformation.

The Museum Vrolik shelves hold perhaps 100 glass containers of conjoined, cyclops, dwarf, and other abnormally structured babies impossible to describe here. What can go wrong, clearly did go wrong with pregnancies in the 19th century before modern medicine.

Unlike Philadelphia's Mütter Museum, the Vrolik collection can be viewed without all the red tape. It is an education not to be missed.

Chapter 16

Bogdan Dragnea—
Physical Virology & Harnessing Viruses

Photo, courtesy Bogdan Dragnea

7/20/2018

Something in the way they move—viruses, that is—
fascinates Indiana University physical chemist Bogdan
Dragnea. Dragnea calls it "cooperativity." Luis Villarreal calls it
"gangen." But it's clear from recent Zika and Ebola epidemics that
understanding the path of a virus continues to be frontier science.
Dragnea, whose roots are in a small town in Romania near the
Ukraine border, has been investigating the structural properties of
viruses, and in recent years "[p]hysical principles in the self-
assembly of immature HIV-1 particles." He is now at
work harnessing the powerful path, the motion of viruses—
although he does not consider viruses live organisms.

The Dragnea Group is experimenting with using viruses as a
scaffold to make nanoscopic light for laser-guided surgery—

among other lab projects sponsored "through the years" by DOE, NSF, NIH, the US Army Research Office and Human Frontier Science Program.

Aside from nanophotonics and the physical principles that "govern" morphogenesis, research interests include bio-inspired materials and the thermodynamics of small systems.

Bogdan Dragnea's latest scientific papers appear in the Royal Society of Chemistry journal *Soft Matter* (self-assembly of convex particles on spherocylindrical template); Springer (in vitro assembly of virus shells around nanoparticles) and *ACS Nano* (virus coat protein assembly around metal nanorods).

He is Provost Professor in chemistry at Indiana University (but says he has "no administrative function"). In naming Dragnea Provost Professor, the university expressed the following:

> *"Dragnea is a leading researcher in physical virology whose work has helped place IU Bloomington at the forefront of the field. Part of the physical chemistry group in the Department of Chemistry, he conducts research on the assembly, disassembly and intracellular tracking of viruses in living cells.*
>
> *He was among the first researchers to recognize that protein self-assembly used in nature to create virus particles could be exploited to create nanoparticle "cages" with well-defined structures and novel physical properties. He more recently developed a new research direction seeking to understand the assembly of immature HIV-1 particles; the research explores early events of HIV-1 budding and assembly, with the long-term goal of developing ways to inhibit growth of the virus."*

Bogdan Dragnea is also a professor of physics at IU. Outside of his research lab and teaching, he enjoys hiking Indiana's trails, sculpting wood and building timber frames.

Dragnea told me he gets back to Romania a couple of times a year to see his parents. While in Romania, he visits key scientific institutes there and is a member of the Horia Hulubei Physics Foundation in Bucharest. He reports that interesting research is taking place in Romania.

His PhD is from University of Paris-Sud and his undergraduate diploma from University of Bucharest—both in physics. Postdoctoral research, with Stephen Leone, was in near-field optics at JILA (Joint Institute for Laboratory Astrophysics).

I spoke recently by phone with Bogdan Dragnea at his lab in Bloomington.

Suzan Mazur: Are you related to the Romanian politician with the same last name who's been in the news?

Bogdan Dragnea: No, I'm not. My family name, Dragnea, is relatively widespread in Romania.

Suzan Mazur: Where are you from in Romania?

Bogdan Dragnea: From a town of about 20,000 people in the northeast bordering Ukraine.

Suzan Mazur: Do you come from a science family?

Bogdan Dragnea: My dad is a veterinarian and my mom has a college degree in biology. She taught elementary school.

Suzan Mazur: Do you get back to Romania from time to time?

Bogdan Dragnea: Yes, once or twice a year. My parents live there.

Suzan Mazur: Is important scientific research being done in Romania these days?

Bogdan Dragnea: Yes. The resources, of course, are different from what we have in the US, but science in Romania has come a long way in terms of organizing itself and establishing focus areas. Each time I visit I spend some time talking to people at research institutes.

Being part of the European community is a big factor in promoting science there. But science is not as popular as when I was growing up in Romania. There are now more lucrative professions, I guess, for young people.

Suzan Mazur: Your research has significant US government support—DOE, NIH, NSF, Army Research Office. What is the Army's interest in your work?

Bogdan Dragnea: To be honest, one never knows. You send a proposal and the Army Research Office advises whether it likes it or not. It is interested in fundamental problems or fundamental questions that may lead to unexpected consequences.

So, if it's new enough, I think that's the criteria—at least the program that funds me—if the research is new and interesting, it will fund the research. If there is something really interesting that comes up in the research that we cannot predict, then it is going to take the project to a different level.

Suzan Mazur: Is the Army currently funding you?

Bogdan Dragnea: It is funding me at present for things that I want to do. I think it's because the research that we are doing here seems creative.

Suzan Mazur: Can you say what you're working on for the Army?

Bogdan Dragnea: I can say I work on principles of organizing soft condensed matter using radiation fields, using light basically. The project that is funded concerns the ability of changing the organization of colloidal particles by using light, lasers. The phenomenon of self-organization, bioinspired phenomena.

Suzan Mazur: Your PhD is in physics but you are Provost Professor in chemistry and you're studying viruses. You're a physical chemist?

Bogdan Dragnea: Professionally I think of myself as a physical chemist. I found that depending on where I am active, people are going to consider me one thing or another. My background, as you said, my degrees are in physics, but when I came to the US I was advised that the kind of physics we like to do here is chemistry. So, it depends more on the local perception than on my own perception.

I think of myself as a physicist but I am interested in chemical problems and biological problems. It's where the edge is.

Suzan Mazur: You are Provost Professor in chemistry. Is this administrative?

Bogdan Dragnea: The Provost (was called Chancellor a few years ago) elected to give me this title but I am not a provost. I have no administrative function.

Suzan Mazur: I understand that you have an expertise in optics and have been studying virus morphology with state-of the-art microscopy. What are some of the tools you're using and what are you seeing now that couldn't be seen without such tools?

Bogdan Dragnea: We use atomic force microscopes to probe how viruses deform on contact. When viruses infect they have to first bind to the cell membrane. At that point there is a tug of war between the cell and the virus. We have a mechanical deformation problem.

Atomic force microscopes can image very, very small objects— objects such as viruses, a few tens of nanometers across. By tapping a virus with a nanoscopic probe—this is a physically sharp silicon pyramid that we bring in close contact to the virus—it allows us to actually detect its morphology and changes in response to pressure.

Suzan Mazur: You can see this tug of war going on.

Bogdan Dragnea: Yes.

Suzan Mazur: Are you using the transmission electron microscope also?

Bogdan Dragnea: Yes. For us that's more of a routine technique we use to check the quality of virus particles and substrates.

Suzan Mazur: What is your perspective on the importance of neutron science, using neutrons to probe materials, including living cells to study structure, motion and function. The Spallation Neutron Source at Oak Ridge National Lab in Tennessee is being expanded. China Spallation Neutron Source is under construction in Dongguan. And there are several neutron science facilities currently operating in Europe with a dozen countries involved in the research. The European Spallation Source at Lund University in Sweden (48% complete) is being touted as the most sophisticated facility for neutron science.

Bogdan Dragnea: Neutron scattering has been used very early on in the study of viruses. This is how we learned where the genome was located with respect to the protein shell, when no crystallographic (X-ray) data was available. As brighter sources are coming on line, new progress is expected in understanding the protein-nucleic acid interaction in fully formed virus assemblies.

Suzan Mazur: Do you consider viruses live organisms since viruses can recognize their targets, attach, and infect their hosts— most viruses using a tail spike and needle—and as you've noted, they can "drive large-scale phenomena across the entire biosphere"?

Bogdan Dragnea: No, I don't. I will stick with the definition that requires for a living organism to reproduce and produce mechanical work in a thermodynamic cycle. If it could do that, then I would say it's alive. But the virus cannot do mechanical work as part of a cyclic transformation. That is because they do not have a metabolism. A virus can do mechanical work, but not as part of a cycle, that is, returning to an initial state after extracting energy from environment. It doesn't do it in a cycle like we do it.

Viruses are part of the fabric of life for sure. They are extremely important for evolution, from very local to very global phenomena, but they are not organisms.

Suzan Mazur: There was an NSF-sponsored meeting in May in Alexandria, Virginia on synthetic cell development and one of the presenters, Richard Murray, an engineer at Caltech, said that as an engineer he doesn't consider replication necessary for making a synthetic cell. Is it a matter of opinion or is there a scientific right or wrong on this, factual basis? By the way, Eugene Koonin sees viruses as active organisms.

Bogdan Dragnea: When you write an article or a paper and want to make a point you have to define your fundamental concepts. The definition for life in Philip Anderson's paper stuck with me, which is, that you have to have replication and you have to have at least one cycle that produces mechanical work. The organism has to go from an initial state, produce some work and come back to the same initial state—by regaining its energy somehow from somewhere.

Suzan Mazur: Phil Anderson, the Princeton professor? I spoke with him at the 2013 Princeton Origins of Life conference.

Bogdan Dragnea: Yes, the Nobel laureate. That's the definition for life I think makes sense. According to that definition [Anderson's definition], viruses are sort of borderline citizens of the biosphere. They're not quite alive.

But I know that viruses tend to be very complicated, so complicated sometimes that they closely resemble bacteria. Scientists have had a hard time distinguishing large viruses from bacteria. If viruses have their own metabolism or rudiments of a metabolism, then the line is blurry. It's okay to be blurry.

Why do we have to have a sharp line between life and non-life? [emphasis added]

Suzan Mazur: What self-organization principles governing morphogenesis of viruses have you identified in your research?

Bogdan Dragnea: In my lab here at Indiana University we look at viruses as systems of molecules that have very strong cooperative properties. The molecules tend to have evolved in such a way that the effect they have is larger than the sum of the parts. We are tracking and establishing how those cooperative interactions can be used either by the virus to perform its functions or by us in our attempt in the lab to modify the virus to perform functions the virus has not evolved itself.

Suzan Mazur: You've said viruses can drive large-scale phenomena across the entire biosphere. Would you give an example?

Bogdan Dragnea: Every form of life is going to have a virus. You have viruses that prey on bacteria, viruses that prey on plants, on mammals. The phages, the ones that prey on bacteria, are especially important because bacteria are important.

A large amount of carbon is fixed by bacteria in ocean water and the number of bacteria fixing that carbon is regulated by phages. **They are the dark matter of the biological universe.** [emphasis added].

Viruses make a difference in the balance of carbon in oceans.

Viruses also make a difference in how large organisms, like humans, function. There are roughly three or four pounds of bacteria in the human gut. Bacteria allow us to digest our food. Those bacteria are kept in a certain equilibrium by phages. So there's a whole universe—

Suzan Mazur: Eugene Koonin has said animals, plants and fungi all live within the context of the microbiome, within the network of microbes and viruses.

Bogdan Dragnea: Yes.

Suzan Mazur: Would you say a bit more about virus shells—I assume you mean capsids—possibly being "useful in facilitating accelerated photon emission from a quantum coherent collective state, at room temperature"?

Bogdan Dragnea: Think about photosynthesis, how sunlight is collected by the photosynthetic machinery of a leaf and transformed into sugar. You take CO_2, you take photons and water and oxygen and transform them into one of the molecules of life.

At the heart of this is an antenna that captures the light. There's a chemical antenna inside every leaf, a nice little ring of chlorophyll. Chlorophyll molecules are pigments. These pigments are making the leaf green. They absorb the photon in such a way that they take its energy and then allow for very fast transport of this energy to where the reaction actually happens. They channel that energy to the tiny chemical reactor, which can harvest the energy and put it to work—to take CO_2 and make sugar out of it, glucose.

So I'm thinking. . . At the heart of this there is an antenna formed of molecules, of chlorophylls and these chlorophylls work together. The inverse of an antenna would be a light source. You take an ordered group of molecules and you make them act in a concerted fashion in order to emit light not to absorb light. That's what we are trying to do using a virus. To make a strong nanoscopic, very tiny source of light for use in facilitating, for instance, laser-guided surgery.

There is a lot of imaging done now that does not use coherent emission. When you get coherence, you get more powerful, much stronger light intensities. We are trying to use the virus as a scaffold that connects emitting molecules.

The symmetry is very important. That's why I've been interested in how viruses obtain these symmetries, how they assemble. How to control and harness those properties.

Suzan Mazur: That's fascinating. This is your current research.

Bogdan Dragnea: I'm writing a paper on this right now.

Suzan Mazur: Do you think Earth's viruses are of Earth origin and are you a member of the NASA astrovirology community?

Bogdan Dragnea: No, I'm not a member, but I'm not surprised people are thinking about this because viruses can be very resilient entities. I've read about lab viruses that can be carried up by the wind and they end up in the clouds, high up in the stratosphere. I've read reports that viruses have been found in the clouds at about 30,000 feet. It's really cold. The sun radiation is very strong. The viruses are stuck in the little grains of ice that make high altitude clouds. Then the viruses eventually come down and they're fine and can infect a crop of tomatoes.

Suzan Mazur: What do you think about the emphasis now on mechanobiology? In fact, at the NFS-sponsored synthetic cell meeting I mentioned earlier, Eberhard Bodenschatz, the presenter from Max Planck said that in its development of the synthetic cell it was going to see how far self-organization would take them without introducing a genome.

Bogdan Dragnea: It's not surprising about this approach by Max Planck. It gives more control. Waiting to see what can happen. All sorts of things can happen.

Regarding mechanobiology, there's a great introduction to it from 2006 by Rob Phillips and Steven Quake in *Physics Today*. It has a wonderful easy to grasp picture of how at the scale of biological organelles below 100 nanometers many phenomena have characteristic energies that converge there.

For instance, energies related to an electron confined to a box several nanometers in size. Thermal energy. Mechanical energy. And chemical energy. Especially those bonds that are prevalent within the molecules of life. They all converge in magnitude at that spatial scale. There is cross-talk.

This means you have the link between mechanics and thermodynamics and the link between thermodynamics and quantum mechanics and they all mix there in the region between 10 nanometers and 100 nanometers. It's that area, in particular, of mechanobiology that's going to be extremely interesting and challenging because of the mixing of these scales. [emphasis added]

Suzan Mazur: Is this movement in science coming from East to West or is this focus on mechanobiology due to advancements in microscopy and other tools?

Bogdan Dragnea: It's more of the latter. It's not socio-geographical. Science is pretty much a delocalized thing now. Someone discovers something in Beijing, it's going to be immediately picked up somewhere else.

It's more like you said: the instrumentation became so great that we can now measure precisely the masses of hundreds of molecules working together. This was never possible before. We can use electron microscopes to see single atoms. We can probe the forces of single atoms using different kinds of tools. The change in the infrastructure is huge. [emphasis added]

Suzan Mazur: Do you find time for activities outside science like art, sports, or mushroom hunting?

Bogdan Dragnea: Yes. Yes. Sometime. Not a whole lot. I hike, so from time to time I spot a mushroom but I don't go especially for mushrooms. I do like to spend time carving wood.

Suzan Mazur: Making sculptures?

Bogdan Dragnea: Yes. Sculptures. I also like the old way of wood construction, timber frames, for instance. I'm passionate about learning and trying my own construction skills. To build a shelter. Or garage. A play room. Things like this. Around the house.

Suzan Mazur: Is there a final point you'd like to make?

Bogdan Dragnea: I guess the take home message would be the point of cooperativity between molecules, which the viruses are excelling at. There is a lot that biomedical engineers can learn from viruses and get inspired by the cooperativity manifested by the molecules making a virus.

We took this research in two directions, one is mechanics, the other is photonics. Both pretty promising. I guess you'll see me doing the same thing in a few years.

Chapter 17

"Astrovirology" Chief Ken Stedman—
Earth Origins for Viruses

Photo, courtesy Ken Stedman

2/19/2018

If viruses originated on Earth—which is NASA astrovirology chief Ken Stedman's "best guess"—just why do we need a new field called astrovirology? What would Jerry Fodor have said?

Ken Stedman, whose day job at Portland State University is investigating the viruses of archaebacteria found at geothermally heated hot springs, nevertheless, thinks exploring for viruses and their biosignatures in space using state-of-the-art microscopes "needs to be done."

But why? Stedman says five years ago his discovery that viruses can be frozen in silica and then recover their infectivity as their glass coating dissolves, led not only to his startup company StoneStable, Inc.—which is now developing technologies to deliver vaccines that would not depend on refrigeration—but peaked his curiosity about the ability of viruses to hitch a ride in the atmosphere.

Stedman now serves as chief scientific officer of StoneStable. He says silica is common to many planets and he obviously wonders whether viruses exist elsewhere in the universe, how far such viruses might be able to travel remaining intact, and by what means.

Stedman's recent 12-page article: "Astrovirology: Viruses at Large in the Universe" published in *Astrobiology* journal by privately held Mary Ann Liebert, Inc. caught my attention, partly because it's behind a $50 paywall! And partly because *Astrobiology* journal is such an incestuous publication with most of its editors and editorial board tied to NASA!

The astrovirology paper's first author is Aaron Berliner (NASA affiliation: Mars terraforming), now a PhD student at the University of California-Berkeley and the Arkin Laboratory on Martian Ecopoiesis. Berliner's research focus is synthetic viruses, extremophile biology, DNA nanotechnology, and making mars-in-a-jar reactors.

The paper's other author is Tomohiro Mochizuki, an ancient virus specialist at Tokyo's Earth Life Science Institute who has been studying viruses and microbes at the Jinata (earth hatchet) hot springs in Japan's Izu archipelago.

Ken Stedman is a professor of biology at Portland State University's Center for Life in Extreme Environments. Among his many honors are: Portland State University Foundation Philanthropic Cultivation Award (2017); Oregon Museum of Science and Industry Science Communication Fellow (2017); BioMed Central Research Award (2012, Best Paper in *BioMedCentral* journals); BioMed Central Research Category Award (2012, Computational and high-throughput studies in genomics and systems biology); Chair (elected), Gordon

Research Conference on Archaea (2011); John Eliot Allen Outstanding Teacher Award (2003-2004) (partial list).

In addition to his position at PSU, Stedman teaches at Oregon Health and Science University. He's been a research fellow at Montana State University as well as at Wageningen University in The Netherlands. His post-doctoral research was with Wolfram Zillig at Max-Planck Institute for Biochemistry in Germany. Ken Stedman has also worked in industry as a biotechnician at Sandoz Pharma, Ltd. in Switzerland and as a researcher at Genentech, Inc. in San Francisco.

His PhD is in molecular and cell biology from the University of California-Berkeley and his BSc in chemical engineering from Stanford University.

I spoke by phone recently with Ken Stedman at his lab in the Pacific Northwest, where he enjoys a view of the mountain of fire—Mount St. Helens. Our interview follows.

Suzan Mazur: The astrovirology article you co-authored: "Astrovirology: Viruses at Large in the Universe" is currently featured in *Astrobiology* journal, one of 80 some publications privately published by a company headquartered in New Rochelle, New York called Mary Ann Liebert, Inc. Mary Ann Liebert, Inc. also published the *NASA Astrobiology Strategy* Executive Summary, the *European Astrobiology Roadmap*, as well as the NASA-supported *Astrobiology Primer*—whose editor-in-chief is an episcopal priest, a lead author on the current *NASA Astrobiology Strategy*, and one of 24 religious scholars NASA/Templeton funded (2015-2017) to investigate how the religious community would respond to the discovery of life in outer space.

Astrobiology journal bills itself as "the most-cited peer-reviewed journal dedicated to the understanding of life's origin, evolution, and distribution in the universe" and it carries the following disclaimer:

"The views, opinions, findings, conclusions and recommendations set forth in any Journal article are solely those of the authors of those articles and do not necessarily reflect the views, policy or position of the Journal, the Publisher, its editorial board or any affiliated Societies and should not be attributed to any of them."

What the *Astrobiology* journal disclaimer does not say is that most of *Astrobiology* journal's editors and editorial board, and often its authors are tied to NASA. For example, the first author on your article, Aaron Berliner, worked at NASA with senior planetary scientist Chris McKay—*Astrobiology*'s deputy editor—to develop the Mars terraforming timeline. You chair NASA's astrovirology focus group and co-authored a virus paper with Sherry Cady, *Astrobiology* journal's editor-in-chief.

You note in your *Astrobiology* journal article that one of your priorities is reaching out to the general public "regarding the ubiquity and role of viruses." Much of what you present is, indeed, already public knowledge—referenced in six pages of end citations.

My question is why didn't you publish your astrovirology article independently? Why publish in a journal that despite its disclaimer is seen as a propaganda arm of NASA and "the Darwinian government"—as the late, great philosopher Jerry Fodor once characterized it—a publication put together around the kitchen table of Sherry Cady and managing editor/hubby, Larry Cady, who is a fiction writer?

I mean there are red flags everywhere. It's like astrobiology according to the Book of Mormon. Why did you not publish independently?

Ken Stedman: Why did we not publish independently? The main reason we didn't publish independently is that I promised Sherry that I would write something for *Astrobiology* journal. That's the number one reason. A second one, and probably more important, is that even if this is a propaganda arm of NASA—those are the kinds of people that we're trying to reach with this particular article.

Yes, I am also incredibly dedicated to the general public knowing about this and I am doing my best to inform the public, which is partly why I'm talking with you about this idea. But I don't see that the astrovirology article, per se, in *Astrobiology* journal as being outreach to the general community. I see it as being outreach to the readers of *Astrobiology* journal, most of whom I think are involved with NASA. Those are the people who read these things, and hopefully are also the ones who will be interested in following up.

Suzan Mazur: The public is very interested in the virus narrative and NASA seems to want to control the narrative and control the technology using public funds. This is a problem. The public doesn't have any control over where the public funding is going or realizing profits made from spinoff companies. The public is cut out. I was giving you credit for posting this as an outreach to the public, but now you're saying that that wasn't even your intention.

You've got mainstream venues now picking up your astrovirology story without questioning what's going on. That's dangerous. Eighty publications, and the *NASA Astrobiology Strategy* Executive Summary and the *European Astrobiology Roadmap*, etc. There's something deep state about this.

Ken Stedman: I would disagree with you on that. I can mention what the editorial input was by the Cadys, and it was practically none in this case. There were maybe two or three recommended changes in the whole manuscript and those were perfectly reasonable editorial issues that made no change whatsoever to the text, which we—Aaron Berliner and myself and Tomohiro Mochizuki—came up with. So I think there is very little influence of NASA on this.

Suzan Mazur: But you're coming from NASA. You chair NASA Astrobiology Institute's Virus Focus Group. Is that a paid position, by the way?

Ken Stedman: It is a completely volunteer position.

Suzan Mazur: I like very much that you're investigating viruses, but I think the venue where you're presenting your discussion of astrovirology is a bit thin on credibility at this point.

Ken Stedman: I completely hear you on that. One of the beefs that I actually have with the article, if I may be so blunt, is that it is not available to the public. It's behind a paywall, thanks to the publishers. And I have been asked probably by 30 or 40 people, at least, to please send them a copy of the article because they are not able to access it because of the behind-the-paywall aspect.

Suzan Mazur: Anyone can access the article for $50 but for a 24-hour view only, and only if you promise not to circulate the article in any form.

Ken Stedman: I completely agree with you on that one.

Suzan Mazur: And you have six pages of references. So this story is largely already out there. You give it a twist but a lot of this information is accessible in an online search.

You're telling me you wrote this story for *Astrobiology* journal because Sherry Cady asked you to?

Ken Stedman: Yes. I think there is a certain readership of *Astrobiology* journal that does not think about viruses and those are some of the people I would like to reach in this process. Hopefully, to be perfectly honest, those are people who are going to start to think about viruses and are spending public money on NASA missions and on NASA experimentation.

Suzan Mazur: Isn't it a bit premature to speak of astrovirology since viruses have not even been found at the level that jet airplanes fly, i.e., the stratosphere?

Ken Stedman: I would beg to differ on some of those things. People have found both microbes and viruses or things that look like viruses under those conditions. In fact, one of our previous papers talks about viruses spread through the atmosphere. And potentially at those kinds of levels.

Suzan Mazur: What levels are you talking about?

Ken Stedman: Viruses and microbes that have been found at some of these levels.

Suzan Mazur: What levels are you talking about?

Ken Stedman: I don't know exactly at what level. But I know that Andrew Schueger has collected samples quite high in the atmosphere. There's some very nice data looking at transfer of microbes from the Sahara to the Caribbean. There's definitely transfer that happens, exactly at what level I don't know.

[Note: Smith, Schueger et al. in 2010 reported bacteria and fungi (not viruses) at 12.4 miles over the Pacific Ocean.]

Suzan Mazur: I think I know the article you're referring to. But viruses were not found above the jet plane level.

Ken Stedman: So at what level is it?

Suzan Mazur: It's below the level that jet planes fly [i.e., below the stratosphere, at the troposphere level].

Ken Stedman: I don't know. That's why I was curious.

Suzan Mazur: You've said "to visualize most virion morphologies, a transmission electron microscope (TEM) is required" but it's unlikely that you'll be able to put one "on a spacecraft in the foreseeable future." Can you say why?

Ken Stedman: These are very large instruments and require large amounts of power:

Suzan Mazur: Also, Eugene Koonin has said this:

> *"Traditionally, microbes have been studied in isolation, but to do that, a microbe or virus has to be grown in a laboratory. While that might sound easy, only 0.1% of the world's microbes will grow in artificial media, with the success rate for viruses even lower."*

Doesn't that put a serious damper on the usefulness of a TEM in space investigation of virions?

Ken Stedman: If we're actually going to study whatever we find there, yes, I completely agree with you. You have to have them in culture.

We have exactly that kind of problem in my research lab right now. We've discovered viruses in the absence of a host and are unable to culture them in the lab. We're trying very hard to find the hosts and grow them in the lab. So, again, getting back to what we mention in the paper—putting TEM on a spacecraft to identify something morphologically as a virus, those kinds of experiments, in my opinion, need to be done.

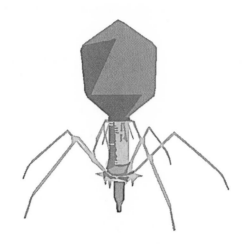

Then, I would say, if we found something that looks basically like a lunar lander. These viruses do look like lunar landers.

There is nothing abiological we know of, or have been able to come up with, that in my opinion is credible, that would make a particle that looks like that. Even if you don't have a host and even if you can't grow it in the lab.

In fact, people do give me electron microscope images quite often and say: Does this look like a virus? I will tell them yes or no. At least in my considered opinion. So, for that reason I think that getting very high resolution images of whatever particles we can find would actually be useful.

Suzan Mazur: No viruses have been found in meteorites to date.

Ken Stedman: Correct.

Suzan Mazur: What other biosignatures are you proposing might be used to search for viruses extraterrestrially?

Ken Stedman: There are a couple of things. My lab has been investigating how lipid biosignatures can be used with regard to viruses. Lipids have been found in very ancient rock and used as biosignature evidence, although all of those to date have been cellular specific. Viruses that have lipids are few and far between and most of those virus lipids are identical to cellular lipids. But there are a few viruses that have lipids that are different from cellular lipids. My lab is trying to find those particular viruses that have these different lipids.

There's a published abstract online, from a paper my postdoctoral scholar and I put together a few years ago. Basically, we're looking for these lipids as biomarkers. Such lipids would much more likely be found in a rock record on Earth.

Another biosignature would be a morphological marker, as I've mentioned. If the TEM could be carried on a spacecraft to identify known viruses, like, for example, the lunar lander shape [icosahedral head-tail morphology]. That brings up the question: What if the virus-like particle doesn't look like a known virus?

We now know that of the viruses found on Earth, the vast majority have very geometrically simple virions. So those geometries are incredibly specific to viruses. If we can find something that has the appropriate geometry, that would also be a very good virus biosignature.

Suzan Mazur: Thank you. You cite Forterre & Prangishvili in your article suggesting that ancient viruses were already rich in morphological diversity at the time of LUCA. And a recent article by Seligmann and Raoult on template-free RNA also reports "evidence for ancient precellular origins and recent *de novo* emergence of viroids." Could you expand on this a bit? Are you familiar with the Seligmann and Raoult paper?

Ken Stedman: I saw the title and abstract but have not yet had a chance to read the article. I do know the work of Forterre and Prangishvili very well. Their interpretation is that since there is so much morphological diversity—admittedly based on many of these same geometries that I was mentioning—that you find all of this diversity in multiple different viruses and multiple different lineages of hosts. And that backwards calculation, which is always going to be a prediction, would be that there were probably multiple different morphologies. Again, precellular or at least around a LUCA kind-of-time.

As far as the emergence of viroids, capsidless viruses—that some of them have arisen recently is a very reasonable hypothesis. But, again, I don't know the Seligmann and Raoult paper very well.

Suzan Mazur: Ricardo Flores and others think that a viroid-like entity was there at the beginning because viroids don't need protein.

Ken Stedman: Right. That makes sense. I think that's very reasonable, in the absence of a time machine. It's very hard to check those hypotheses.

Suzan Mazur: **Didier Raoult argues against a Tree of Life, he sees all life as a mosaic. He sees a Tree of Life concept as a biblical vision and Darwin as the father of intelligent design.** [emphasis added]

What is your understanding of stem-loop RNA hairpins? Do you work in that area?

Ken Stedman: I do not work in that area but I know some things about them. Lots of RNAs can make stem-loop hairpins. But in terms of their activities, I don't know.

Suzan Mazur: And DNA also. I did an interview about this last year with Georg Urtel, who was working in the lab of Dieter Braun at the time. There was a return of the hairpins in his experiment. He was working from synthetic DNA.

Ken Stedman: Yes. The fact that DNA and RNA can form these very interesting structures is, I think, absolutely fascinating. One of the viruses we're working on probably makes a very interesting double hairpin structure, but exactly what that structure looks like in a cell or for that matter in just the DNA itself, I really don't know.

Suzan Mazur. Would you say a bit about StoneStable, your spinoff company that was started with funding from NASA?

Ken Stedman: Our company was not started with funding from NASA. Our NASA-funded research led to the founding of the company. It was money for virus research. We looked at viruses in the rock record. Looked for biosignatures for NASA. The biosignatures we got were completely worthless, but the technology turned out to be useful for vaccine stabilization.

So, yes we did some work for NASA looking for virus fossils. The results we got were not funded by NASA at all. It's something that came out of the scientific process, whereby we then discovered something that is now funded by NIH.

Suzan Mazur: Would you say more about this technology that's proved useful for vaccine stabilization?

Ken Stedman: So, we got funding from NASA to look basically for virus fossils. The geologists will complain and say they're not fossils, they're just mineralized—mineral on the outside of the biological entity. We were very interested in how old the viruses were. In fact, going back to your question just a second ago, viruses being precellular, etc.—the direct evidence for viruses, particularly virions, is at most thousands of years old in terms of virus disease. Regarding being able to visualize virions, it's only been possible since the electron microscope was developed in the late 1930s. Being able to visualize virions is very, very recent.

The question is: How old are viruses? There's pretty good evidence that microbial fossils, cellular fossils are billions of years old. But what about virus fossils? Are they there but we just can't detect them, at least not unambiguously—getting back to the biosignature question—or are they just not there? Maybe they are very recent, maybe viruses haven't been around that long. [emphasis added]

We thought, and this is in fact what NASA funded, that if we're going to find virus fossils, we should find the more mineral-shaped viruses and we'll find them around hot springs. The vast majority of my research work is studying viruses in hot springs. I've been doing that for 20+ years now.

The reason that we thought we'd find mineralized viruses in and around hot springs is because the super-heated water, which comes up at depth, will go through all the minerals. It will leach out those minerals because it's superheated. Once it gets to the surface, that superheated water, which is now saturated in minerals, cools down. As it cools down all of those minerals start precipitating out of the solution. They will precipitate on whatever is there.

We work on viruses at hot springs, so we know there are viruses at hot springs. We know that the minerals will precipitate on those viruses. Now what we need is a way to detect those viruses that the minerals have precipitated on.

So instead of going to the hot springs, which are very complicated, at least chemically, we decided to basically make an artificial hot-spring-like condition in our research lab together with a virus with a very well known morphology—the bacteriophage HT4—the morphology that looks kind of like a lunar lander with the icosahedral head on top of a tail.

Suzan Mazur: Which is most viruses.

Ken Stedman: Exactly. Well, there's a paper that just came out in *Nature* that said that may not be true. But we thought that if we're going to find something, we should see mineralization of bacteriophage HT4. And if we're going to continue to see this amazing morphology while minerals are precipitating on it, we should do it under controlled conditions in the lab.

So, again, funded by NASA, we looked at these conditions and we saw beautiful coatings of silica that were detectable in the transmission electron microscope coating bacteriophage HT4 for up to about three days. After three days, they became completely unrecognizable blobs. Fossils older than three days were not detectable even using TEM.

Suzan Mazur: Are you saying that some sort of protective coating could be used by viruses coming from space to Earth?

Ken Stedman: Right, if there was an appropriate condition to coat them.

Suzan Mazur: Are you thinking silica or something else?

Ken Stedman: In this case we used silica, which is common to many planets.

Suzan Mazur: Would that be protection enough traveling through space?

Ken Stedman: That was one of the next things we did. We looked at those viruses to see if they were protected under those kinds of conditions. But there are two different ways of thinking about protection. One would be protecting the shape, the morphology. The other one is protecting infectivity.

What the graduate student working on this found was that when you did this silica coating, which is basically glass, once you coat a virus in glass it loses its infectivity. The big surprise was that this coating is reversible. When the coating comes off, the virus regains some of its infectivity.

Suzan Mazur: But you don't know what can happen to viruses with the radiation actually out there.

Ken Stedman: Right. One of the things my student did was even under these controlled conditions in the lab he found that after two months even with the nicely coated viruses, all infectivity was gone and could not be recovered. So it was literally a process of months, not the—what is the minimum transit time from Mars to Earth? A lot longer than months. At that point I would say silica coating will not protect viruses for a long enough time to transfer from one planet to another.

But while two months is clearly not enough time in terms of a virus hypothetically traveling from Mars to Earth, two months is plenty of time to get a vaccine from a distribution center on Earth where it's being produced to people living in the backlands worldwide where these vaccines might be needed. So that's the foundation of the company.

Suzan Mazur: What's your best guess as to where viruses or RNA or viroid-like entities originated? Do you think it happened on a comet, an asteroid, on Earth? Where do you think it happened?

Ken Stedman: **My best guess is it happened on Earth probably under very similar conditions in which cellular life was also developing, at about the same time.** [emphasis added]

Suzan Mazur: How do you feel about public funds being allocated to scientific investigation by the scientific establishment with the public essentially cut out of the picture, which has its roots post-WWII? As science and technology historian David F. Noble once pointed out to me, the way they kept the public out was through peer review. This is another beef that I have about *Astrobiology* journal. Noble regarded peer review as censorship, a way to control the narrative.

Ken Stedman: I wouldn't go quite that far. One of the things that I do is I try and communicate my science to the public as much as possible. Because I completely agree that if public money is being used to fund research that I do, I am obligated to tell the public about it.

Suzan Mazur: But the situation is much stickier than that. In 1980, there was an amendment to the Patent Act—the Bayh-Dole amendment—where companies ever since have been able to approach universities where 90% of the research is publicly funded, and where companies can lay down money for monopoly rights. Noble characterized the Bayh-Dole amendment as "the biggest give-away in American history."

I think these issues of democracy and science that David F. Noble championed need to now be seriously revisited so that the public is cut in not out of the decision-making regarding allocation of public funds to science as well as the resulting profit.

Chapter 18

L-forms: A Chat with Leeuwenhoek Medalist Jeffery Errington

Photo, courtesy Jeffery Errington

2/22/2017

Having published a book on origin of life, somehow I missed wet-lab microbiologist Jeffery Errington's cutting edge investigations of wall-less organisms called "L-forms." Not surprisingly, Errington—who resembles Edward Fox a bit (*Day of the Jackal*) —was awarded the Royal Society's Leeuwenhoek Medal in recent years for his "seminal discoveries" in cell morphogenesis and research on L-forms. But aside from being a distinguished scientist, Errington is also an occasional footballer during time off from the lab he directs at Newcastle University in the UK, and knowing how critical teamwork is to victory, accepted the Leeuwenhoek saying the Royal Society honor really belonged to his team.

It is one of many awards Errington's received through the years, others include: Lwoff Award and Medal (Federation of European Microbiological Societies); Novartis Medal and Prize (UK Biochemical Society); 20th Anniversary Medal and Prize (Biotechnology Organization and Biological Science Research Council).

Jeffery Errington is a Fellow of the Royal Society and a Fellow of the Academy of Medical Science, and has been elected to the European Academy of Microbiology, American Academy of Microbiology, and EMBO (European Molecular Biology Organization).

Errington serves on the editorial boards of *EMBO Journal*; *Molecular Biology*; and *Current Opinion in Microbiology*. He's co-chaired two Gordon Conferences and organized numerous others.

He is an entrepreneur as well, founder of two spin-out companies working in drug discovery and is currently director of Demuris Ltd., based in Newcastle, north of London on the river Tyne.

Jeffery Errington's PhD is in bacterial genetics from the University of Greenwich and his BSc from Newcastle University in genetics and zoology. Errington's postdoctoral research was done at Oxford University where he later became Professor of Microbiology in the Sir William Dunn School of Pathology. He is presently Director of the Centre for Bacterial Cell Biology, Medical School, Newcastle University, where he works with a staff of 300. Errington is also Professor of Microbiology at Newcastle.

I recently spoke with Jeff Errington by phone at his lab, mostly about his curiosity about L-forms as models of primordial cells, their role in infectious disease, and their potential use in medicine.

Our interview follows.

Suzan Mazur: Congratulations on being honored by the Royal Society with the Leeuwenhoek Medal for your discoveries in cell morphogenesis, and, in particular, for your work with the wall-less L-form bacteria and its potentials for medicine, in developing antibiotics and other drugs.

L-forms were first defined more than 80 years ago by Emmy Klieneberger-Nobel who thought they represented a phase that bacteria go through, some under normal cultural conditions, and others only when exposed to abnormal conditions. In her 1949 paper, Klieneberger-Nobel characterizes the following medium as "ordinary conditions": "boiled blood agar made from ox-heart infusion peptone broth enriched with horse serum."

Through the years specimens have been scraped from some of the most intriguing corners of life for experiments to transform bacteria into an L-form-like, wall-less state. You've said that there's been a resurgence of interest in L-forms in recent years because of genome sequencing and advances in microscopes. Does science at the moment have any idea how extensive L-forms are in nature or may have been in evolutionary time?

Jeffery Errington: There are several answers to that question. I became interested in the problem because I was aware of L-forms from the scientific literature of the 1950s and 60s. Curiously, however, right around the end of the 1970s or so, publishing on L-forms just sort of petered out. I haven't really been able to get to the bottom of exactly why that happened.

A lot of people were excited by the notion that L-forms might be involved in infectious disease or chronic or recurrent infections. But if you look at the publications from the 50s and 60s—and there were many of them—a lot of those were single patient case studies that were not very carefully controlled.

There was also the problem of investigators looking at specimens under the microscope and seeing L-forms indiscriminately in blob-like objects. It was the pre-molecular era and there just weren't incisive methods to demonstrate that objects under the microscope were of bacterial origin. And even if researchers had an L-form line that could be bred in the lab, investigators had no way to work out what kind of walled bacterium it came from. So there were all sorts of technical issues about even defining precisely what an L-form was, never mind working out the relevance to disease. All of the above held back the field, and, as mentioned, it petered out in the 70s. It's only in the last 10 years that more rigorous scientific papers on L-forms have begun to be published.

Suzan Mazur: How pervasive are L-forms in nature now and earlier in evolution?

Jeffery Errington: There are a few bacteria that are naturally cell wall-deficient, like *Mycoplasma*, which is a pathogen, and *Phytoplasma*, which inhabits plants. They're both cell-wall deficient, but if you look at the evolutionary history of these organisms, it's quite clear they're derived from much more ancient bacteria – probably resembling modern clostridia, which have conventional cell walls. So the thinking now is that this is retrograde evolution—*Mycoplasma* lost the ability to make a wall while evolving into specialized pathogens.

Suzan Mazur: Are you saying that this group, *Mycoplama*, *Phytoplasma* and related species are the only cell-deficient organisms that now exist naturally—without being generated in the lab?

Jeffery Errington: No. It's clear that there are L-forms in nature. What I'm saying is that an ancient ancestor of modern *Mycoplasma* probably started out as an L-form in the distant past and then evolved down a side track becoming a pathogen, meanwhile losing many genes needed for life outside the specialized environment in the host.

Suzan Mazur: Klieneberger-Nobel also pioneered the study of M*ycoplasma*, is that right?

196

Jeffery Errington: She was one of the people who was working on these organisms, although the history is a little difficult to reconstruct right now. Scientific papers from that time indicate that researchers couldn't tell whether this was *Mycoplasma*, a highly evolved bacterium, or the temporary variant of a walled bacterium, i.e., an L-form. They just didn't have the molecular tools to easily make the distinction. The general term PPLO (pleuro-pneumonia-like organism) became used for the whole group of organisms, perhaps reflecting uncertainty about their origins and identities.

Suzan Mazur: What are some of the L-forms occurring naturally that have been identified?

Jeffery Errington: This is really where the cutting edge is presently. Now that we understand the molecular basis for the L-form transition better we're in a much stronger position to work out the extent to which bacteria live in the L-form versus the walled state. The jury is still out. We just haven't done enough work on this.

But my lab is now working hard on whether we can find L-forms in various clinical situations, especially involving chronic or recurrent infections. None of this is published but we're quite excited about the results we're getting, especially with recurrent urinary tract infections.

Suzan Mazur: So you tend to think L-forms were extensive in earlier evolutionary time.

Jeffery Errington: Yes. For example, what we're finding is that very similar triggers to those that will turn a Gram-positive bacterium [i.e., bacteria with a single thick peptidoglycan wall] like *Bacillus subtilis* into an L-form will also convert *E. coli* into the L-form state. And these two species of bacteria are separated by about a billion years of evolution.

Suzan Mazur: That's fascinating.

Jeffery Errington: This suggests to us that this is a general physiological state that's very ancient.

Suzan Mazur: Some L-forms can slip back and forth from walled to wall-less states, does that particular talent indicate the organisms are *more* evolved or *less* evolved than other life forms?

Jeffery Errington: This ability to change between the two states begins to seem quite a general property of bacteria, which to me suggests that this is a very ancient trait that's been retained by modern bacteria because it has adaptive significance in situations that are not especially rare. [emphasis added]

For example, if the cells experience conditions where lots of osmolytes [like sucrose in plant sap] are present, giving a sufficiently high osmotic pressure around the cell—the organism doesn't really need its cell wall, and in principle it can slip into the L-form state, dispensing with the wall. We may have missed this in the past due to microbiologists historically using a particular kind of agar [gelatinous substance derived from red algae] to grow bacteria, which is usually incompatible with the growth of L-forms.

Suzan Mazur: Do viruses play a role in regulating L-form bacteria?

Jeffery Errington: That's a good question. Of course, much of the research on bacteriophages has shown that they tend to bind to components of the cell wall, so certainly you'd anticipate that L-forms would be resistant to many forms of virus. But I don't know if much work has been done on this.

Suzan Mazur: You've said "a vast number" of bacteria can be induced to an L-form state. How many species have you been able to convert to an L-form-like state?

Jeffery Errington: According to the scientific literature, a very wide range of pathogenic bacteria can switch to L-form state. There are historical reviews by Gerald Domingue. In our lab we've chosen to work with about a half dozen bacteria—organisms from very diverse backgrounds. They mostly seem to behave in more or less the same way if we give them an osmoprotective agar medium and trick them with a particular antibiotic, most will switch to the L-form state.

Suzan Mazur: You say it's basically simple geometry to transform a walled bacterium into an L-form, that it's a matter of making excess membrane which results in deformation of the cell, that is, you drive changes by increasing surface area. L-forms then reproduce by non-binary fission via membrane tubulation and also blebbing, i.e., they generate blob-shaped descendants. Is that right?

Jeffery Errington: Yes.

Suzan Mazur: Getting back to the *Mycoplasma*, have you been able to induce wall-less bacteria like *Mycoplasma* or *Phytoplasma* to form a cell wall and would it be useful to try and do so?

Jeffery Errington: That's a really interesting question. My feeling is that because they've been evolving for hundreds of millions of years without a wall, and they've lost most of the genes needed to make the wall that—it would be pretty difficult to do that.

However, the L-forms we make in the lab from walled bacteria can generally switch back into the walled state relatively easily.

Suzan Mazur: Some scientists characterize reports about horizontal gene transfer (HGT) being rampant in evolution as a reflection of "HGT industry" hype and say that HGT has been a "negligible factor" in evolution. But you've said, assuming that the vesicles of ancient organisms had similar structure to today's organisms, and that they used L-form proliferation, that horizontal gene transfer would have been massive because vesicles would have contained multiple genomes. Can you say a bit more about this?

Jeffery Errington: I think it's likely that HGT was fairly rampant in the primordial L-form-like cells. However, my feeling is that invention of the cell wall (perhaps separately in archaea and bacteria—which have completely distinct cell wall structures) could have brought an abrupt halt to the primordial HGT. Once the wall was in place, new mechanisms of HGT may need to have emerged to enable DNA transfer across the wall barrier.

Suzan Mazur: You've also said "It seems likely that further detailed studies of the cell envelopes of deeply rooted bacterial groups will provide insights into the early evolutionary history of the bacteria," and that "sequenced-based analytical methods are still inadequate for defining early steps in bacterial radiation."

If you were laying out a Tree of Life, how would you organize the domains in light of these difference in cell wall structure since you say that the ingredients for cell walls are produced within the cell itself and then flipped to the outside?

You go into some interesting detail in your Royal Society paper about bacteria having either (1) one thick PG (peptidoglycan) wall or (2) one thinner PG wall *plus* an outer membrane; and archaea exhibiting a variety of protective layers—most often a paracrystalline proteinaceous shell (otherwise known as an "S-layer")—with some families of archaea displaying a PG-like layer (called a pseudomurein) but made via a different pathway than a true PG wall is made. Eukaryotes, on the other hand, don't have either a PG wall or a paracrystalline proteinaceous shell.

So the question is how would you organize the domains on the ToL?

Jeff Errington: I think it's curious, really curious that the archaea and the bacteria have a fundamental difference in terms of their cell development structure. It reflects also the very fundamental differences in the way they replicate, transcribe and translate DNA.

Suzan Mazur: And the archaea are antibiotic resistant, aren't they?

Jeffery Errington: Yes, in general, because they're much more like eukaryotes, and so lack the molecular targets of antibacterial compounds. For example, all of the antibiotics we use that act on the PG wall of bacteria don't work at all on archaea. As I mentioned before, one of the ideas I particularly like is that a key step in the evolution of cellular life was the invention of a cell envelope structure that would allow cells to survive outside of the "muddy puddles" that Darwin suggested may have been the birth place of life.

There were two distinct evolutionary solutions to the problem of how to tolerate osmotically unstable conditions. One was the PG wall, which is common to all modern bacteria, and the other was the pseudomurein or proteinaceous "S-layer"-type walls, which were invented by the ancestors of the archaea. I like this explanation, but of course, it's difficult to go back in evolutionary time to do experiments!

Suzan Mazur: There's an interesting challenge coming from the North, from Charles Kurland and Ajith Harish in Sweden, who think we only assume bacteria are the earliest organisms, that this reflects Aristotelian thinking. Their perspective is that the modern ToL is a rerooted tree from a now extinct biosphere and that the most recent common ancestor was actually a complex organism. They base this on their computations that 75% of the Superfamily proteome of the three domains—archaea, bacteria and eukayotes —are shared ancestral Superfamilies. Some of their work has been supported in part by the Nobel Committee for Chemistry of the Royal Swedish Science Academy. Any comment?

Jeffery Errington: I have a colleague here at Newcastle University named Martin Embley who's been very prominent in this ToL discussion. Martin and his team have done incisive work that I think supports the idea that there are only two domains and that the eukaryotes are derived from a group within the archaea rather than being an out group and separate from the archaea. The latest textbooks are starting to show the two-domain tree instead of the Woese three-domain tree.

Suzan Mazur. You started two spin-out companies that are working on discovering and developing antibiotics. Are any of these products close to phase III trials?

Jeffery Errington: No, they're really still in early development.

Suzan Mazur: Can you talk about it?

Jeffery Errington: Yes. I've been involved with this for about 20 years now. The first company was started while I was at Oxford. I was at Oxford for about 25 years, latterly in the department where Florey, Chain and co-workers first purified penicillin in the 1940s. [**Note**: Jeff Errington was Professor of Microbiology at Oxford University's Sir William Dunn School of Pathology.] So I was acutely aware of the importance of antibiotic discovery.

My interest really began at the end of the 1990s when the pharmaceutical companies switched the way they did drug discovery to a new "target led" approach. The idea was that to find new antibiotics, you should go after essential genes within the bacteria that hadn't been targeted by existing antibiotics, and then look for chemical compounds that work specifically on the new targets. The thinking was that you'd find new chemistries and new antibiotics. Companies at the time were limited in their development because of the poor understanding then about basic bacterial science.

We were working on a number of genes and proteins that are involved in fundamental aspects of bacterial life, such as the cell division machinery, and we tried to find chemical inhibitors of some of those compounds. We set up the first company, called Prolysis, in Oxford. We went through about £15 M in funding. To make a long story short, a couple of new compounds were very promising but the company wasn't able to raise enough funds to take these compounds into clinical trials. The two compound series are still in play, though, with a couple of biotech companies on the East Coast of the US. Years later, here in Newcastle, I founded Demuris.

Following from the Prolysis experience we realized that if you try to find chemicals that work on a single enzyme target, you're almost always going to come up with a problem of resistance. It turns out to be very easy for bacteria to make very small, simple, genetic changes to the enzyme that will prevent the compound from binding without compromising the activity of the enzyme.

The resistance frequency turns out to be the most difficult problem to get around. Our present strategy is to return to looking at natural product molecules made by bacteria. These organisms have been carrying out a kind of biological warfare for perhaps a billion years. To have been retained by evolution these molecules are much more sophisticated. They often either have a double mode of action, so simple mutations don't generate resistance, or they work on a non-protein target, such as binding to the cell wall. It's very difficult for the bacterium to alter the chemistry of its cell wall without changing many genes.

So Demuris is going back to old-fashioned natural product discovery but using modern methods to try and find compounds that work in different ways from the compounds that have been discovered in the past. We have several very promising molecules that look as if they have novel modes of action, but they're still pretty early-stage.

Suzan Mazur: Fascinating. Good luck with your ongoing investigations.

Jeffery Errington: Thank you.

Suzan Mazur: Oxford University physiologist Denis Noble once said, "No one needs to be just a scientist." Noble, for instance, likes to perform medieval Catalonian songs of love and chivalry as much as possible with his group, the Oxford Trobadors. Do you make time for recreation outside of the lab, do you still have an interest in football, for instance?

Jeffery Errington: Soccer for you in the US. Football is more like English rugby, you need to be either very big or very fast when you play that sort of game. I play soccer. I actually played last night. It's great when I'm running around chasing a ball, all my worries and concerns, scientific models and contrary data are forgotten about for at least an hour. . .

I like music as well, and travel. I get to travel a lot as a scientist. Yes, I'm enjoying life and science immensely. It's a fantastic career, as a scientist. I feel hugely privileged to be able to do this.

Chapter 19

Antonio Lima-de-Faria:
The Law of Biological Periodicity

A. Lima-de-Faria photos, courtesy Lima-de-Faria

7/25/2018

Thirty-five years ago a highly vivid and provocative book was published by Elsevier titled *Evolution without Selection: Form and Function by Autoevolution.* It was translated into several languages and apparently sold thousands of copies in Russia alone but only a couple of hundred in the United States. The book's author, Antonio Lima-de-Faria, a cytogeneticist at Lund University—with aristocratic Portuguese roots and dubbed "Knight of the Order of the North Star" by Sweden's king for his work in science—was also one of the Osaka

205

Group of "structuralists," whose other members included Brian Goodwin, Mae-Wan Ho, Peter Saunders *et al.*

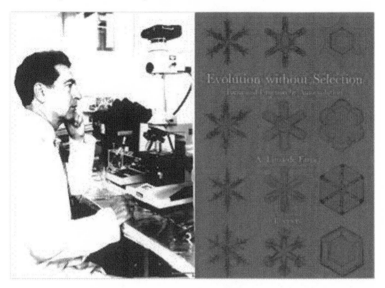

Lima-de-Faria is now an emeritus professor at Lund University and, at age 97, has just written another book whose central theme is that the recurrence of form and function in biology makes possible a periodic table similar to the periodic table of chemical elements (a subject first explored in his 1983 book) and reveals the "law of biological periodicity." The new book (there have been several in between) is: *Periodic Tables Unifying Living Organisms at the Molecular Level: The Predictive Power of the Law of Periodicity.*

Lima-de-Faria opens the new book with "The Search for the Physical Rules that Predict the Atomic Behavior of DNA and of Proteins" and highlights Sweden's neutron scattering facility at Lund University—ESS (European Spallation Source, under construction—48% complete).

European Spallation Source, Lund University, Sweden

He notes that neutrons can probe matter—including biological molecules—enabling measurement of structure from micrometers to one-hundred thousandth of a micrometer *plus* motion from milliseconds to ten-million-millionths of a millisecond.

It is interesting that the world's "most powerful spallation source" should be under construction at Lima-de-Faria's university, since the packing of matter is one of the threads of his work through the years. In *Evolution without Selection*, Lima-de-Faria writes:

> *"Minerals and other pure chemicals have no genes, yet they already display these two basic features: constancy of pattern and ability to change it by forming a very large number of forms."*

Lima-de-Faria thinks ESS opens a window to a deeper understanding of the physical evolution of DNA and other atomic complexes, saying further:

> *"Every structure and function is the immediate product of a molecular cascade having its origin in atomic and ultimately in electronic events."*

One fascinating chapter in the new book is on carnivorous plants. In the section "Periodicity of Plant Carnivory," Lima-de-Faria makes the argument that "carnivory evolved independently on at least ten separate occasions," that the current genera belong to 12 families, and that there are 300 carnivorous species worldwide!

Chapter 20

Oak Ridge Biophysicist John Katsaras:
Neutron Science Transforming Biology

Photo, courtesy John Katsaras

"The target vessel is a steel structure containing 50 tons of swirling liquid mercury. During neutron production 60 pulses of protons collide with the target vessel releasing energy roughly equivalent to a stick of dynamite exploding every second. When high-energy protons hit the nucleus of a mercury atom, 20 to 30 neutrons are "spalled" or released. Those neutrons are guided into beam tubes attached to instrument stations. The neutrons coming out of the target must be turned into low-energy neutrons suitable for research—that is, they must be moderated to room temperature or colder."—**Oak Ridge National Laboratory**

9/14/18

Oak Ridge National Lab biophysicist John Katsaras chaired one of the sessions at the February 2018 National Science Foundation conference, "Progress and Prospects in Neutron

Scattering for the Biological Sciences," and he has been working in the neutron science field for a quarter century or so—both in the US and Canada. However, unlike the NSF's May symposium on synthetic cell development—whose video presentations were posted online—the public remains largely in the dark about what transpired at the NSF neutron science meeting last February. Katsaras tells me we can expect to see the NSF neutron scattering and biology report sometime early next year.

Probing material with neutrons—neutron scattering—enables minute and precise measurement of structure and function without damage to even living material. So why all the suspense?

The insight of science and technology historian David F. Noble is relevant here:

> *"By about 1943-44, there was a discussion about what the postwar scientific establishment would look like. . . .Vannevar Bush and his friends put together a counterproposal calling for a "National Research Foundation"—which became more or less what we have in today's National Science Foundation.*
>
> *The Vannevar Bush et al. legislation said essentially that science would be funded by the taxpayer but controlled by scientists. Again, scientists—this is important to emphasize—are not simply scientists, but scientists and the corporations they work for."*

So NSF may be trying to figure out exactly what to say in its 2019 report to the American people. Indeed, there are sensitive points.

One—the Oak Ridge, Tennessee facility—Spallation Neutron Source—which at the moment is the largest spallation source in the world (26 neutron scattering instruments and beam lines) is expanding from 1.4MW to 2MW to be more competitive with the European Spallation Source (ESS) in Lund, Sweden, which is designed to eventually be a 5MW facility (it's 48% complete now). The projected MW numbers in both cases seem to be somewhat fluid. The US is also planning a second target station.

Two—Oak Ridge currently uses "50 tons of swirling liquid mercury" in its spallation process. And expanding power will require dealing with the current limits of its steel vessel in order to prevent mercury leaks. Mercury pollution is a global environmental problem, causing nerve damage, in particular, across the spectrum of life.

The Swedish ESS facility does not use mercury and seems to have met the demands of Europe's environmental community.

Construction began in 2017 on a mercury treatment facility at the Oak Ridge Y-12 National Security Complex, which was formerly used for H-bomb production. The *Washington Post* noted in 1983 that DOE reported 2.4 million pounds of mercury missing from Oak Ridge over a 13-year-period beginning in the 1950s, which had most likely escaped into the pristine Tennessee countryside. When completed in 2024 the treatment center will apparently help to reduce the amount of mercury released from the demolition of Y-12.

But what about the mercury factor at SNS? Should the Oak Ridge facility be redesigned along the lines of the more environmentally friendly ESS? We will probably have to wait for next year's NSF report to see if that's even on the boards for discussion.

Three—the High Flux Isotope Reactor, which provides a steady stream of neutrons for scientific research at Oak Ridge still uses highly enriched uranium to do so. The scheduled move from weapons-grade to low-enriched uranium doesn't happen until sometime in 2020.

I decided to ring up John Katsaras at ORNL to discuss his research on cell membranes using neutron scattering. In 2017, Katsaras and colleagues at ORNL were successful in carrying out the first direct nanoscale investigation of a living cell membrane, finding that lipids gathered with other lipids of their type within the cell membrane to form "rafts." These rafts or domains help facilitate cell-cell communication but are too small to be seen using standard optical instruments.

Coincidentally, as I write, John Katsaras is moderating a panel discussion at Lund Institute of Advanced Neutron and X-ray Science on "Dynamics of Membranes and their Constituents."

John Katsaras is "Senior Scientist Biological Systems/ORNL Distinguished R&D Staff, Large Scale Structures Group, Neutron Sciences Directorate" at Oak Ridge National Laboratory. He is also on the faculty at the University of Tennessee's Bredesen Center for Interdisciplinary Research and Graduate Education as well as UT's Institute of Biomedical Engineering, and a professor in UT's Department of Physics and Astronomy. Katsaras is an adjunct professor in the physics department at Ontario, Canada's Brock University St. Catharines.

He serves as associate editor of the journal *Chemistry and Physics of Lipids* and is on the editorial board of the journal *Membranes*. He holds two patents with several others pending.

Among his honors are: Fellow, Neutron Scattering Society of America (2018); Fellow, American Institute for Medical and Biological Engineering (2018); Oak Ridge National Laboratory, Significant Event Award (2017); NRC/Steacie Institute for Molecular Sciences, Annual Award for Improving Life in the Institute, Canada (2007); NRC/Steacie Institute for Molecular Sciences, Outstanding Achievement Award, Canada (2001, 1999).

As a Canadian—he adores the Tennessee outdoors. And his fascination with acceleration is evident even in his avocation—collecting racing bikes.

John Katsaras first studied psychology—BA, Concordia University, Montreal—and then biology —BSc, Concordia. His MSc and PhD are both in biophysics from Canada's University of Guelph. He was a postdoctoral research fellow at Guelph (with R.H. Stinson and J.H. Davis) and at McMaster University (with R.M. Epand) as well as a post rouge fellow at CRPP-CNRS (with J. Dufourcq) in France.

My recent conversation with John Katsaras follows.

Suzan Mazur: Neutron scattering has been around for a while, why all the excitement now? The Europeans have formed LENS (League of Advanced European Neutron Sources), and Sweden is building the next generation spallation source with apparently unprecedented brightness at Lund University (48% complete). Oak Ridge National Laboratory is expanding its facilities. There are also upcoming conferences on neutrons and biology. Why all the excitement?

John Katsaras: Neutron scattering is comprised of many different techniques, each requiring its own approach—one can say that about other techniques, such as microscopies. As far as biology is concerned or soft materials, the real excitement is that you can probe these materials at the nanoscale. We've shown here at ORNL that you can probe cells when they're living with nanoscopic resolution.

Currently there are no other techniques that can accurately probe living materials at the nanoscale. There's a lot of debate about that. To the best of my knowledge, neutron is the only one, as we've demonstrated here.

Moreover, there are very few techniques period that can probe soft materials on the nanoscale in a disordered state. When you crystallize things, there are scattering techniques that can be used, for example, electrons and x-rays. But when material is not crystallized, neutrons have a distinct advantage. [emphasis added]

Neutrons also come in different flavors. You can look at static structure. You can also look at dynamic structure. In static structure you are studying the time averaged structure. In the case of dynamic structure, by definition things are moving around and

213

you are capturing snapshots of the structure. So with neutrons you can study a range of things from—collective motion—molecules moving together in some synchrony, or individually.

Suzan Mazur: Thank you. Cytogeneticist Antonio Lima-de-Faria from Lund University, where they're building the European Spallation Source, refers to "enormous accelerators of electrons and neutrons elucidate[ing] DNA's own evolution—determination of exact position and movement of atoms." Do you agree with that?

John Katsaras: I agree in the sense that you can observe how DNA's structure evolves in real time as a function of changes in temperature, pH or ion content, for example. Depending on the timescales, which can range from fractions of a second to hours, these kinetic measurements can be done with x-ray and neutrons, although neutrons are better able to capture the slower kinetics due to their lower flux compared to x-rays.

Suzan Mazur: Lima-de-Faria has also said neutrons can probe matter including biomatter enabling measurements of structure from micrometers to one-hundred thousandth of a micrometer plus motion from milliseconds to ten-million-millionths of a millisecond. Do you agree with that?

John Katsaras: Basically yes. You can look at things from the micron scale, which corresponds to optical techniques that provide complementary data. And then you go to angstroms with neutron crystallography. Neutrons can be understood as similar to x-rays in crystallography, where you obtain atomic positions with angstrom resolution, corresponding to 1×10 to the minus 10 meters. So, yes you can. And the dynamic information with that can be accessed with neutron ranges from the picosecond to the hundreds of nanoseconds.

Suzan Mazur: Is every structure and function the immediate product of a molecular cascade originating in atomic and electronic events?

John Katsaras: That's a good question. I don't know how to answer it. Of course structure has a role in how function is expressed. One such case is the so-called raft hypothesis in membranes, for example. Something we've been investigating here at Oak Ridge.

Suzan Mazur: That was actually my next question. Your team at Oak Ridge has done the "first ever direct nanoscale examination of a living membrane." What can we now see that we couldn't see without these advanced measurements and instruments?

John Katsaras: But it's not necessarily the instruments that make the difference. It's the approach to the problem. Sometimes there's an overemphasis on hardware. The best hardware doesn't always lead to the best science. Of course you need access to the very best instruments you can find. But if you don't have the right questions and if you don't have the right sample, it will result in a poor or mediocre experiment. What's needed most is a great experiment. In the membranes experiment we did here we engineered the bacteria so we could visualize its membrane, using neutron scattering.

But coming back to the question of structure and function. The way DNA is organized, for example, DNA's structure is integral to its replication process.

Suzan Mazur: Your membranes research revealed that lipids gathered with others of their type.

John Katsaras: Right. The cell makes thousands of different types of lipids. In the plasma membrane, which is the outer membrane of the cell, there are hundreds or, maybe thousands of different lipids. The question is, why does the cell expend so much energy to make all of these different lipids.

You could say, well, maybe they have all different physical properties.. As a result, mixtures of lipids may come together to create an environment for a protein enabling the protein to perform its function.

How does this happen? Are these passive processes driven by thermodynamics or are they active processes where the cell makes these things, puts them in place, and then continues to micromanage them? This remains an open question. [emphasis added]

Suzan Mazur: Is the Oak Ridge Spallation Neutron Source (SNS) the only neutron scattering facility in the US?

John Katsaras: Not the only, however Oak Ridge is the largest US facility—both the Spallation Neutron Source and the High Flux Isotope Reactor. There's also the NCNR [Center for Neutron Research] in Maryland. A small facility in Missouri [University of Missouri Research Reactor]. And a spallation source similar to SNS at Los Alamos [LANSCE], although I am not sure if it is currently open for civilian research.

Suzan Mazur: Are you collaborating with Europe on investigations?

John Katsaras: I have a collaborator in Austria, Georg Pabst at the University of Graz. We've been developing an asymmetric membrane with a model system. Since model systems are much simpler than functional biological membranes, they allow one to get a handle on what's going on in real systems.

It should be pointed out that membranes have two bilayer leaflets. In functional cells these leaflets are chemically different, i.e., the leaflets contain different lipids. The inner or cytoplasmic leaflet differs from the outer leaflet chemically. One can argue as to why that is.

When you make model systems you generally mix these lipids and they will always randomly distribute equally in both leaflets. The chemical makeup of that bilayer will be the same for both leaflets or very close. There may be some factors that may make the lipid prefer the inner lipid versus the outer bilayer leaflet. But for the most part, the leaflets are symmetrical.

We've been developing something that is asymmetric, to better mimic the biological membrane. That's one of the things our lab is working on with Georg Pabst and his group. We're also working with other people here within the United States and Canada (e.g., Fred Heberle, Drew Marquardt and Erwin London).

This has been written up in *Nature*—Protocols, which will be coming out very soon.

Suzan Mazur: What does this mean for synthetic cell development?

John Katsaras: The systems that we work on are created to understand biological membranes. That's our focus. Now, of course, you can use cells to create and encapsulate material. These are useful in industry and drug delivery. You can send them to image parts of the body. So you can develop model membranes with all these different functions.

Suzan Mazur: But do you envision down the road being able to see more and more of what is happening inside the cell to determine position, measure, etc.

John Katsaras: Scientists have done that over many years. You can do electron microscopy, for example, and look at a cell, at 10 angstroms or whatever the sample allows you. And you can look at the organization of cells at some resolution. In most cases, the cells are dead.

With living systems it becomes much more difficult to study systems with good spatial resolution. Some of the ways you can do it is optically. Then it's a question of resolution. So people are looking at creating model cells. But as far as I know, they are almost always inert.

The other thing that's becoming really important is the computational aspect of science, which means you now have data with which you can better understand the structure-function relationship, for instance.

Suzan Mazur: But are we closer to understanding the origin of life because of advanced neutron scattering?

John Katsaras: You can start putting the pieces together regarding big scientific questions about the origin of life, which will lead to a better understanding of what's going on regarding disease. [emphasis added]

Experiments have been going on for a long time regarding the origins of life. The techniques themselves are needed but insufficient in understanding the fundamental problem. In science you have to come up with an idea. The science is the idea. Technique is part of the story, but in the end, you always have to have a good idea to work from.

Suzan Mazur: What are the hazards working in the areas of neutron scattering? The use of deuterium, for instance.

John Katsaras: It's not hazardous at all because deuterium is not radioactive, it's stable, an isotope of hydrogen. As long as you don't drink it. And even if you drank some of it, nothing would happen to you. Just don't drink too much.

Suzan Mazur: Do you see the US moving more into neutron science the way the Europeans are?

John Katsaras: Well we are. SNS is a great example. ESS in Sweden will be more powerful but America is planning a second target station that will be very competitive.

Suzan Mazur: Where will that be, the second target station?

John Katsaras: We don't know. There are ongoing discussions. If it does come to fruition, it will be tailored to look at biological materials and soft materials. If it does happen, then I would very much like to have that machine because its characteristics will be effectively maximized for the type of science I'm interested in.

[Note: John Katsaras has emailed the following update: *"[The second target station] STS will be next door to the first target station (FTS) and would be ideally suited for studies of Advanced Materials, which include quantum phenomena, engineered materials, soft matter, and biological materials (for further informtion please visit: https://neutrons.ornl.gov/sts and the corresponding STS fact sheet:*

https://neutrons.ornl.gov/sites/default/files/STS%20Brochure%2 011×17%20%202018.pdf)."]

Suzan Mazur: How long have you been working in neutron science?

John Katsaras: I've been involved with membranes research my entire career. I began as a graduate student in 1984. I've worked in neutron scattering since 1994, starting at the Chalk River Laboratories in Canada. Those are very similar labs to Oak Ridge. They were developed during World War II and the Canadians had the heavy water reactor concept, which they developed in the 40s and 50s. The first really big reactor in Canada built was called NRX—National Research Experimental. Canada then developed the National Research Universal reactor.

Suzan Mazur: You've seen quite a lot. Do you expect to continue with your research for some years to come?

John Katsaras: Well, I haven't stopped. I've been at it since 1984 and I don't plan to stop anytime soon. One of the reasons I came to the United States was to make sure my career could continue. Canada's NRU reactor was shut down this year. That I knew was going to happen because the reactor became operational in 1957. The writing was on the wall as far as its longevity was concerned. Its lifespan was clearly coming to an end. That would be it. I moved to Oak Ridge in 2010.

Suzan Mazur: You were born in Canada?

John Katsaras: I was born in Greece. On the island of Rhodes. My mother and I emigrated to Montreal when I was two years old and I came to the US when I was 52. It's been a very good place to live and work, and ORNL has experienced a revitalization of its facilities over the last 15-20 years.

Suzan Mazur: What do you expect from the research in the way of applications?

John Katsaras: I don't think of science that way. Putting applications before science is like putting the cart before the horse. It's important to address basic questions. From those answers all kinds of possibilities emerge. We're too preoccupied now with technology and outcomes. Discovery happens when you least expect it. A lot of practical applications often emerge when you're not trying to make practical applications.

Successful breakthroughs happen because you have some of the brightest people researching, scientists who are allowed to think and work on basic problems that are of tremendous interest. It's been proven over and over, that this is the best way to do science.

Even with the atom bomb, for example. The basic physics aspect of creating an atom bomb had been worked out. The building of the bomb was the real problem. It was an engineering problem. Then, of course, the politics of the day came into play, because billions of dollars had to be found to create a device.

Suzan Mazur: Is there a final point you'd like to make?

John Katsaras: Any country that wants to be at the cutting edge of science has got to have excellent basic research. The United States has hugely invested in basic research over the years, and as such continues to attract the best scientists. Once you have such an investment in basic research, important technology flows.

Suzan Mazur: What kind of budget does Oak Ridge have?

John Katsaras: Its annual operating budget is about $1.6 billion dollars.

Suzan Mazur: That's quite a substantial amount.

John Katsaras: And now you have China coming into the frame. It has put an enormous amount of money into basic science and is attracting a lot of Western talent.

Suzan Mazur: China is building a spallation neutron source in Dongguan.

John Katsaras: Just outside of Hong Kong.

Suzan Mazur: Do you get back to Greece?

John Katsaras: Once a year to visit my mother. I travel to Canada quite a bit.

Suzan Mazur: Do you have interesting hobbies outside the lab?

John Katsaras: I play a lot of hockey. I fish. I love history, including science history. I cycle and am a big collector of European racing bikes from the 50s and 60s, but I'm also interested in the ones Schwinn made at its Chicago factory.

The bicycle is still the most efficient human-powered machine. Roads were actually built for bicycles, not cars.

Neutron Science Facilities Worldwide:

Oak Ridge Neutron Facilities (SNS/HFIR)
NIST Center for Neutron Research, Maryland
Los Alamos Neutron Science Center (LANSCE)
University of Missouri Research Reactor Center
European Spallation Source, Lund University, Sweden (48% complete)

ISIS Neutron and Muon Source, UK
Institut Laue-Langevin (ILL), France
Laboratoire Leon Brillouin, France
Helmholtz-Zentrum Berlin, Germany
Jülich Centre for Neutron Science (JCNS), Germany
FRM II, Munich, Germany
Budapest Neutron Center, Hungary
Swiss Spallation Neutron Source, Paul Scherrer Institut
Frank Laboratory of Neutron Physics, Dubna, Russia
China Spallation Neutron Source, Dongguan, China
Bhabha Atomic Research Centre, Mumbai, India
Japan Proton Accelerator Research Complex (J-PARC)
JAEA Research Reactors, Japan
High Flux Advanced Neutron Application Reactor, South Korea
Australian Centre for Neutron Scattering (ACNS)

Recent and Upcoming Conferences:

National Science Foundation Workshop on "Progress and Prospects in Neutron Scattering for the Biological Sciences," Alexandria, Virginia, US, February 20-22, 2018

9th Workshop on Neutron Scattering Applications in Structural Biology, Oak Ridge National Laboratory, Tennessee, US, June 11-15, 2018

American Conference on Neutron Scattering, University of Maryland, College Park, US, June 24-28, 2018

"Membranes Beyond," International Workshop on Status and Perspectives in Research on Membrane Structures and Interaction, McMaster University, Hamilton, Ontario, Canada, July 2-4, 2018

15th International Surface X-ray and Neutron Scattering Conference, Pohang Accelerator Lab, Pohang, South Korea, July 15-19, 2018

"Dynamics of Membranes and their Constitutents," Lund Institute of Advanced Neutron and X-ray Science, Lund, Sweden, September 12-14, 2018

Neutrons and Biology Conference, Carqueriranne, France, September 16-19, 2018

High Brilliance Workshop, Cologne, Germany, October 4-5, 2018

ISIS Large Scale Structures User Meeting, Abingdon, UK, November 1-2, 2018

Gordon Research Conference on Neutron Scattering, Hong Kong, China, May 5-10, 2019

European Conference on Neutron Scattering 2019 (ECNS), Saint Petersburg, Russia, July 1-5, 2019

Chapter 21

"Neutrons for Society"—
A Chat with Sweden's Tommy Nylander

Photo, courtesy Tommy Nylander

> *"I'd like to say that ESS [the European Spallation Source] is nothing magical, strange or science fiction. It is a powerful tool that people are welcome to use. That is said not only in the spirit of openness but to communicate that we are making ESS for the benefit of society. These are 'neutrons for society.'"*
> **—Tommy Nylander**

9/23/2018

Lund University physical chemist Tommy Nylander likes to thoroughly punctuate his personal communications with exclamation points! That's just the way he sees life! And so neutron scattering science in Sweden could not have a better ambassador!

"Neutrons for society" is what Nylander is promoting. Neutrons for peace, prosperity, and for big leaps in scientific research with unparalleled accuracy possible for observation—including for the biological sciences. Neutrons can pinpoint where hydrogens are within a protein, for example, as well as reveal the molecular dynamics of cells.

And ESS at Lund University (construction now 48% complete) is slated to become the world's most powerful facility for neutron science—eventually 5MW—with its neutrons generated via spallation. No nuclear reactor involved. ESS is also mercury-free.

Nylander has worked in neutron science for over a quarter century. In recent years he's been using neutron scattering to look at biological surfaces—like in the interaction of proteins and lipids.

He's also researching the interaction of RNA and lipid membranes and has been a trailblazer in investigating the surface properties of DNA. Nylander in our conversation that follows tells me he thinks advances in neutron scattering technology will lead to an understanding of the DNA "wrapping process."

Last year the Swedish Chemical Society awarded Tommy Nylander its Norblad-Ekstrand medal for "outstanding scientific research" in physical chemistry. Richard Campbell of France's Institut Laue-Langevin expressed the following regarding Nylander being honored:

> *"There could not be a more deserved recipient of the Norblad-Ekstrand medal than Tommy Nylander! First and foremost, his research towards the understanding of interfacial interactions of lipid phases and a broad range of amphiphilic systems in soft matter and biology is highly distinguished. His work relies on a range of experimental techniques and supporting computational calculations, but in particular he is a strong enthusiast of neutron science, not only at the ISIS pulsed source in the UK and the ILL in France, where he has acquired a large amount of his scientific data, but also many other facilities worldwide. Furthermore, his exceptional dedication*

needs to be mentioned as clearly he offers more support than most academics to further the careers and aspirations of the young scientists who have the fortune to work with him."

With his warm, open style of dialogue, Tommy Nylander has been successful not only in educating the public about the virtues of ESS but also in reassuring the public that ESS—a pan-European project—is environmentally friendly.

Indeed, earlier this year representatives from all member countries of the UN Security Council visited ESS to assess the facility, apparently giving their nod of approval as well.

ESS uses a rotating helium-cooled tungsten target wheel for its neutron source rather than the liquid mercury target used at facilities in the US and Japan. Per the ESS literature:

"The spallation process takes place when the accelerated proton beam hits the Tungsten bricks of the 11-tonne target wheel. At ESS, this will produce unprecedented neutron brightness for scientific experiments across multiple disciplines."

Tommy Nylander is a professor of physical chemistry at Lund University with 70% of his focus on research, particularly at NanoLund—the university's nanoscience lab. He is currently PI (principal investigator) on a half dozen projects funded by the Swedish government and European Commission.

Nylander is a member of the editorial boards of *Chemistry and Physics of Lipids* and *Biophysical Journal*. He serves as chairman of the Review Panel for Biology at MLZ (Heinz Maier-Leibnitz Zentrum) neutron research center in Germany. Nylander was main organizer of the European Conference on Neutron Scattering in Lund (2007), among many other distinctions.

Tommy Nylander's PhD is in chemical engineering/biophysical technology from Lund University and his MSc in chemical engineering/food technology also from Lund. He was a postdoctoral research fellow at Australian National University.

My recent conversation with Tommy Nylander follows.

Suzan Mazur: Congratulations on being awarded the Norblad-Ekstrand medal by the Swedish Chemical Society. You've been working in neutron science for a quarter century in various countries, I understand, and you are also at the cutting edge of investigations on biological interface, protein-lipid interactions, as well as the surface properties of DNA. Can you say a bit more about your current research?

Tommy Nylander: I'm very interested in different structures that can occur in living cells. In particular, structures generated by lipids, or fats, if you want. Previously lipids were considered as only a building block with no or very minute function. Merely a support.

Suzan Mazur: Cell membranes are made of lipids.

Tommy Nylander: Yes. Today it's realized that lipids can perform various functions that can be very important for cell maintenance and various cellular processes. I'd like to know more about how biomolecules interact with cell membranes, which are curved, and with lipids that form at this curved membrane.

There has been increased attention to this aspect of biological interface. Neutrons are especially useful for the study of lipids and other biomolecules. You can play a bit of a trick with something called selective deuteration, since ordinary water and heavy water have very different scattering properties.

When we do neutron scattering, this is what enables us to look at one part of a molecule at a time. We then mix H2O and deuterium oxide or D2—ordinary water and heavy water to match out different parts of structure. That is really the power of neutrons.

Another important aspect of neutrons is that they are not so harmful. Neutrons can pass through matter more easily than X-rays and they don't destroy cells.

You know when you go for an X-ray, the doctor goes out of the room and you're left alone with that buzzing machine. That's because X-rays are, I wouldn't exactly say harmful, but they are more intense.

Suzan Mazur: You're also looking at the surface properties of DNA. Can you say a bit about that?

Tommy Nylander: Yes. DNA contains the information code for transcription, for making protein and passing information into and out of cells. It is also important in cell division. DNA is a long double-helix strand, a meter or so long in a cell. To make this long strand, this long molecule fit into the cell, DNA wraps with a protein called histone. We think it's important to understand how this wrapping process occurs. One can regard this wrapping process as a mutational process.

Suzan Mazur: And neutron scattering can help us understand how this wrapping process happens?

Tommy Nylander: Yes. Sometimes DNA becomes damaged, i.e., the code goes wrong. There's an idea that if you want to repair DNA inside the cell, you can introduce healthy DNA to the cell using a small torpedo-like entity. It's somewhat futuristic, but can be done to an extent now. Neutrons offer new possibilities to help us look at this phenomenon.

Suzan Mazur: Thank you. Regarding the growing interest in neutron science in Europe, is the League of Advanced Neutron Sources (LENS) now replacing the European Research Infrastructure Consortium (ERIC) or do these two organizations remain separate? There are roughly a dozen European countries in each of these organizations.

Tommy Nylander: These consortia are a way for different countries to pool their resources, not only money but also in terms of competence and science.

Suzan Mazur: In-kind contributions.

Tommy Nylander: In-kind contributions but also general knowledge as well as in preparing the European Spallation Source (ESS) user base.

Suzan Mazur: Is LENS replacing ERIC or will they remain two separate consortia?

Tommy Nylander: ESS is within the concept of ERIC, within the legal framework of ERIC, which is a non-profit organization. LENS is more of a networking-type organization.

Suzan Mazur: Sweden and Denmark took the lead in building ESS? Is that right?

Tommy Nylander: Sweden and Denmark took the lead to build ESS. Denmark and Sweden each had a neutron research facility previously. Denmark's facility was quite famous—a reactor in Risø, near Roskilde Sweden had one at Studsvik, south of Stockholm.

The one in Denmark was very important for building up the research community and it had quite some impact. It was initiated by Niels Bohr, one of the principal physicists in Denmark—as you well know, a great scientist. The facility was built in a beautiful area just outside Roskilde. I did an experiment there once. The facility was nice, but it was a small neutron source and was closed for safety reasons. The reactor had passed its lifetime.

The Danes and Swedes came together to plan a new research facility. Since land around greater Copenhagen is expensive, some visionaries in Lund suggested constructing the facility here where it would be cheaper to build.

Suzan Mazur: What is the ESS operational target date and are we talking about a 2MW beam power or 5MW beam power?

Tommy Nylander: First there will be 2MW in 2023 and then it will be ramped up.

Suzan Mazur: My understanding is there are six main benefits to using neutron scattering: (1) probing structure and function in living cells, (2) high penetration, (3) precision, (4) sensitivity and selectivity, (5) probing for magnetism, (6) probing fundamental properties. Is that right? Did I leave anything out?

Tommy Nylander: That is quite a good summary of what you can do.

Suzan Mazur: Imaging living organism-level complexity will be possible with ESS. Is this what's called neutron tomography?

Tommy Nylander: Neutron tomography is an imaging technique and it is a rapidly evolving technology. With new detectors, we now have the resolution to look at living cells. This is quite an exciting development. And compared to X-ray, neutron scattering is still a relatively new technique.

Suzan Mazur: Will ESS be able to "elucidate DNA's own evolution"?

Tommy Nylander: Even with large and fancy equipment like this for addressing complex issues you need other techniques. Even with the power of neutrons, you need other types of measurement. But the reason why neutron scattering has become a good tool for life science is that scientists have been developing an environment in which they can grow living cells using neutron beams.

Neutron science started, was initially run by physicists, mostly nuclear physicists. Now you see biologists and researchers within medicine taking an interest in neutron scattering with measurement methods becoming increasingly important. The user communities are developing rapidly.

Suzan Mazur: Can you say briefly what the essential principle of neutron scattering is? How it works.

Tommy Nylander: Neutron scattering. One can regard neutrons as any kind of radiation like X-rays, the same sort of physics is valid. The only difference between neutrons and X-rays and photons is that neutron scattering is based on a particle that is neutral, i.e., the neutron can penetrate deep into matter without being destructive. The reason also for neutrons being very good for life science is that water scatters neutrons very well.

You know when you go to the doctor and have an X-ray of your soft tissue—a contrast solution is used that is sensitive to X-rays. This solution is generally based on a heavy metal complex. But water scatters neutrons very well, so you can look at water and at structure without the high contrast solution required for X-rays.

There is a famous picture of an operating car engine done with neutron tomography that was published by BMW and recorded in Munich. You can see through the engine parts, the dark part, the non-transparent part that stands out is the water vapor. So neutrons scatter different things than X-rays.

In some cases X-ray is better because it is more intense and can detect different things than neutrons can. But neutrons are particularly good because you can not only look at the location and structure of water better, but you can also look at the dynamics of water in living systems.

Suzan Mazur: ESS will have to its benefit the brightness factor as well.

Tommy Nylander: Yes. Of course, neutrons are very scarce. There are very few of them. So you need to have a strong source, a highly optimized source. As mentioned earlier, most of the facilities previously developed were designed from a physicist's point of view to optimize and measure certain things. But ESS is different because the technology is also inspired by the needs of a whole new user community working in life science and soft matter. From its inception, ESS was adapted for life science with the development of instruments, etc.

Suzan Mazur: There was a 2013 meeting of origins of life/synthetic cell development scientists at CERN, a meeting that I also attended. Will scientists at ESS be investigating origins of life/synthetic cell development?

Tommy Nylander: I'm sure there will be scientists investigating this, but there will also be a lot of other research, maybe not as spectacular, but clearly things that will benefit our daily life.

Suzan Mazur: Regarding benefitting our daily life—I've read that some of the projected uses are for dentistry and looking at bone structure.

Tommy Nylander: This is very good. Today we don't fully understand how bone mineralization happens on the molecular level. It's believed the mineralization process not only involves the mineral itself—calcium phosphate—but different proteins. Neutron scattering can be a very powerful tool in this investigation.

Suzan Mazur: Neutron science has been used to investigate viruses for a number of years. What will ESS enable us to see that previous neutron science could not?

Tommy Nylander: It's true, the structure of viruses is to some extent known. But a brighter source will enable us to better understand structure as well as the dynamic process, the mechanism of action of the virus.

Suzan Mazur: On the cultural front—ESS will also be used to examine ancient artifacts in new ways. Will this tool somehow enable a better read of fragmentary DNA and bone structure from say a 10,000-year-old skeleton?

Tommy Nylander: There are some people working on this issue with various techniques and I think the knowledge you gain from neutron experiments might help. The challenges are large though. You can recover some of the fragments in the DNA. But to encode the complete sequence of DNA you'd need a lot of different techniques, some computer modeling, etc.

ESS may help us to unravel the mysteries as to why the dinosaurs died out and things like that. Some prominent American researchers investigating this are using multiple techniques—not only neutron scattering but DNA sequencing.

Suzan Mazur: Thank you. Has there been any noticeable opposition to the construction of the world's most powerful spallation source at Lund University? Are there hazards?

Tommy Nylander: There was some resistance in the beginning. I happened to be at some of the very first meetings when the ESS project was discussed with environmentalists and local politicians. Colin Carlile—the first director of ESS—had a very good approach to this. He was very open and welcomed discussion.

I remember at one of these early meetings where there was a very open dialogue—an environmentalist, a very prominent young woman who opposed ESS, voiced her skepticism. The main concern of environmentalists at the beginning was that ESS would have a mercury target like the Spallation Neutron Source at Oak Ridge National Laboratory in the US.

Suzan Mazur: ESS will use a rotating, gas-cooled tungsten target in its neutron production unlike the liquid-mercury target both Oak Ridge and the Japan Proton Accelerator Research Complex use. Correct?

Tommy Nylander: Yes. The main environmental concern in Sweden was the large amount of mercury. This prominent environmentalist I just mentioned was successful in forcing engineers and decisionmakers to come up with a different construction. One that did not contain mercury. A tungsten wheel instead, which causes much less waste material and you don't have to pump mercury.

So that was a result of the discussion with the environmentalist. And I remember another meeting about ESS, where I was on a panel talking about my science with other panelists painting a very dark picture of nuclear waste. It was quite a horrible experience.

I turned to a young woman on the panel, an environmentalist, and I said: "Well I guess no one is interested in my science talk then."

And she looked at me and said: "I am very interested."

So that was the importance of public openness from the start.

Suzan Mazur: Other panelists were painting a very dark picture of nuclear waste. What was the nuclear issue?

Tommy Nylander: ESS is an accelerator. It accelerates protons. There is a nuclear aspect because it's a spallation. Neutrons come from the center of the atom so in that respect it's a nuclear process. It's not like in a nuclear reactor though where there's a chain reaction that you initiate which then generates a lot of energy. With ESS, when you shut off the proton accelerator that hits the target, the thing stops. To stop a nuclear reaction in a reactor, you have to put in rods that cool down the neutrons. So there's a fundamental difference.

Suzan Mazur: Europe has been hugely training the next generation of neutron scattering scientists. There in Sweden, you have SwedNess, a graduate school for neutron scattering operated by six universities. You also have the Nordic Neutron Science Programme. In April of this year, a delegation from the UN

Security Council visited ESS to have a look-see. Where's it all heading?

Tommy Nylander: ESS was not only envisioned as a neutron facility. It also contributes to society's excitement about science. If you look at all these projects that have been created. Take ILL, for instance, Institut Laue-Langevin in Grenoble, France. It was conceived as a peace project. It was created after the war to bring German, French and British people together. I think ESS can be similarly regarded as a way to bring people together, to help maintain peace and prosperity in Europe and beyond.

Suzan Mazur: ESS has been very transparent in communicating with the public the nature of the project and providing project updates. It's interesting that America's National Science Foundation held a meeting in February of this year on neutron scattering and biology. Biophysicist John Katsaras—a senior scientist at Oak Ridge National Laboratory—who participated in that NSF meeting, told me in a recent interview that America is planning "a second target station that will be competitive to ESS."

However, there is so far no public access to information from that NSF meeting, whereas NSF held a meeting in May on synthetic cell development with videos posted on the Internet. I understand a report on the NSF neutron scattering meeting may be coming out early next year. But when it comes to science, we just don't seem to have the same healthy transparency here in the US as you have there in Sweden.

Tommy Nylander: I know John very well and he is a good friend of mine. The thing is that, at least in our country, most people in government understand that they are entrusted with public money to create something good and beneficial for the society. And many scientific researchers, although not all, feel that they are public servants and want to share their work with the people of Sweden because we are funded by them. When you meet people in the street and mention ESS, there is real interest and enthusiastic support. This is because it has been a very open process.

Suzan Mazur: Your commitment to your work and to the public's perception of your work is inspiring. Do you have time for activities outside your work? Hobbies?

Tommy Nylander: I am an avid gardener and I do horseback riding. I love cooking also. We have a young son. So I'm really enjoying life.

Suzan Mazur: Is there a point you'd like to make that I may have missed?

Tommy Nylander: I'd like to say that ESS is nothing magical, strange or science fiction. It is a powerful tool that people are welcome to use. That is said not only in the spirit of openness but to communicate that we are making ESS for the benefit of society. These are "neutrons for society."

Part 3

Reframing Origin of Life

Chapter 22

Reframing Origin of Life

"There is this general question when the science experiment ends. Peter Galison has written a book, How Experiments End. Nothing is ever proven in science. At some point the community decides this is no longer the most pressing problem. That's it. The investigation moves on from this to that."—**Steve Benner** in conversation with me at Princeton, 2013, *The Origin of Life Circus*: *A How To Make Life Extravaganza*

6/22/2018

The problem with the origin of life investigation was neatly summed up in two recent articles. One was published in *Life*, co-authored by University of Wisconsin-Parkside chemistry professor Vera Kolb, a former protégé of legends Stanley Miller and Leslie Orgel. The other paper appeared in *Nature*, co-authored by MRC chemist John Sutherland, a co-coordinator of the Simons Collaboration on Origins of Life (SCOL), and with Matt Powner, winner of Harry Lonsdale's Origin of Life Challenge in 2012. Kolb and Sutherland are both on the same page in their assessments of origin of life.

John Sutherland: *"It follows that the sequence of events that led to life must have been highly contingent and the origin of life as we know it could have been **a low probability event**."*

Vera Kolb: *"We proposed the "comet pond" model as a way to create such a pond, even though it would be **a very low probability event** due to the challenges of landing pristine cometary material. . . .Nonetheless, some organic molecules are expected to survive in their original form. Over time, with large numbers of cometary impact, a significant inventory of organic material may be delivered. However, because comets did strike the planetary surface in a stochastic manner, there is **a vanishingly low probability** of two or more comets impacting the same area in a geologically short time interval."*

With that as backdrop—there are three relevant chats about origin(s) of life scheduled in the next few months. The first conference, opening June 24 at McMaster University in Hamilton, Ontario, Canada, is being called "Science of Early Life." Why the downgrade from origin(s) to early life? Does it signal that the caravan has already moved on?

The Canadian event (admission C$520) was organized by biophysicist Paul Higgs and colleagues at McMaster's Origins Institute. Paul Higgs was—along with Portland State University chemistry professor Niles Lehman —a Lonsdale Origin of Life Challenge research grantee.

What would Harry say about the Canadian event being framed as "Early Life"? Lonsdale considered his role in the origin(s) investigation "the second biggest thrill" of his life. With Lonsdale's death in 2014, the investigation may indeed have lost its most enthusiastic supporter.

Lynn Rothschild is the McMaster event's keynote speaker. That's Lynn J. Rothschild, the astrobiologist at NASA Ames married to NASA Ames research scientist Rocco Mancinelli—not to be confused with Lynn de Rothschild, former wife of Andy Stein now married to Sir Evelyn de Rothschild.

LJ Rothschild is also a biology professor at Boston University as well as at UC-Santa Cruz, and co-founding editor of the journal *Astrobiology*. Rothschild has recently said on one of NASA's online sites: "Charles Darwin always inspires me."

Will Rothschild stick to the Darwinian script in her upcoming McMaster talk: "Towards a universal biology"?

Big name presenters include: Dave Deamer, Steve Benner, Dimitar Sasselov, Irene Chen, Sukrit Ranjan and Andrei Lupas.

Also significant is CAS Conference 2018 on "Recreating the Origins of Life," a meeting, taking place in Munich, Germany, October 11-12 at Literaturhaus Munchen, organized by Ludwig-Maximilians University biophysicist Dieter Braun. The event is partly funded by the Simons Foundation. Braun is part of the Simons Collaboration on Origins of Life.

Some of the meeting's notable speakers are Matt Powner, Dimitar Sasselov, Irene Chen, Philip Hollinger, Andrei Lupas, Niles Lehman, Sheref Mansy, Stephen Mojzsis, Robert Pascal—several of these SCOL members.

It is disappointing to see a reference to Darwinian evolution in the promo for the Munich event: "How can Darwinian evolution emerge?" Disappointing because Dieter Braun told me months ago in an interview: "We're getting a good corps of people now who are reshaping the field in a completely new way."

I assumed from that conversation that meant letting go of Darwinian natural selection:

> *"**Suzan Mazur**: One of the problems in funding origins research is that it still seems largely angled to Darwinian evolution, which has been seriously challenged over the*

last decade. . . . There seems to be a need for new terminology, new language in the field to describe this. Selection isn't an accurate description.

Dieter Braun*: That's a big difficulty in the field, absolutely. Selection, if I say that to biologists, to physicists, to chemists, it has completely different meanings to each. . . . It would be a great advantage to have more precise language. We will find this as we continue to communicate across disciplines, In the end, experiments will be our common language."*

Another issue with the CAS conference promo is its peculiar arrogance:

"Only the combined effort from renowned experts from various disciplines can be successful in retracing the origins of life under experimental conditions and pave the way towards answering some of the most pertinent questions: how did the very first genetic material in lifeforms develop?"

Such a claim runs contrary to comments by:

Freeman Dyson*:"We are all equally ignorant when it comes to origin of life."*—**Dyson** at *Charlie Rose* roundtable

Steve Benner*: "There are no experts."*—**Benner** in conversation with me at Princeton Origins conference, 2013

and

Bob Hazen*: "We've got to draw the circle wider. Even the idea of a professional scientist versus a knowledgeable reader. There's a continuum here. And we're all part of this search for trying to understand*

where we come from and who we are."—The Altenberg
16: An Exposé of the Evolution Industry

With some of the €19 million in funding from the Dutch government awarded for synthetic cell development, scientists in The Netherlands have organized the "1st International Symposium on Building a Synthetic Cell."

The event takes place in South Holland at Delft University of Technology, August 28-29. Key speakers include: Bert Poolman, Matthias Heinemann, John Sutherland, Eugene Koonin, Michael Jewett and Eors Szathmary, among others.

I traveled to The Netherlands last October and met with scientists at the Dutch Origins Center, headquartered (virtually) at the University of Groningen. One of them, Bert Poolman, a principal of the Dutch synthetic cell development team, said their reason for building the cell was to "better understand biology." Poolman said further:

> *"**Bert Poolman**: We received a grant of €19 million from the Netherlands Science Foundation last summer for our synthetic cell development project. The award went to 15 working groups—15 groups working in this area is substantial. We will probably appoint 30-80 PhD students. But some of our labs also have national grants and so the 15 groups could each include 10 to 20 researchers.*
>
> *The 15 PIs have already individually been working on aspects of synthetic cell development. But for the first time there is proper funding for tackling larger scale problems.*
>
> ***Suzan Mazur**: Why are you developing a synthetic cell?*
>
> ***Bert Poolman**: The reason for us is basically to better understand biology. . . .*

Suzan Mazur: How close at this point are you to making the synthetic cell?

Bert Poolman: We're still decades away. This has to do with the middle part, what I call information processing. The most difficult aspect is probably protein synthesis because protein synthesis involves more than 100 components. And to build a ribosome in vitro, *from scratch, that is an enormous challenge.*

So information is stored in DNA—although it could also be something else—it doesn't have to be DNA. We need to replicate it because that's something necessary for life. DNA is replicated to make a copy of itself for the daughter cell when a cell divides. But DNA also needs to be decoded or 'read' to make new proteins. This is something that all living cells do and that we try to reconstitute from molecular components, which is extremely difficult because of the many molecules involved, their complex assembly, and lots of processes we do not understand yet."

Missing from all three events is Nobel laureate Jack Szostak, who announced at World Science Festival 2014 he'd have "life in lab" in three years. Harvard astrophysicist Dimitar Sasselov predicted five. . .

Chapter 23

ISSOL's Niles Lehman &
Templeton Cash Cow

"If you still want to chat and can stick to a scientific agenda, check back in a couple of weeks when I have a bit more time. . . .I think everything regarding the JTF project(s) is above board. Please tell me if I'm wrong."
—**Niles Lehman, March 2018 email to me**

4/5/2018

It's like a madcap scene from the Marx Brothers' *A Night in Casablanca*, where to the dismay of the Nazis the trunk that's packed for the getaway is empty because the clothes keep walking away. Templeton continues to pour millions of dollars into origin and evolution of life projects that result in fiasco: (1) the 2013 origins conference at CERN; (2) funding of religious scholars by NASA & Templeton to investigate how the religious community would respond to the discovery of life in outer space; (3) the dig through 18 levels of civilization for religious evidence at 10,000-year-old Çatalhöyük—to cite just a few. But science is not being compromised for big laughs, it's being compromised by greedy academics and their university money managers who, with a wink, look the other way while Templeton's Big Creep mission blurs the lines between science and religion.

One of the stickiest origins projects Templeton has recently funded is "Cooperation and Interpretation in the Emergence of Life," which looks to find purposeful RNA fragments that agree to cooperate. Six hundred thirty thousand dollars ($630,000) has been awarded for said project to the team of Christopher Southgate—a British theologian/biochemist, and Portland State University chemistry professor Niles Lehman.

Lehman was recently elected president of the nonprofit origin of life society "ISSOL" replacing Sandra Pizzarello. As ISSOL president, Lehman will now also be majorly soliciting funds, including more from Templeton.

Lehman and Dave Deamer, who served as ISSOL president from 2011-2014, were both Lonsdale origins research darlings. But with philanthropist Harry Lonsdale now gone. . .

I decided it was time to request an interview with Niles Lehman. So I emailed him a week or so ago. But Lehman was defensive about a conversation and dictated terms. He would not agree to questions about the politics of science, for example, only about science—despite the fact that he is a publicly funded scientist and is now looking for public investment in ISSOL.

I never did interview Niles Lehman for my first book on origin of life. Lehman's embrace of autocatalytic sets, and Nobel laureate Jack Szostak's dismissal of the concept, which follows, gave me pause:

> *"Autocatalytic sets is one of those concepts where the people who came up with the original idea, like Stuart Kauffman, rather than admit being wrong kept changing their story until it was basically the same concept everybody was already working on.*

The original idea was that there would be large numbers of compounds where one would help another to replicate, and that one could help some other one to replicate, and that somehow out of this huge population of interacting molecules autocatalytic replication would emerge.

In my opinion that was never chemically realistic. Now you see people talking about non-enzymatic RNA replication and calling that autocatalytic sets. If that's what you want to call it, that's fine. But it seems like the concept has lost all meaning."

However, I did interview Lehman's former graduate student, Nilesh Vaidya, who told me in January 2013 at the Princeton origins conference that the secret to making RNA fragments come together in his 2012 experiment with Lehman was simply adding magnesium. Similarly, Georgia Institute of Technology chemist Nick Hud commented in a 2013 videotaped review of Lehman's research funded by Harry Lonsdale that the aggregation of RNA shown on Lehman's slide was likely due to manganese in the mix.

"I didn't think that I could sneak that past you.," Lehman responded to Hud's observation. "I wasn't trying to do that."

The bottom line is that the stitching together of RNA in Lehman's experiment was not due to smart RNA.

But Lehman, now partnering with Christopher Southgate (Certificate in Theology—University of Exeter, and General Ministry Certificate—Church of England), in this his second grant from the John Templeton Foundation, is pursuing just that angle—purpose "all the way down" to single RNA molecules.

Meanwhile, Southgate, per his online CV, has been engaged by Templeton numerous times over the last two decades, (1) to develop a course on science and religion; (2) to develop a textbook on science and religion; (3) as a contributor to a "high-level

246

Templeton Colloquium on Deep Incarnation"; and (4) as grant assessor for both the John Templeton Foundation and Templeton World Charities Foundation. It is unclear how much money has changed hands.

Southgate's forthcoming book from Cambridge University Press is *Glory and Longing*, in which he proposes "a new way of understanding the glory of God in Christian theology, based on glory as a sign."

Southgate has done six interviews on science and theology for the PBS television program *Closer To Truth*, which is funded by Templeton. He's currently teaching such university courses as: "God, Humanity and the Cosmos" and "Evolution, God and Gaia."

Furthermore, Lehman and Southgate cling to discredited Darwinian theory in their Templeton-funded project, despite the following voices of reason:

> *"Sometimes when I'm in a mildly bitter mood I think, look the trouble with Darwin is he believes in Intelligent Design. He never really got it clear to himself that there really isn't a designer. So it's questionable whether you can take artificial selection as a model for natural selection the way he did. When you try to do that you can't work it out."*—**Jerry Fodor** *talking to me in 2008*

> *"Perhaps making all these parallels between natural selection and artificial selection, the way Darwin does in his book, could be somewhat dangerous because in artificial selection there is someone who is selecting, even if unconsciously. In that respect, the evolutionary process is very different in nature where nothing is there to actually select. . . . No one in the mainstream scientific community now takes selection literally."*—**Eugene Koonin** *in conversation with me in 2017*

> *"The circulation of the proof copy of What Darwin Got Wrong, the product of a noted philosopher and a prominent student of linguistics and cognitive science, has resulted in a volume of critical comment from biologists and philosophers that has not been seen since 1859. . . . Not to be misunderstood, perhaps biologists should stop referring to "natural selection," and instead talk about differential rates of survival and reproduction."—Richard Lewontin, New York Review of Books, 2010*

And while I don't see eye-to-eye with University of Chicago's Jerry Coyne on his enthusiasm for Darwinian natural selection, I do find his dissection of the Templeton threat to science right on the money (even if he did try to claim my NASA-Templeton report as his). Following are Coyne's blog comments regarding the recent lecture by philosopher Orestis Palermos, part of a University of Edinburgh Coursera course that Templeton bankrolled:

> *"In the end, this whole course seems like a Templeton-funded endeavor to cast doubt on evolution—and perhaps on science as a whole. That, of course, comports perfectly with the John Templeton Foundation's agenda to blur the boundaries between faith and science, making both seem like faith-based enterprises that, taken together, can tell us "spiritual truths" and answer "the Big Questions". (That was, after all, Sir John's purpose in creating the Foundation.) Let nobody say that Templeton has decided to abandon religion and cast its lot fully with science. It may pretend to do that, but behind the scenes it's still funding courses like this one."*

We have a wall between church and state in America, but in recent years we've seen attempts to destabilize that wall. The 2015-2017 $3M funding by NASA & Templeton to two dozen religious scholars was one of them. The Freedom From Religion Foundation took action filing a Freedom of Information Act request for documents regarding the matter, which should have led to housecleaning of NASA personnel. But how much the Trump administration cares about maintaining this particular wall is questionable.

Chapter 24

NASA & Templeton Fund Misty Quest
For What "Life" Is

"Therefore, perhaps, life 'is what it is not, and it is not what it is.'"—**Takeuchi, Hogeweg, Kaneko quoting Jean-Paul Sartre**

1/15/2018

Reunited following their collaborative funding of a $3M investigation to determine how the religious community would respond to the discovery of life in outer space—NASA Astrobiology Institute (NAI) and John Templeton Foundation, directly and through Templeton-funded entities: Templeton World Charity Foundation and ELSI Origins Network, are principal supporters of a Royal Society year-end publication that seems to want to redefine "life" in order to justify further adventures (space as well as lab).

[Note: Royal Society papers discussed in this article are funded in whole or in part by NAI, Templeton or Templeton-funded entities, unless otherwise indicated.]

Titled: "Re-conceptualizing the origins of life," theme issue 2109 of *Philosophical Transactions of the Royal Society A* is really all about re-conceptualizing the living state. Manipulating the definition for what "life" is is the easiest way to ensure that you find "life" where you want to find it in the universe (that would include inside synthetic cell labs).

Curiously, the Royal Society journal cover imitates the Templeton nautilus spiral signature, while inside the articles that are funded by Templeton distance themselves from Templeton views and bear the following disclaimer:

> *"The opinions expressed in this publication are those of the authors and do not necessarily reflect the views of the John Templeton Foundation."*

But if the views of the authors don't reflect the views of Templeton, why is a disclaimer necessary? It's because Templeton is known to support a pairing of science and religion. Plus the Freedom From Religion Foundation filed a Freedom of Information Act request regarding the 2015-2017 collaborative funding of religious scholars by NAI and Templeton.

Marshall, Murray and Cronin in their Royal Society article supported in part by Templeton (how much support is not disclosed) argue:

> *"A generalized approach that aims to evaluate complex objects as possible biosignatures could be useful to explore the cosmos for new life forms. . . . By remaining too tied to the details of terrestrial biology we risk missing biosignatures presented to us due to our assumptions about what life must be like."*

Lee Cronin further entertains this idea as part of a $860,802 grant from Templeton (2016-2019) to develop what he calls a "Universal Life Detector." Here's Cronin's proposal:

"We will explore this by comparing the complexity of simple molecules to those complex ones found in biology and aiming to establish a threshold to discriminate if the molecule in question could have been generated by a non-biological process, or if it has originated in a living system, either directly as a metabolite, or indirectly by a person (e.g. Earth or Alien chemist), or a living proxy (robot)."

What I'm saying is that by expanding the definition for what life is—beyond biology—as active matter, live systems, whatever—as suggested in the Royal Society origins issue—scientists seem to be embarking on a kind of fantastic voyage, clearly in contrast to what investigators not affiliated with the Royal Society issue have told me in recently published interviews about the days of origins fishing trips being over.

The Royal Society origins issue grew out of a March 2014 white paper on the subject involving Piet Hut at Japan's Earth-Life Science Institute (ELSI), Nicholas Guttenberg also at ELSI, Norm Packard at ProtoLife *et al.* Curiously, in a March 2013 book interview, Piet Hut told me he was "new to the origins of life field":

"I'm actually new to the origins of life field. I've been largely involved with physics and other areas of investigation. It was only in December of last year as the Earth-Life Science Institute in Japan started up that I found myself one of the principal investigators, when we decided to delve into the topic of origins of life."

In the 2014 white paper, Guttenberg—who now also serves as chief data scientist at ARAYA Brain Imaging, Inc. in Japan as well as research associate at ELSI—commented:

"[I]t may be useful to shelve the question of 'what is life?' for a while and try to look at the phenomena we associate with emergent structures of this era independent of our biocentricism. Rather than saying 'what properties are necessary to define life?', we should ask 'what broad and

252

qualitatively different properties do we often see in living things that we don't yet know how to explain?'"

The white paper next led to a Carnegie Institution conference in 2015 chaired by Paul Davies protégé/surrogate Sara Walker, a physicist at Arizona State University. Walker was also co-compiler of the Royal Society year-end theme issue. Through the years Paul Davies, director of ASU's Beyond Center, has been both a major adviser to Templeton and substantial beneficiary of the foundation's philanthropy.

The Carnegie conference featured Bob Hazen (Carnegie), Piet Hut (ELSI/IAS), Nigel Goldenfeld (UIUC), Norm Packard (Protolife), Nicholas Guttenberg (ELSI), George Cody (Carnegie), among others.

Further scrutiny of the Royal Society theme issue reveals:

(1) Scientists do not understand what existing life is and so they think that by trying to make life in the lab they may be able to begin to figure it all out. No news here. This is something Jack Szostak said years ago. Walker, Cody and Packard note in their introductory piece (which states Walker, Cody and Packard "received no funding" for the article):

> *"[I]t is precisely in attempting to understand the transition from non-life to life where we have our best hope of understanding those properties of life that are its most fundamental."*

(2) Walker, Cody and Packard further indicate that scientists think "information may be a key factor" in the origin of life, although investigators don't understand what "information" is either. I interviewed both Packard, known for chaos theory, and Walker for my book on origin of life. Sara Walker offered this definition for "information" during our 2012 comversation:

> *"Information can be loosely defined as events that affect and direct the state of a dynamic system. Saying that*

information is algorithmic really means that specific events are programmed to have specific outcomes in biological systems. So it's really the processing of the information that's unique about how biology operates."

(3) Takeuchi, Hogeweg and Kaneko, in an opinion piece funded by the Japanese government and EU, work around the classic definition for life being linked to Darwinian evolution, noting:

"We can conceptualize the origin of life as the origin of evolution and the evolution of life. Therefore, evolution is at the centre of the origin of life, where the two lines of enquiry must meet."

They conclude by quoting Jean-Paul Sartre: "Therefore, perhaps, life 'is what it is not, and it is not what it is.'"

(4) Goldenfeld, Biancalani, Jafarpour, in an article funded by NAI on universal biology, recognize a transition to Darwinian evolution following a collective stage—the communal stage is Carl Woese's 1970s idea—and they identify these two features common to life: (1) the "canonical genetic code," and (2) biological homochirality—saying both emerged prior to the *Last Universal Common Ancestor state* (emphasis added). Goldenfeld *et al.* look to statistical mechanics to support their argument.

Carl Woese collaborated for many years with Nigel Goldenfeld, who is currently director of the NAI Center for Universal Biology at the University of Illinois, Urbana-Champaign and heads the Biocomplexity group at UIUC's Carl Woese Institute for Genomic Biology.

Goldenfeld told me this in a 2014 book interview:

"Early life was much more collective, much more communal than it is today, particularly the core cellular machinery, such as translational machinery, etc., which was horizontally transferred. We don't know how that happened. It may well have been that there was massive

254

endosymbiosis, meaning organisms were very porous and could crash into each other and absorb each other on a massive scale and that's how cellular functions were transmitted. That was an idea Carl proposed in the 1970s in one of his papers."

Following the death of Carl Woese several years ago, Goldenfeld revealed: "Carl had a sub-clinical Asperger's type of personality, and this meant hat he was unable to put himself in the mind of the other person."

[Note: Charles Kurland has said more recently that the concept of endosymbiosis was born in a 1960s pipe dream: *"The 60s was a time when many were discovering drugs and the endosymbiosis model is a fitting product of that period. It is a pipe dream."***]**

Carl Woese was funded by both NASA and NIH in the 1970s for his work on the Three Domains of Life. In our October 2012 interview, Woese described LUCA this way:

> *"The universe is a process. Alfred North Whitehead said with biology and other things, we are not dealing with a procession of forms. . . .we are dealing with the form or forms of process. In that distinction lies the essence of what this astrobiology institute here in Illinois is all about. We are really going to study the evolutionary origin of life. Anybody who looks at biology now, with a one percent exception, can feel—anyone with biological intuition can feel—that life is an evolutionary process. As I said, it's not just a procession of forms."*

(5) Adam, Zubarev, Aono, Cleaves say our current theories (thermodynamic, chemical, physical and information) are all inadequate to explain life's origins and they discuss the "new guiding principle" of *subsumed complexity*:

> *"Within the framework of a new guiding principle for prebiotic chemistry called subsumed complexity, organic compounds are viewed as by-products of energy*

transduction phenomena at different scales (subatomic, atomic, molecular and polymeric) that retain energy in the form of bonds that inhibit energy from reaching the ground state. There is evidence for an emergent level of complexity that is overlooked in most conceptualizations of abiogenesis that arises from populations of compounds formed from atomic energy input. We posit that different forms of energy input can exhibit different degrees of dissipation complexity within an identical chemical medium. By extension, the maximum capacity for organic chemical complexification across molecular and macromolecular scales subsumes, rather than emerges from, the underlying complexity of energy transduction processes that drive their production and modification."

(6) Ikegami, Mototake, Kobori, Oka, Hashimoto in their paper funded by the Japanese government—*"Life as an emergent phenomenon: studies from a large-scale bold simulation and web data"*—**think a definition of "life" should include the Internet, World Wide Web and social media!**

(7) H. James Cleaves (ELSI/IAS) and Markus Meringer (German Aerospace Center) envision "a very different chemical trajectory":

> *"First, as it is now clear that the abiotic organic chemical space of the Universe is very large, it must be acknowledged that far less is known about prebiotic chemistry which led to the origin of life than has perhaps been presumed.*
>
> *Second, as many of the secondary metabolites which make up the grand diversity of biological natural products come from metabolic transformations mediated by evolutionarily derived enzymes, and the chemical space to be explored is so incredibly large, it is likely that there is little overlap of the compounds with abiological samples, and possible that an independent biochemistry might develop along a very different chemical trajectory."*

(8) Mamajanov & Cody consider the possibility "that catalysis may have originally been performed by hyperbranched polymers."

(9) Kacar, Guy, Smith, Baross look at the deep past by reconstructing sequences of proteins that might have existed in ancestral organisms—palaeophenotype reconstruction. (See also Kurland & Harish on Deep Evolution.)

(10) Santa Fe Institute's Jessica Flack worked with two Templeton grants for her research on "Coarse-graining."

(11) Even Bob Hazen's research was supported by Templeton. Hazen takes a physical science perspective to life's origins in his Royal Society article, saying, (1) there are a "range of probabilities for many natural events," and (2) just because you can't make it happen in the lab doesn't mean it is not inevitable on an Earth-like planet.

Hazen, in response to Jerry Fodor's comment to me: **"Astrobiology doesn't exist. What are its laws?"** said this in defense of the field in our 2008 book interview:

> *"Of course astrobiology exists. Any human endeavor "exists" where there's a group of people, in this case probably 1,000 researchers, who have a common set of goals and aspirations."*

As part of Hazen's $400,000 grant (2017-2020) from Templeton, he plans to produce 15 seminars and public lectures on origins of life and astrobiology.

Several of the Royal Society articles discuss the importance of computation to the field. Among them: "Origin of life in a digital microcosm"; "An intermediate level of abstraction for computational systems chemistry"; Bulk measurements of messy chemistries are needed for a theory of the origins of life"; and "The thermodynamic efficiency of computations made in cells across the range of life."

The Royal Society issue is largely about science that Darwin never dabbled in, and may never have even dreamed of, and yet there is an inclination in the issue to cling to the Darwinian cliff. Nonetheless, it is good to know what the scientific establishment are up to and this collection of articles is open access.

The big question is: Are scientists reaching out to inspire and be inspired by the public or publicly engaging to solicit funds for a ramping up of space adventures and for basic research that looks to spin off discoveries commercially?

Chapter 25

Steve Benner—Origins of Life Funds & Origins of Life Jewelry

1/9/2018

Five years ago at an origins of life conference at Princeton University, I suggested to Andrew Pohorille—NASA's senior-most scientist on the subject of origins, and synthetic biologist Steve Benner—who runs his own non-profit research institute in Florida, that they take the origins discussion to public television like Paul Nurse did with science, bringing in Pfizer to sponsor a 13-part program on *Charlie Rose*. Pohorille at the time thought the subject was "too esoteric" for public television. Benner liked the idea and I received an email from him several months later while on Crane Island in the San Juans saying that he was almost booked on *Charlie Rose*. But initial interest was in

Benner's findings on primate evolution and the consumption of alcohol, and his guest spot never did materialize.

Photo of Steve Benner, NASA

With the *Charlie Rose Show* now swept away by scandal, and PBS late night television without a suitable replacement really, Benner has recently taken to the stage on Manhattan's Lower East Side (admission $20@) to discuss origins of life at a performance space described as a cross between the Harvard Club and CBGB. I'm told the podcast of the event will soon be publicly available.

Benner is one of few scientists with that kind of range. Britain's Nick Lane, a biochemist at University College London and popular science writer, is another. Lane is known to Irish fiddle in pubs on weekends and has recently been coaxed onstage to play with origins of life—sans fiddle. But origins of life with fiddle could also draw a crowd. So could an opera with full orchestra.

Steve Benner is a self-described "crackpot synthetic biologist to some extent" (i.e., he thinks outside the box). As an entertainer, he's got perfect timing. His father was an inventor and engineer and his mother a musician. But Benner's wit is uniquely his own. For instance, one way he's raising money for origins research is through the sale of origins jewelry, as FfAME, his non-profit foundation, advertises:

"Impress your friends with your understanding of the most recent theories for how life originated on Earth. Each necklace is individually handcrafted by Mary Margaret Andrew, with a black diamond representing carbon (the central element in RNA, which originated life), pink tourmaline (delivering borate needed to stabilize ribose, the "R" in RNA), blue apatite (delivering the phosphate of RNA), and olive green peridot (the serpentinizing mineral that provides the alkali that gets it all to work together)."

Benner's outreach is not as unconventional as it may seem, however. He's managed to secure a $5.4 million grant from the Templeton Foundation for origins research. In Benner's announcement of the Templeton award on his FfAME web site, he credits Harry Lonsdale for getting the origins research funding ball rolling with some of "his personal fortune," and NASA for its ongoing support for astrobiology. Benner had this to say about the Simons Foundation, which is substantially throwing money into origins investigations:

"The Simons Foundation portfolio is largely classical, devoted mostly to research strategies that were defined a half century ago. We are hoping in our Templeton program to support more innovative ideas, ideas that have a chance of solving paradoxes related to origins that will remain even if all of the classical questions are answered."

It is curious that Benner's appearance on the Downtown Manhattan stage was sponsored by the Simons Foundation. And even more curious that the host of the show—who writes for the *New York Times*—still believes in tooth fairies like natural selection.

Speaking of tooth fairies, as previously noted here, for the past two years NASA and Templeton have funded religious scholars in a $3 million inquiry about how the religious community would respond to the discovery of life in outer space. The sole representative from NASA to that inquiry was Frank Rosenzweig, apparently the grandson of Franz Rosenzweig, the Jewish theologian who, with Martin Buber, translated the Bible into German. The irony is that there are a significant number of scientists at NASA, I'm advised, who don't think we will find life anywhere else in the solar system. And I'm further advised that the instruments to detect biomarkers on the exoplanets are "decades away" from development. Not to mention the lack of consensus about what life even is. . .

Benner is now scheduled to address origins funding options at the January 14-19 Gordon Conference in Galveston, Texas, as well as discuss how to commercially spin off origins research. To shed further light on Benner's strategic thinking along these lines, following are excerpts from our 2013 Princeton conversation, from my book, *The Origin of Life Circus: A How To Make Life Extravaganza.*

January 2013, Princeton

"**Suzan Mazur**: I was just stepping into the discussion about origin of life in 2008. I thought it was important to talk to a diversity of people, including amateurs and mavericks, because who knows where the great idea comes from.

Steve Benner: Exactly. As I mentioned and you quoted me, none of us are experts and we don't really know what we're doing with this.

Suzan Mazur: Since the Princeton conference is about the RNA world, would you comment as to whether you think things in the RNA world have moved significantly forward in the last few years?

Steve Benner: Yes. They really have. In part, because there's been a swing back and forth between two major themes. One theme emerged in the 1980s, the discovery of catalytic RNA, which led the community, myself included—I was just a pup at the time—to think the problem was a lot simpler. The discovery by Sid Altman, Tom Cech, Norm Pace and various people, that there was a potential for RNA being a catalytic molecule was certainly something.

It went back a lot earlier. Carl Woese had this on his mind. You can go all the way back to Alex Rich in 1962. As far as I know, Rich was the first person to actually suggest RNA could perform both the catalytic and genetic roles.

I thought it would be a much easier process. By the 1990s it was quite clear—as evidenced by Stanley Miller's paper from 1995 or 1996—that it was going to be a hard slog to get RNA in its oligomeric form because of the instability of its various pieces. Again, a downer from the 1960s when people were finding prebiotic ways, all sorts of things based on Stanley Miller's earlier work.

Leslie Orgel was one scientist. Joan Oró. All these people found lots of these things going on quite quickly. But in the 1990s we hit another wall with the research. And by the year 2000 scientists were saying—like my good friend Pier Luigi Luisi, who you've noted has referred to the RNA world as a baseless fantasy. Luigi and I were colleagues at the ETH in Zurich for 10 years, by the way. In the 1995-2000 period, scientists were in despair.

Suzan Mazur: But Luisi is up to date about developments in the RNA world.

Steve Benner: The way he states the case is probably a bit stronger than he actually himself believes. All of us do this in speaking to the Fourth Estate.

Suzan Mazur: He told me something even worse.

Steve Benner: Even worse?!

Suzan Mazur: I asked Luisi if funding was the issue slowing down progress in the origin of life field. He said that is not the problem. Luisi said there are no new ideas, we need "mindstorms."

Steve Benner: There is a shortage of ideas plus there's a shortage of funding to pursue the ideas that we do have. It's an interesting question whether putting more money in will result in more substantial ideas. It's a cycle you can't anticipate, you have to try. . .

Suzan Mazur: Lonsdale wanted to go really public with the origin of life message. He saw that I'd been on the *Charlie Rose Show* and asked if I could introduce him. I told him what I knew in terms of doing science roundtables these days on the program, which is what Paul Nurse told me in 2008 at his Rockefeller University Evolution symposium. That is, if you want to do a science roundtable on *Charlie Rose*, you need a corporate sponsor like Pfizer, which Nurse brought in for his 13-part series.

Steve Benner: I didn't know that.

Suzan Mazur: Some think orign of life is too esoteric a subject for a public discussion, but Princeton and NASA made the wise decision to stream the Princeton conference over the Internet. I think Lonsdale is right. There should be a series of *Charlie Rose* origin of life roundtables.

Steve Benner: I agree.

Suzan Mazur: Luisi says there are no new ideas. Why not widen the discussion circle? Freeman Dyson was on *Charlie Rose* talking briefly about origin of life. Why not bring Freeman Dyson in again and many others for an in-depth conversation?

Steve Benner: Science, to the public, is at one level the memorization of facts based on an authority—your teacher, who has the cosmic authority of the expert. You'll see this all over— "four out of five dentists agree." The appeal to authority and consensus of opinion.

But science is also the opposite. I'm a great fan of Richard Feynman who comments that science begins with a denial of the opinion of experts. Science begins when you say NO. The perceived wisdom is wrong. Feynman's opinion is exactly the opposite of what many people think science is, the memorization of facts taught to you by an authority.

Suzan Mazur: That was the view of the late science and technology historian David F. Noble, who told me, "A consensus of scientists. Well, when you have a consensus of scientists, that should set off alarms."

Steve Benner: Scientists must be trained. This is a problem. Feynman goes on to point out that there's an enormous amount of what goes on in the public sphere in term of science that is mostly not scientific at all. He also says there's an enormous amount of intellectual tyranny in the name of science.

Suzan Mazur: Noble thought that peer review was at the heart of the problem. He considered it censorship.

Steve Benner: Well, it's a big problem. I'm a very soft peer reviewer. I think if you want to publish something that makes you look like a fool—go ahead. Be my guest.

Suzan Mazur: Yes. You have a right to put it up there. Lynn Margulis courageously fought PNAS over its system of anonymous peer review.

Steve Benner: Exactly. This is how I don't get asked to review very often. . . .

Suzan Mazur: So is the origin of life field exploding within the scientific community?

Steve Benner: We now have the ability to address most if not all of the 1990s objections to the RNA World. That means we have ways to get ribose directly. We have ways to get ribose and its nucleotides indirectly. Some of that progress is due to the work of Sanchez and Orgel. Some of these are very old ideas. John Sutherland has amplified these splendidly. There is essentially nothing from the 1995 critique of the RNA world that does not have an answer.

Suzan Mazur: But it will be a creation scenario that COULD have happened. Not what did, in fact, happen.

Steve Benner: There is this general question when the science experiment ends. Peter Galison has written a book, How Experiments End. Nothing is ever proven in science. At some point the community decides this is no longer the most pressing problem. That's it. The investigation moves on from this to that.

It's a matter of opinion as to whether the solutions to the 1990s' objections regarding the RNA world are sufficiently robust to allow people to move on from them to something else. It is a little early to say that. Right now what's emerging in the RNA world, which Irene Chen talked about here at Princeton, is that we don't know how useful function is distributed among sequence spaces.

You have 4 raised to the power 100 different sequences of RNA 100 nucleotides long. We don't know how productive function is distributed there compared to destructive function.

One of the things about the model of autocatalysis is that we have many molecules and this increases the chance of having one that does something productively but it also increases the chance of doing something else destructively.

Well, very often when you add things, it's bad. It destroys interaction. It inhibits interaction. It catalyzes undesirable side reactions. It depletes material. . . .

Suzan Mazur: Are you involved in making a protocell?

Steve Benner: We're not. There are a lot of very bright people in that business. A lot of them are in Europe.

Suzan Mazur: Are scientific fields here in the US integrating as they are in Europe?

Steve Benner: I saw a piece of yours a while back about the CERN meeting coming up. Partly because of the European funding structure, which we got a taste of in Antonio Lazcano's talk regarding Mexico. Lazcano said that if you are a professor, you have a chair which has an endowment associated with it so you have a certain amount of research without having to go outside. It makes people lazy and that's one of the criticisms Americans will direct at the European system. But it also permits imagination and broad-based interest.

If you go to France, you see people coming up with cutting-edge advances in sort of this evolution fringe.

Suzan Mazur: This is good.

Steve Benner: Of course it's good.

Suzan Mazur: Well there could be more public interest and more funding in the US. How do you get the public enthused? Do a 13-part series on origin of life on *Charlie Rose*.

Steve Benner: All of this is coming from Europe. I had 10 years in Europe where I had the ability to do crackpot things. It is because of the funding structure in Europe.

I worked for 10 years in Switzerland at the Swiss Federal Institute of Technology, and I was the beneficiary of the European funding system, for which I'm eternally grateful, and for which major advances came out that would not have been conceivable at all in the United States.

You heard Eric Goucher's talk here at Princeton, where he was resurrecting ancient enzymes. We were the first people to do that, we did that in Europe. We would never have done that in the US. I proposed that to the NIH when I was just a pup in the mid 1980s, but the NIH panelist reviews were scathing. And I've kept them.

The second thing is that we reinvented the genetic alphabet. Put 12 letters into DNA and the four ACTG. But go around the world and ask where has synthetic biology expanded on the notion of what might constitute a genetic system. Well in Belgium there's Piet Herdewijn. You go to Albert Eschenmoser at ETH in Zurich, my former laboratory. This is all coming from Europe. There is nothing of this power originating in the United States.

Suzan Mazur: But you're a synthetic biologist now in America.

Steve Benner: That's right. A crackpot synthetic biologist to some extent. Synthetic biology is now mainstream. It was certainly not mainstream in the early 1980s. Or in the 1990s when Piet Herdewijn was getting started in Belgium.

It was only because of the funding structure of Europe where you were allowed to bring together—you were mentioning this in the protocell area, but this is 20 years ago—the molecular biology needed to do this, the synthetic organic chemistry needed to do this, the physical chemistry, the biophysics, this concept about origins of life to inspire. **You didn't see that anywhere in the United States until after Europe took the lead. That is a direct assignment, you can attribute that directly to funding."** [emphasis added]

Chapter 26

Biophysicist Dieter Braun—
Origin of Life Investigation Renaissance

Photo, courtesy Dieter Braun

9/11/2017

Redford-style good looks have not been enough to divert Dieter Braun from his research interest in nonequilibrium conditions on the microscale, and what is now a central role in the investigation into the origins of life. Braun—a professor of systems biophysics at Ludwig Maxmilians University in Munich, a Simons Foundation collaborator on the origins of life, and scientific coordinator of the OLIM initiative (Origin of Life Munich)—says a whole new breed of scientists, "experimentally driven," have entered the field as funding opens up and that origins of life research is no longer a "side activity," fishing expedition, or place for dreamy "pet theories."

I first became aware of Dieter Braun several years ago when Rockefeller University physicist Albert Libchaber spoke to me of

Braun's star quality as an origins investigator in his lab (postdoctoral research 2000-2003). I next noticed Braun on the Simons origins page also featuring Jack Szostak, Dimitar Sasselov, John Sutherland and Matt Powner, and finally contacted him about a recent paper he coauthored on hairpin structures. Since Braun was not first author on the paper, he tossed his hat to postdoc Georg Urtel who was, and who agreed to be interviewed.

I couldn't make it to the recent kickoff of the Dutch Origins Center, where Braun gave a talk on "transport phenomena and nucleic acid replication," so I made another story pitch.

As our interview that follows reveals, Braun grew up in a village in the German countryside, was a computer geek by high school but saw physics as far more challenging. His diplomas are in physics from the University of Ulm and Technical University Munich, and his PhD, *summa cum laude,* from Max Planck Institute of Biochemistry, also in physics.

Following his years at Rockefeller University, Braun led the Munich-based independent Emmy Noether research group at LMU on biomolecule thermophoresis and thermal trapping. A spinoff company, NanoTemper Technologies (now with 100+ employees), was founded by two of the group's students. Braun currently heads a new research group at LMU focused on "recreating the origin of life."

Along the way he's toyed with something he calls "bookkeeping mechanics," producing a paper: "Nonequilibrium Thermodynamics of Wealth Condensation"—which may have also caught Jim Simons' attention.

Among Dieter Braun's awards are—Deutscher Grunderpreis (2015, for NanoTemper); Simons Foundation Collaboration on the Origins of Life (2014, $1.5M); Prodekan (2012); Step Award (2012, for NanoTemper); Deutscher Innovationspreis (2012, for Nanotemper); Klung-Wilhelmy Weberbank Price (2011, Germany's top award (€100,000) for physicists age 40 or younger); European Research Council's Starting Grant (2010, €1.5M).

I was particularly impressed that Braun indicates on his CV—"2005 Parental Leave: half time position for 1.5 years," and as a committed parent has taken an active role (Chairman of the Board) in the running of the "midday care" school association in his alpine neighborhood outside Munich.

I reached Dieter Braun by phone last week at his lab at LMU for this conversation.

Suzan Mazur: You've recently said that you are not an artist but photos of you have a certain Redford aesthetic.

Dieter Braun: [Laughter]

Suzan Mazur: Your online biography is a bit sketchy. Do you come from an art family? A science family? An industrialist family? Are you possibly related to the motorcycle racer Dieter Braun?

Dieter Braun: Not that I know of. I came from a small village in the German countryside. My father played the organ. There are a lot of musicians in the family, although I am not one.

Suzan Mazur: But where does your color sense and style come from?

Dieter Braun: My father was into photography. He had a dark room and photography equipment. He was the guy who was kind of the official photographer of the village.

In science I think it matters a lot how you make a point so that people can grasp the message fast. It makes sense to take time to make pictures, graphs, and other images.

Suzan Mazur: I gather your family did not take an active role in your early science career by building a lab for you in the basement and providing chemicals like Jack Szostak's did?

Dieter Braun: No. I did a lot of programming when I was a kid. I earned my first money selling program code to small journals. Back in the 1980s people bought small magazines and typed programs from them. I was a computer geek more than anything else.

Suzan Mazur: Your interest in science began when?

Dieter Braun: When I was 17 I made a decision that informatics was probably a little bit too boring so I chose physics. I was also inspired by my older brother who studied physics.

Suzan Mazur: Your wife, Veronica Egger, is a scientist too.

Dieter Braun: Yes, she's involved with two-photon microscopy and a professor of neurophysiology at Regensburg University, about an hour and a half from here by train. She was previously at LMU's Munich Center for Neurosciences—Brain & Mind, although it didn't work out that we were at the same LMU location.

Suzan Mazur: Are you an athlete?

Dieter Braun: Not really. Where I grew up in southern Germany I did a lot of bike tours. We now live outside Munich in the Alps, Bavaria. We like to hike.

Suzan Mazur: You're being funded, in part, by a Simons Origins Foundation grant of $1.5M. Aside from that research grant and your EU funding, are there European philanthropies supporting your origins investigation?

Dieter Braun: That would be interesting, but no, there is not the kind of philanthropic culture here in Germany to fund science as

272

there is in the US. The universities here are very good, studies are free. But philanthropy, giving back to universities doesn't exist here.

Suzan Mazur: Jim Simons told me this about research funding in Europe and the US:

> *"Philanthropy doesn't happen in Europe very much period. . . . Philanthropy in the United States, per capita, is far greater than it is in Europe. We have a very old tradition of philanthropy. . . . Private enterprise used to do more of it [support research] in the United States, in particular. Big companies, most notable would be Bell Laboratories. . . .*
>
> *When I got my PhD, the best place in the world to study what's now called condensed matter physics, and in those days it was called solid state physics, was at the Bell Telephone Labs. That was a better place than Harvard or MIT or anyplace else. They did the best research. . . . It was a remarkable institution. But when the telephone company was broken up, when AT&T was broken up, none of the individual companies really had enough money to so generously support that kind of enterprise".*
> —**Jim Simons**, *The Origin of Life Circus: A How To Make Life Extravaganza*

What do you think about the John Templeton Foundation funding origins of life research?

Dieter Braun: We're getting a good corps of people now who are reshaping the field in a completely new way. It's clearly a time to invest in origins research. We'll see solid science back from these investments.

In the past, origins of life was a side activity for older, established scientists. Now young people are entering the field who are much more experimentally driven. They don't write long papers about their pet theories without solid experimental proof. It becomes a real scientific exercise now, particularly as funding becomes more available.

Suzan Mazur: The Templeton Foundation is known for its coupling of science and religion and there's a good deal of controversy about that. Would you accept Templeton funding for origins research?

Dieter Braun: I haven't fully look into that. Professional funding now should be without strings attached.

For the Simons Foundation, for example—you make a proposal, two pages, saying roughly what you will do. The rest is mostly based on trust. Simons is bringing good professional practice to the field. . . .

Suzan Mazur: What do you think about NASA and Templeton funding a $3M inquiry into how the religious community would respond to the discovery of life in outer space?

Dieter Braun: Actually our university, LMU, includes a theological faculty. They're very serious and down-to-earth people. If people are serious, I can imagine that serious research can be possible.

I would hesitate taking money from NASA though because it's very often geared to engineering and space missions. That would inhibit our freedom in doing experiments much more than the Templeton Foundation, which seems to try to explore a little bit more on the right and left side of things or fund projects that normally are not funded by the science community.

Suzan Mazur: The Simons Foundation seems to have a continuing interest in origins research.

Dieter Braun: The Simons Foundation does a good job connecting the origins community and in structuring things so that people really are collaborating.

Suzan Mazur: Your current Simons Foundation grant expires in 2019. Will you be refunded?

Dieter Braun: There's some hope. In parallel, I submitted an ERC Advanced proposal to EC for a five-year grant to pursue research, which I almost got last year. Let's see. We try to secure funding from various sources to keep us independent. If we depended solely on the Simons Foundation, it could limit our freedom.

Suzan Mazur: One of the problems in funding origins research is that it still seems largely angled to Darwinian evolution, which has been seriously challenged over the last decade. A recent *Spectator* magazine article noted that Darwin's "theory quickly outstripped his scientific data and instead became a grand narrative seemingly capable of explaining the entire history of life on earth."

Eugene Koonin, who—like Nigel Goldenfeld and Carl Woese—thinks that biology is on its way to becoming the new condensed matter physics, has told me this:

> *"No one in the mainstream scientific community now takes selection literally."*

It appears that continued use of the term selection in scientific papers is seen as one factor preventing biology from becoming a hard science. Would you comment? Do you see biology as the "new condensed matter physics"?

Dieter Braun: That's a long discussion. Basically, the term selection in biology is one that is used for already existing life, right? So we can study selection and evolution for example at the bacterial level and molecular level for things already replicating. But I do think it's important in this field [origins] to be precise regarding the term selection.

Suzan Mazur: But who's doing the selecting?

Dieter Braun: In our experiments, for example, we use tiny rock compartments as traps (mimicked by fluid-filled glass capillary tubes), driven solely by a heat flow. A physical mechanism, temperature difference, accounts for accumulation of molecules in one spot. It brings the molecules inside the compartments together. It chooses larger molecules over smaller ones, and oligonucleotides with similar sequences and binds them together. That physical mechanism of bringing molecules together has nothing to do with biological selection, but could be seen as a first step in physically selecting long molecules with similar sequences.

The idea is that you have porous or volcanic rock. If you walk over Iceland, you find conditions like this where hot water vapor comes out and volcanic fire and you think of what might be possible in these pores. For such experiments [thermophoresis], you only need temperature difference. I'm not saying this is a solution. We try to make something step-by-step (1) that we can do in the lab, and (2) might have had similar boundary conditions on early Earth.

Suzan Mazur: There seems to be a need for new terminology, new language in the field to describe this. Selection isn't an accurate description.

Dieter Braun: That's a big difficulty in the field, absolutely. Selection, if I say that to biologists, to physicists, to chemists, it has completely different meanings to each. In science we have trouble writing papers because we run into these ambiguities in different fields. That's what's going on right now in the origins field. Things are increasingly interdisciplinary. It would be a great advantage to have more precise language. We will find this as we continue to communicate across disciplines. **In the end, experiments will be our common language.** [emphasis added]

Suzan Mazur: Do you see biology now as, or as becoming, the new condensed matter physics?

Dieter Braun: What do you mean by "the new condensed matter physics"?

Suzan Mazur: That biology is developing into a hard science. It's not fuzzy Darwinian science anymore.

Dieter Braun: Biology isn't about Darwinian evolution even if you just look at the cell as it is. Many solid, quantitative studies are now being done on this with serious modeling similar to, say, condensed matter physics. And if you look at how the cell evolves, how it varies, how extensive the mechanism is that's going on—biology is relying increasingly on quantitative analysis [emphasis added].

We have to push further toward an explanation that fully explains things from bottom up.

Suzan Mazur: How much of getting to the bottom of the origin of life depends on redefining what life is?

Dieter Braun: I think in a way quite a bit. What we try to do in the lab is start with a certain idea of life. We do an experiment and we think of all the things we might need for evolution. The result might be very primitive. We then go out to the scientific community for response. Other investigators might say: "You need to explain this and this and this." We then go back to the lab and try to add that too. Does it work? It will be progress with a lot of feedback loops. Communicating with biologists as well as many other disciplines. Eventually we ask: "Look, is this life or not?"

I think what will be found is an experimental question. We hope we might even persuade biologists to say, "Oh, I can see a logical line from the early Earth all the way to the cell." However, a lot of things still need to be shown experimentally.

Suzan Mazur: Do you think 4 billion years is enough time to take us from nucleic acid to *Homo sapiens*?

Dieter Braun: Absolutely yes. I'm optimistic. That is driving us because we think that if we have the right conditions, we can do the crucial steps in the lab. I would argue that if we needed to have a long time and very strange, not understandable processes for this to happen, then we couldn't do the experiment in the lab. So, yes, I am optimistic.

Suzan Mazur: Do you think RNA may have been premixed in an Earth-bound meteorite?

Dieter Braun: All the data that's in on what is coming from space, my rough idea—this should all be based on data—is that comets give up quite a number of complex molecules but from all that we've seen, it's not yet giving us nucleic acid. It's giving us amino acids, short peptides, but not nucleic acid. Part of the ingredients come from outside Earth, similar to where most of our water originated. **Simple molecules came from outside Earth, but the evolutionary process probably happened on Earth.** [emphasis added]

Suzan Mazur: And you continue to favor the thermophoresis hypothesis regarding origin of life?

Dieter Braun: Everyone has a pet theory to push an experimental line as far as he/she can make progress with it. We do, still do, so we continue that route. Science is about making hypotheses and about being honest if the hypothesis is falsified by experiments. You can never prove a hypothesis.

Suzan Mazur: You've got Albert Libchaber as an ally. He told me this in his office at Rockefeller University:

> *"Yes, and my interest lately focuses more about life originating in thermal vents deep in the ocean. In thermal vents you have large temperature gradients because water comes out of the vents in a high temperature.*
>
> *The little volcanoes that make thermal vents are full of porous material, and those pores hold all the temperature gradients you need. What was shown is that with this*

temperature gradient many nonequilibrium processes exist.

For example, we discovered that polymerase chain reaction (PCR) is possible under thermal convection. There's nothing but thermal convection. In the center region of a convective cell double-stranded (DS) DNA melts and in the side single-stranded (SS) DNA is copied. We thus made the smallest PCR machine, centimeter in size. . . .

We did that when Dieter Braun was here as a postdoctoral fellow, about 10 years ago.

We also showed that if you have a very thin geometry, water cannot move because of friction to the wall but the suspension moves. So in a temperature gradient, you can accumulate the suspension.

There can be a huge accumulation. We saw that you can accumulate, you can amplify, you can even select length. So all those processes may have played a role at the origin.

This is one of the questions always asked. How do you reach a critical concentration? Well, temperature gradient can do that. It can also amplify, it can select size. It can select even some sequences."—**Albert Libchaber**, *The Origin of Life Circus: A How To Make Life Extravaganza*

Dieter Braun: Being a postdoc in Albert's lab was a great experience. He gives a lot of freedom to his researchers and freedom is important to do good science.

Suzan Mazur: How did you find living in New York?

Dieter Braun: This was a great experience. I am always happy when going back. Nevertheless, with kids, life is way more simple—and cheaper—here in Germany.

Suzan Mazur: How close are we to understanding the origin of life and/or making life in the lab?

Dieter Braun: We're getting quite close. Jack Szostak and many other origins investigators are making fast progress. We will have replicating systems and see the evolution of these sequences probably within the next 5 - 10 years. Defining a very minimal way of life.

Suzan Mazur: There are now a half dozen or so origins centers in America, Europe and Japan. Is throwing more funding at the problem the way forward or do we need new "mindstorms," as Pier Luigi Luisi has said. Are we really going to be there in 5 - 10 years or do we need new approaches?

Dieter Braun: In the past there was no money in this field at all. If we'd made our origins proposal 10 - 15 years ago, we would not have been funded. People now see that origins experiments can be solid. Even to the point that you get biotechnology from them.

We secured funding in the physics world by arguing that non-equilibrium effects are interesting. People agree on that. Meanwhile, we can say we produced new biotechnology.

Two former students of mine spun off their own nanotechnology company—NanoTemper Technologies, which now has more than 100 employees. They first studied the movement of molecules by a thermal gradient and developed the idea to measure how strong biological molecules bind. Pharmaceutical companies use the technique now to develop new drugs. More money is currently paid to Germany in taxes from this spin-off than was ever spent on our lab.

Suzan Mazur: So the origins investigation is no longer regarded as a fishing expedition?

Dieter Braun: Yes. That's a big change of gears. Our lab experiments are interdisciplinary ones tackling core questions of how information in terms of sequences emerged in realistic Earth conditions.

Suzan Mazur: How was the Dutch Origins conference kickoff at Groningen?

Dieter Braun: It showed how many scientists representing many disciplines—far apart—can come together. Groningen is in a good position now to do what other Origins centers are doing, like Harvard, Scripps, ELSI, etc.—as well as the one we're trying to create here in Munich—that is, securing funding to further grow the science. It's important that there's enough money. Serious experiments are not so cheap.

Compared to funding for other scientific disciplines and the overall funding of science—$2.5M for Origins research is not a lot of money—it is baby steps for getting this going as a real field.

Chapter 27

(What Would Harry Lonsdale Say?)
The Dutch Origins Center Kickoff

Image source, Dutch Origins Center

8/27/17

There hasn't been much fanfare about it—the Dutch like to approach things quietly, preferring substance to bluster. But it's clear what Dutch ingenuity can do. I'm writing from New York, for example, which once was New Amsterdam.

The present story opens at Groningen in the north of Holland, home to one of the largest natural gas fields in the world, and site of this week's inauguration of the Dutch Origins Center, which kicks off with a symposium at the University of Groningen— "Fundamentals of Life in the Universe" (August 31-September 1). Organized under the auspices of the Royal Netherlands Academy of Sciences, the event features some of the most relevant names in science presenting around these five themes: (1) origin of the

Earth and life; (2) predicting evolution of life; (3) building and directing life from molecule to biosphere; (4) life in extraterrestrial environments; (5) emergence and bridging of temporal and spatial scales.

Of the five themes, the emergence and bridging of temporal and spatial scales seems most intriguing. Principals involved with the center—its manager is Jan-Willem Mantel—think it's crucial to develop multiscale mathematical models to make sense of interactions of the chemical, biological, physical and astrophysical dimensions of our reality, noting the following:

> *"For the biological and physical sciences, these developments will help us understand how molecules can self-organize into self-replicating, living cells, how cells can join forces to form multicellular tissues and organisms, and how organisms form ecosystems."*

The Dutch Origins Center, a virtual project, has been led by Nobel laureate Ben Feringa (2016, Chemistry)—keynote speaker of this week's two-day conference. The project is a Dutch national initiative involving 17 of the country's universities and institutes.

Other high-profile conference presenters include Dieter Braun, a Simons Collaboration on the Origins of Life investigator, who will address "transport phenomena and nucleic acid replication." Of course, John Sutherland, one of Harry Lonsdale's top Origins prizewinners as well as a SCOL investigator, will be there spinning heads about systems chemistry. Tetsuya Yomo will enlighten about the artificial cell.

Curiously, Steve Benner's $5.4M Templeton-funded Origins project isn't represented, but inorganic chemist Lee Cronin—who's developing a "Universal Life Detector" with big bucks from Templeton—will address this week's gathering. Cronin, based at the University of Glasgow, has been attempting to make matter come alive.

One of most notable presenters at the event is astrobiologist Bob Hazen, who told me he is "very sympathetic to people who see echoes of biology in mineralogy." Hazen explained his perspective to me at length in a 2008 book interview:

> *"I want to make very clear what I mean by evolution. It's not just change over time. In this case it's diversification or complexification over time.*
>
> *Let me give you a brief abstract of this idea. All terrestrial planets like Earth, Mars and Mercury and their moons, etc., begin in a pre-solar cloud of dust and gas. In that pre-solar cloud, there are microminerals—about a dozen different minerals: diamonds, graphite, corundum, spinel—all together about a dozen different minerals.*
>
> *And as you clump those together to form the earliest bodies and meteorites and asteroidal bodies, you get about 60 different minerals through heating of the sun in the primary formation of minerals. About 60 different minerals that form the most primitive minerals in what are called chondrite meteorites.*
>
> *And then you go through periods of aqueous alteration. And then these planetismals get larger. You get up to about 250 different minerals. You see increasing complexification, from 12 to 60 to 250 to 350 in a place like Mercury, to 500 in a place like the moon. And with plate tectonics you add more minerals and you go to 1,000. You go to 1,500 and finally when life kicks in on Earth you get maybe another 3,000 known minerals. So about two-thirds of all the known minerals on Earth actually result in a very complex feedback mechanism with life.*
>
> *That's what we call "mineral evolution". . . That's something I see as a process of evolution, which in many ways, is parallel to biological evolution. . . .*
>
> *You have species. You have diversification. You have extinction. You have punctuation. You have selection.*

Those five characteristics and others as well are common to all evolving systems whether they be minerals or language or biology or microbes or bears. And the fact is that there are also fundamental differences amongst those different systems.

I'm very sympathetic to people who see echoes of biology in mineralogy or echoes of biology in language."—**Bob Hazen**, *The Altenberg 16: An Exposé of the Evolution Industry*

So Hazen and Cronin will have a lot to chat about on Thursday and Friday.

I have also spoken with Lee Cronin in recent years and questioned his thinking about "survival of the fittest" as key to making matter come alive—which he vigorously defended. I'm skeptical as well about aspects of Cronin's $860,802 Templeton project:

"Our proposal aims to define, and test a new theory of complexity and emergence in molecular space; asking the question: Can the molecular constructors found in biology lead to highly complex molecules that are simply not found abiotically? We will explore this by comparing the complexity of simple molecules to those complex ones found in biology and aiming to establish a threshold to discriminate if the molecule in question could have been generated by a non-biological process, or if it has originated in a living system, either directly as a metabolite, or indirectly by a person (e.g. Earth or Alien chemist), or a living proxy (robot)."

I won't be attending the Dutch meeting. But somebody please ask Lee Cronin to tell us a bit more about his "Alien chemist."

Missing from the talks is anyone from the recent UK, Canadian and Italian investigation with "first observational evidence that our universe could be a vast and complex hologram."

THE PROGRAM

Conference Location: Energy Academy, Zernike Campus, University of Groningen

Thursday, August 31

Session 1 — Origin of the Earth and Life:

John Hernlund (ELSI, Japan): Building scientific cohesion between disparate scientific fields

Geoff Blake (Caltech, US): Organic material in planet-forming regions

Bob Hazen (Carnegie, US): Minerals and the origin of life

John Sutherland (MRC-LMB): Origins of life systems chemistry

Paulien Hogeweg (U. Utrecht, NL): Prebiotic evolution

Session 2 — Predicting the evolution of life:

Tim Lenton (U. Exeter, UK): Predicting the evolution of biospheres

Tetsuya Yomo (ECNU, CN): Synthesis and experimental evolution of an artificial cell model

Marcel Visser (NIOO, KNAW): Evolution on a changing planet

Phil Donoghue (U. Bristol, UK): The timescale of evolutionary history

Session 3 — Building Life from molecule to biosphere:

Bert Poolman (U. Groningen, NL): Can we build from molecular components a minimal form of life?

Cees Dekker (U. Delft, NL): Synthetic cell division

Origins Center kickoff event: Speed networking

Ben Feringa (U. Groningen, NL): Keynote speech

Friday September 1

Han Olff (U. Groningen, NL): From molecule to biosphere: reductionistic versus emergentistic approaches

Dieter Braun (LMU, Germany): Transport phenomena and nucleic acid replication

Session 4 — Life in extraterrestrial environments:

Giovanna Tinetti (UCL, UK): Biosignatures in exoplanet atmospheres

Inge Loes ten Kate (U. Utrecht, NL): Prospects for life on Mars

Charley Lineweaver (ANU, Australia): What makes planets habitable?

Lee Cronin (U. Glasgow, UK): Towards life in the lab and complexity as a life detection system

Session 5 — Emergence and bridging of temporal and spatial scales:

Peter Sloot (U. Amsterdam, NL): The quantum nature of biology and life

Alexander van Oudenaarden (Hubrecht Institute, NL): Revealing novel cell types, cell-cell interactions and cell lineages by single-cell sequencing

Stan Gielen (NOW, NL): The future of the Dutch National Science Agenda

Charley Lineweaver (ANU, Australia): Are we alone in the universe (public talk, downtown)

Symposium Organizers

Royal Netherlands Academy of Sciences (KNAW)

Faculty of Science and Engineering (FSE), University of Groningen

Nationale Wetenschaps Agenda (NWA)

Max Gruber Foundation

SRON Netherlands Institute for Space Research

Groningen Biomolecular Sciences and Biotechnology Institute (GBB)

Groningen Institute for Evolutionary Life Sciences (GELIFES)

Stratingh Institute for Chemistry

Zernike Institute for Advanced Materials

LKBF

Kapteyn Astronomical Institute

Chapter 28

Jan-Willem Mantel—
Orchestrating the Dutch Origins Center

Photo, courtesy Jan-Willem Mantel

12/2/2017

It was a rainy Sunday morning along the canal on Nieuwe
Doelenstraat in Amsterdam as Jan-Willem Mantel arrived on
his bicycle for our recent origin of life chat at Café de Jaren.
Mantel is a tall, athletic-looking man (perhaps 6'4" or so—I didn't
ask) with hands that appear capable of firing a Hail Mary football.
But he's actually a philosopher and musician who enjoys
gardening and bicycle touring and has now been entrusted to
orchestrate 18 teams of scientists connected to the new Dutch
Origins Center.

It was a focused meeting, although I got the impression that
Mantel could address almost any subject in conversation—a
useful skill since his new role involves not only coordinating

scientific research teams but engaging the public. Including potential origin of life funders.

He says he's comfortable "support[ing] groups and individuals who have highly ambitious objectives in governance, management or operations"—a role he's played for many years as projects and company secretary for the Dutch Natural History Museum, Naturalis Biodiversity Center, and Muziekschool Amsterdam.

Our interview follows.

Suzan Mazur: Are you adviser for the Dutch Origins Center exclusively or do you serve as consultant for other organizations as well?

Jan-Willem Mantel: I work exclusively for the Dutch Origins Center. After I graduated from university—my degree is in philosophy—I left academia and served as company secretary to various institutions. I returned more or less to academia 15 years ago as company secretary to the National Natural History Museum. Since then I've worked within science, always in support roles. I don't publish philosophy papers.

Suzan Mazur: As secretary to various institutions, what did your work involve?

Jan-Willem Mantel: I prepared policy documents, reports, budget estimates. Things like that.

Suzan Mazur: You've also worked in a fundraising capacity?

Jan-Willem Mantel: Yes, that has always been a large part of my job. That is again an important part of my job at the Origins Center.

Suzan Mazur: As manager of the Dutch Origins Center, you are both conferring with its scientists and engaging the public?

290

Jan-Willem Mantel: Yes, I try to organize that.

Suzan Mazur: Are you the press officer as well?

Jan-Willem Mantel: I work through the universities and other organizations. They have their own communications departments. They are better at it than I am.

Suzan Mazur: How much is Ben Feringa involved in the Dutch Origins Center?

Jan-Willem Mantel: In a way he's very substantially involved in that he wants to devote the next few years of his research career squarely in the origins of life field. He's working on molecular systems, trying to understand what asymmetry means in these systems. Of course, as a Nobel laureate, he's participating in all kinds of activities and he likes that as well. But in his research and the research of his group, origins of life is a very important theme.

Suzan Mazur: He's working somewhat with Bert Poolman at the University of Groningen?

Jan-Willem Mantel: Yes, and with other chemists.

Suzan Mazur: On synthetic cell development.

Jan-Willem Mantel: Yes.

Suzan Mazur: They have a good-sized budget, €20 million, I understand.

Jan-Willem Mantel: Yes. There are various programs already running.

Suzan Mazur: What is your interest in origin of life? You said you're not an expert. But then no one is an expert.

Jan-Willem Mantel: I'm generally interested in how did it happen. Where did we come from? Is there life elsewhere? Etc.

Suzan Mazur: What sparked your interest in the Dutch Origins Center?

Jan-Willem Mantel: Frank Helmich chaired a group bringing people together to submit an origins proposal in the context of the Dutch science agenda. At the time, I worked at the Dutch Natural History Museum. I became interested when the University of Groningen decided to organize a team of scientists from all over The Netherlands around origins of life and advertised for a manager. I am now fully occupied by the Dutch Origins Center.

Suzan Mazur: You're a musician as well.

Jan-Willem Mantel: Yes, an amateur.

Suzan Mazur: What instrument do you play?

Jan-Willem Mantel: The bassoon.

Suzan Mazur: I read you were in various orchestras.

Jan-Willem Mantel: At the moment it's a little bit low, I perform with only one small quartet. But, yes, I've played in all kinds of ensembles.

Suzan Mazur: The Dutch Origins Center is a virtual center, but would you say the University of Groningen serves as sort of the hub?

Jan-Willem Mantel: In a way. We try to create a flat network. We have groups in 17 or 18 universities and/or independent research organizations and we try to avoid one university leading or dominating. But, of course, the practical work has to be done somewhere and that is being done by Groningen. In an intellectual sense, however, you can't say Groningen or any one of the others dominates.

The participating groups are at: University of Groningen, Amsterdam, Utrecht, Leiden, Delft University of Technology, Radboud University Nijmegen, VU University Amsterdam, Technical University of Eindhoven, Technical University of Twente, Netherlands Institute for Space Research, Netherlands Institute for Ecology, National Research Institute for Mathematics and Computer Science, Naturalis Biodiversity Center, Erasmus Medical Center, Dutch Institute for Cancer Research—17 or 18 altogether. They're all strong groups, but very diverse groups in these institutions.

The idea was to bring people together to talk across disciplinary boundaries. The methodological assumption is that you get progress earlier and faster when you do that instead of researchers working separately. But it's quite a challenge because we have astrophysicists, mathematicians, biologists, chemists, nanotechnologists, all disciplines of natural science, actually.

Suzan Mazur: How will you report progress?

Jan-Willem Mantel: Our main outlet, of course, will be scientific papers. But we will also communicate to the public. That's part of the Dutch science agenda. It's kind of an experiment. It was started by the former Dutch science minister, who provided an opportunity for the public to submit questions about science. About 12,000 questions were received on practical issues, theoretical issues, and quite a lot about the origins of life, life elsewhere, basic properties of life like evolvability, and more.

So our own starting point is that set of questions. It gave us the opportunity to get organized and funded. To make a start. Of course we will report back to the public who submitted those questions when there is an interesting development.

We have been funded with €2.5 million and have defined a portfolio of projects that should advance the subject of origins of life as well as strengthen bonds between the various institutions. We have also recruited fellows for the Dutch Origins Center who will start in the first quarter of 2018. We've recruited worldwide.

Suzan Mazur: Are you planning public origin of life events?

Jan-Willem Mantel: Yes. In Amsterdam we have NEMO, the Dutch science museum, which has an events program where scientists often speak. And there are others as well. Our plan is to use the existing infrastructure for science communications, which is already quite well developed.

Chapter 29

Biochemist Bert Poolman—
The Dutch Synthetic Cell

Photo, courtesy Bert Poolman

12/10/2017

Wind turbines have replaced windmills in the North Holland farmlands outside Groningen, and Google now has a significant presence in the city itself. Otherwise Groningen looks like a page from Hans Brinker. One in every five residents is a student, many at the University of Groningen. It's a culture where friends still share bike rides on the back fender. With cheese shops featuring shelves and shelves of wheels of exotic flavors from local dairies. And there are, of course, the canals for silver skates in winter. But inside the laboratories at the University of Groningen synthetic cell development is in progress—under the direction of biochemist Bert Poolman—which, if successful, could change the landscape far beyond this Dutch storybook setting (although it's unclear just how). For now, Poolman says the goal is to better understand biology by bottom-up construction of a synthetic cell—"building systems, cellular systems, from molecular building blocks," and he regards even a minimal living cell as "kind of a black box."

I visited Bert Poolman in his office at the University of Groningen in late October. Poolman serves as program director of the Centre for Synthetic Biology and as scientific director of the Groningen Biomolecular Sciences and Biotechnology Institute. He also chairs the Membrane Enzymology group at Zernike Institute for Advanced Materials and at Groningen Biomolecular Sciences and Biotechnology Institute, in addition to his role as professor of biochemistry at the university.

Poolman and his team making a synthetic cell have recently been awarded €19 million by the Netherlands Science Foundation for their research. Bert Poolman is also a principal participant in the new Dutch Origins Center, which has received separate funding of €2.5 million.

Poolman's research interests include synthetic cell development, i.e., "bottom-up construction of functional far-from-equilibrium systems"; bacterial cell-volume regulation; and traffic of membrane proteins.

He's a member of the Royal Netherlands Academy of Arts and Sciences; a Faculty 1000 member; editor of the journal *Molecular Biology*; flagship manager of Synthetic Biology in the public-private research program BE-Basic, among other distinctions.

As a Fulbright Scholar a dozen or so years ago, Bert Poolman was a visiting professor in biochemistry at CalTech in Pasadena and before that a scientist at Genencor Inc. in San Francisco.

Other honors and awards include the Biochemistry Award of the Dutch Biochemistry Organisation; NWO Top-Go subsidy on membrane protein biogenesis; ITN-NICHE grant; ERC Advanced grant (partial list).

Bert Poolman's PhD is in microbiology and his MSc in molecular biology and biochemistry—both from the University of Groningen and both *cum laude*. His undergraduate studies were in Switzerland at the University of Bern, with biochemical training at Medizinisch-Chemisches Institut.

Our interview follows.

Suzan Mazur: Are you starting from scratch? Jack Szostak told me in 2014 that he and his group were the only ones working from scratch.

Bert Poolman: There is a lot of labeling going on in synthetic biology: top-down, bottom-up. Here, what we call bottom-up is actually building systems, cellular systems, from molecular building blocks.

We don't do the type of work let's say that Craig Venter is doing, who is using living cells to make minimal organisms. We try to create life, molecular systems, by using well characterized building blocks and gradually increase the complexity [of the system] so that at some point we have a system that can grow, replicate and sustain itself.

Jack Szostak is also working from scratch because he uses—if you look at the membrane—he uses simple fatty acids to create membrane systems and determines their permeability and stability.

We use real lipids and more complex molecules, but we also include membrane proteins—channels and transporters—to catalyze the transport across the membrane so that we can also build up gradients. Our membrane systems build up osmotic pressure, like current living systems do.

So let's say his [Szostak's] molecules are a little more primitive than the ones we have, and they may relate to the ones that may have been at the origin of life. We take, in principle, any synthetic molecule as long as it has, say, properties that support the embedding and function of transport proteins.

Suzan Mazur: Why are you developing a synthetic cell?

Bert Poolman: The reason for us is basically to better understand biology. In making a minimal cell, you could also make it simpler and try to better understand what is needed. But we find that even a minimal cell is still very complex. It's kind of a black box.

What we try to do is build up a cell-like system by working with fewer components. We then try to understand and to model all the interactions and reactions taking place so we have better control over our system. Of course, you're then further from a system you could call "life."

Suzan Mazur: I noticed in an article that Dutch Origins Center manager Jan-Willem Mantel sent me that you actually define life. Would you repeat your definition for "life" and let me know whether you think it's important to have a consensus on what life is?

Bert Poolman: This is a tricky question. I'm not claiming I have a definition for life. However, we have a working definition for life in the context of what we are doing—building systems—which is: A system that can grow, replicate and sustain itself.

Suzan Mazur: Once you make your synthetic cell, it can only exist within a certain medium?

Bert Poolman: Yes.

Suzan Mazur: This is not something you want to make to send into space, to Mars?

298

Bert Poolman: I don't know what I want to do in 10 years or so.

Suzan Mazur: Is that feasible? It would have to be kept in that same kind of environment.

Bert Poolman: For now it is a system that is contained in a specific environment.

Suzan Mazur: But you don't know what's going to happen until you've finished building it?

Bert Poolman: We're building it on the basis of components we know. But, of course, components you know, if you put them together, may give emergent behavior that you would not have predicted. [emphasis added]

But this is also one of the things we are looking for in order to understand biology in depth. You can do it in two ways. By studying living systems or by trying to make things, systems that have properties of life-like systems.

So, for instance, we also divide our work into modules. One of the modules is a metabolic processor. This is, in fact, the part that I'm mostly involved with—the self-organization of components, catalysis and confinement, transport of food and waste, and making a fuel system.

Suzan Mazur: Self-organization is the tricky one? It's not really understood at this point.

Bert Poolman: No, but if we take simple vesicle systems, you can predict what you will see. That they are bright spherical structures. We can put skeletal structures in. One of our collaborators is reconstituting skeletal structures—and you get these invaginations. This is, of course, what you need for division.

We make sure that ATP is made. If we combine these two modules, we then have a system that can already basically produce two vesicles from one.

Suzan Mazur: How close at this point are you to making the synthetic cell?

Bert Poolman: We're still decades away. This has to do with the middle part, what I call information processing. The most difficult aspect is probably protein synthesis, because protein synthesis involves more than 100 components. And to build a ribosome _in vitro_, from scratch, that is an enormous challenge. [emphasis added]

So information is stored in DNA—although it could also be something else—it doesn't have to be DNA. We need to replicate it because that's something necessary for life. DNA is replicated to make a copy of itself for the daughter cell when a cell divides. But DNA also needs to be decoded or "read" to make new proteins. The process is one in which DNA is transcribed into RNA, which is then decoded by the ribosome to synthesize new proteins. This is something that all living cells do and that we try to reconstitute from molecular components, which is extremely difficult because of the many molecules involved, their complex assembly, and lots of processes we do not understand well.

Suzan Mazur: Albert Libchaber predicted in 2014 when I spoke with him for my book on origin of life that Vincent Noireaux—his former postdoc who has his own lab at the University of Minnesota—would have a minimal cell within five years. And Jack Szostak announced at the 2014 World Science Festival in New York that he'd have "life in the lab" within three years. So far it hasn't happened.

Bert Poolman: I know Vincent quite well. We collaborated in a paper.

I would say five years is very optimistic. But Vincent's definition might be different. Vincent starts from pre-assembled ribosomes that he isolates and then he puts things together to synthesize protein.

But until he can do protein synthesis and have the same machinery make itself and make the ribosome itself—and the ribosome is very complicated. It's not just protein, it's also RNA—to make that cell and to let that fold into a new functional machine, I think that is still a very long way to go and will take more than five years.

Suzan Mazur: But it does seem to be moving along. There's a ramping up of origin of life research and synthetic cell development. Is the interest real or is this just a way to dabble in basic research and get funded? Dieter Braun, also a former Libchaber postdoc, mentioned to me in our recent interview that a whole new breed of scientists has entered the origins field who are experimentally-driven. No more fishing expeditions.

Bert Poolman: I think the interest is real. This is due in part because certain things are now possible that were not possible in the past.

Suzan Mazur: What wasn't possible in the past?

Bert Poolman: At some point we also need DNA to code the systems. The making of synthetic DNA has gotten quite a boost with the minimal genomes that Venter's institute has developed.

The other thing is we can make observations now in a single cell or even at a single molecule level. If you think about the Nobel Prize a few years ago in chemistry, that was for super-resolution microscopy. Super resolution microscopy means that you can observe molecules in living systems with a resolution far better than conventional microscopy.

Suzan Mazur: The tools have improved.

Bert Poolman: The tools have improved in terms of microscopy, also in terms of analysis. If you think of mass spectrometry, the cells that we make are very small and the number of molecules that are on the inside are so small that you need very sensitive equipment to see what is going on. Mass spectrometry has improved tremendously. Super-resolution microscopy, mass spectrometry, synthesis of DNA, to name a few.

Furthermore, researchers from chemistry or true physics have entered biology in the last 15, 20 years, bringing with them their important skills and methods that have boosted the field further.

Suzan Mazur: With the coming together of the sciences, is there a need for a new language to replace obsolete terminology like natural selection, etc.?

Bert Poolman: For me it's a non-issue right now, the terminology.** [emphasis added]

Suzan Mazur: How many scientists would you say are now involved in synthetic cell development in The Netherlands and worldwide?

Bert Poolman: We received a grant of €19 million from the Netherlands Science Foundation last summer for our synthetic cell development project. The award went to 15 working groups—15 groups working in this area is substantial. We will probably appoint 70 to 80 PhD students. But some of our labs also have national grants and so the 15 groups could each include 10 to 20 researchers.

The 15 PIs [principal investigators] have already individually been working on aspects of synthetic cell development. But for the first time there is proper funding for tackling larger scale problems

Suzan Mazur: Where are the synthetic cell development labs? Here in the Netherlands; in the UK—John Sutherland and Matt Powner; in the US Jack Szostak and the Simons Foundation collaborators and Vincent Noireaux in Minnesota; Tetsuya Yomo now in China—

Bert Poolman: There is a parallel program to ours in Germany. Dieter Braun is part of that. There are groups in Switzerland.

Suzan Mazur: ETH.

Bert Poolman: Yes, ETH.

Suzan Mazur: How much money would you say is involved at this point—$100 million or so?

Bert Poolman: Probably around there. But five years ago it was virtually nothing. Yes—$100 million is substantial but only a fraction of what we will ultimately need.

Suzan Mazur: Your connection to the Dutch Origins Center is what at this point?

Bert Poolman: The previous government wanted to give the general public more say in the direction of science. It asked the public to submit questions and among the questions that kept coming up were those relating to origins of life. People had a strong interest in finding out where we come from.

Suzan Mazur: Is the Dutch public okay with synthetic cell development?

Bert Poolman: The majority of people responded positively to that. Of course, there are always some people who worry we might create Frankenstein-type monsters. But the public is very enthusiastic about arriving at a better understanding of origins of life. It was brought up so many times that we said let's organize scientific teams who have an interest in the origins field—from geologists to biologists to astronomers to mathematicians, chemists and physicists. We also have philosophers participating.

We created the Origins Center as a virtual center. We got a little bit of money—a few million euros—that's being used mostly to organize ourselves within The Netherlands and to set up programs of collaborative research.

Suzan Mazur: Do you have any tie-in to Google and its computer system? I understand Google has a substantial presence here in Groningen.

Bert Poolman: Within our synthetic cell development program, which is separate from the Origins Center, people from Google are involved but this is mostly coincidental I would say.

Computer power is very important for us. We also have many people here who do large scale molecular dynamic simulations, to simulate a cell. That of course requires a lot of computer power.

The amount of computer power we need is high but it's relatively small compared to what Google is now setting up in terms of facilities here for data storage. And it probably is relatively small compared to what the astronomers here are using as well.

Suzan Mazur: You're doing both bench and computer chemistry?

Bert Poolman: My group is an experimental group. But one of my colleagues here is entirely computational. We collaborate a lot.

Often in computational studies you need to develop force fields and models and those need to be tested. My group sometimes tests those models so that they can be further built. In turn, we have experimental observations that are somewhat of low resolution, and we ask for help with computational simulations.

There's an intimate interaction among computational people here at all levels—from quantum mechanics, atomistic, to mechanics.

Suzan Mazur: Seems like everything is going computational. Every scientific field is going into quantitative analysis.

Bert Poolman: Yes. There is some resistance and reluctance to it in some sciences, however. Of course, you cannot capture everything in a model, in an equation.

Suzan Mazur: Does the information that's emerging on viruses at all affect your thinking about how evolution works?

Bert Poolman: Viruses are very good at self-assembling. A lot of what we do can be based on things that originally came from viruses, but work on viruses is not *per se* important for what we do.

Suzan Mazur: There are spinoffs possibly resulting from these investigations, useful in medicine, etc. You're thinking along those lines?

Bert Poolman: We always use drug delivery as an example because the systems that we develop, can do sophisticated things already. We can already sense the environment. We can do catalysis in confinement.

Ultimately, if we understand the system, we can build it the way an engineer does—the way they build devices. Engineers can draw things on the drawing table and probably it will work the way they want. This is still our dream. We are far away from that with synthetic cell development. But once we are there, I would say the applications are limitless. [emphasis added]

Chapter 30

Astrophysicist Frank Helmich—
The Dutch Origins Center

Photo, courtesy Frank Helmich

12/5/2017

In recent meetings in The Netherlands with principals of the Dutch Origins Center I was advised that, unlike at NASA, funds there will not be used to address theology. Frank Helmich, who chairs the Dutch Origins Center core group and heads the astrophysics programs at SRON (Netherlands Institute for Space Research)—one of the Center's 18 participating institutes—told me this during a space instruments tour at SRON/Groningen:

> *"We will not make the mistake NASA made."*

Several days later in Amsterdam, Origins Center coordinator Jan-Willem Mantel confirmed that theology is not part of the Dutch initiative.

Over a million US dollars were squandered by the NASA Astrobiology Institute (NAI) for a two-year program (2015-2017) to find out, among other things, how the religious community would respond to the discovery of extraterrestrial life—a story I reported here, which Jerry Coyne picked up a few days later followed by the Freedom From Religion Foundation (FFRF) filing a Freedom of Information Act request. The NAI grant went to theologians roughly two years before the weakening of the wall between Church and State favored by the Trump administration.

FFRF learned through its investigation that the NASA funds were for:

> *"(1) Formulating a "Christian response" to scientific studies on morality. (2) Developing a new model of biblical interpretation. (3) Relating themes from First Corinthians, a book in the Christian bible, to astrobiology. (4) Reconciling a potential astrobiology discovery with Christian theology. (5) Looking at how astrobiology would affect the Christian doctrine of redemption. (6) Examining Christian ethics and Christian doctrines of human obligation. (5) Looking at societal implications of astrobiology with "theological ethics." (6) Writing a monograph on Christian forgiveness."*

As for whether there is life in outer space, Frank Helmich, whose roots are in the exoplanet community, told me in our interview that follows that "there must be habitable planets," but as for whether there is life there: "I don't know, I really don't know." He said further that telescopes for finding the right biomarkers to determine this are "decades away" from being made.

Clearly Helmich is in the know about the latter. He oversees instrument project development at SRON. He's been principal investigator on the Heterodyne Instrument for the Far-Infrared on the European Space Agency's Herschel Space Observatory and lead scientist for The Netherlands on the SPICA/SAFARI instrument, among other projects. He is also a member of the Herschel, GUSTO, and STO-2 science teams.

I first exchanged emails with Frank Helmich while en route to The Netherlands in late October but had not yet fixed an appointment with him when I bumped into him on a train traveling north from Amsterdam to Groningen through Holland's gorgeous farm country. Helmich boarded in Utrecht where SRON has principal headquarters, but I was so exhausted after a long journey from Dundee via Edinburgh via Dublin that I didn't really notice him until we pulled into Groningen station.

From certain angles, Helmich looks a bit like Baryshnikov. From others, Samuel Finzi—German television's amusing Dr. Flemming. Indeed, Frank Helmich's playful humor does seem to rival his professional profile. Our interview follows.

SRON/University of Groningen

Frank Helmich: I was surprised when your article in *Huffington Post* came to my attention—that you were aware of the Dutch Origins Center. I still do wonder, how did you find out?

Suzan Mazur: I saw a brief reference months ago about the Dutch Origins Center conference August 31-September 1, but didn't investigate further. I should have. It would have been good to attend. But I did at least report that the kickoff was about to happen. Dave Deamer sent me a note when the article posted saying Harry Lonsdale would have been delighted.

Frank Helmich: Lee Cronin in his talk at the conference referred to the remark you made in the *Huffington Post* article about his "Alien chemist."

Suzan Mazur: Did he really.

Frank Helmich: He did yes. It was an excellent gathering—to see what's possible, what the boundary conditions are right now. That was the first time that we could really do that. It was also good to be together because most of us don't know each other very well.

It provided momentum that made the symposium so important for us.

Suzan Mazur: Was the decision to make the Origins Center at the University of Groningen at all related to Google's presence here? The computers—

Frank Helmich: No, not at all. It was purely driven by the Dutch science and research agenda. There was a consultation of the general public, initiated by the Ministry of Education and Science and the response was 12,000 questions from the public and also from researchers. Things they found important and needed to be solved by science.

Suzan Mazur: How much funding do you have? You're separately funded from the synthetic cell development project that Bert Poolman is involved with. Right? He said they've received €19 million in funding.

Frank Helmich: We have very different funding areas. For the Origins Center itself—€2.5 million have been given to the Center to start. So we're working with scientists who already have tenured jobs and are willing to contribute, along with their postdocs, to the research. The initiative is clearly national but we're working internationally as well. Science is always international.

Suzan Mazur: You've got 30 or 40 people working with the Dutch Origins Center now?

Frank Helmich: We asked 40 people to be part of the working group, so they came to meetings and we discussed how we should proceed. But the group is much larger if you consider the number of people we invited to all the workshops. We organized several workshops on several topics and at least 200 tenured people attended. If everybody would be interested from the fields involved, we'd have a group of 700. For a small country like The Netherlands, that's not so bad.

So active is probably more on the order of 40 to 100 and we could have 700. But how you manage 700 scientists is a different question.

Suzan Mazur: Dieter Braun told me that there's a new dynamic in origin of life research, that a new generation of experimentally-driven scientists have entered the field. No more fishing expeditions.

Frank Helmich: It's difficult for me to judge, because I'm new to the field, but I think I support that perspective. From what was presented at the recent symposium here and the workshops we had, the research is much more professional than it used to be. I don't think we will see any more fishing expeditions.

Suzan Mazur: Would you tell me how you set up the Dutch Origins Center? Is Ben Feringa involved in a hands-on way or is he the figurehead?

Frank Helmich: Ben Feringa is the patron and figurehead of the whole Origins Center. He also read our proposal prior to submission and corrected it. Ben's research [molecular systems] is also one of the key areas of investigation in origins of life. He is very connected to the Center even though he travels a lot as a Nobel laureate.

Setting up the Origins Center involved a funding agency, NWO— The Netherlands Organisation for Scientific Research. NWO had a large database of people possibly interested in the subject. So together with a colleague from NWO, I sent around emails saying: "Are you interested in participating in a workshop about this topic?"

Seventy people attended our first workshop on the subject. They were very interested in finding out what it was all about, also what kind of funding was attached to it. The general spirit was very good, but we found out that all these scientific disciplines had very different languages. It was difficult for people to talk to one other. They had to explain more than they could really ask questions.

Seventy people also participated in the second workshop, and we were then able to decide:

> *Okay, we can bundle these ideas in five game-changing topics[: (1) origin and co-evolution of earth-like planets and life, (2) predicting evolution, (3) building and directing life from molecule to biosphere, (4) finding extraterrestrial life, (5) bridging long temporal and spatial scales].*

Bundling was necessary because we also had to send the proposal as part of the whole Dutch Science and Research Agenda to the parliament and ministry. When our part all came together, it was about origins of life, thus the name Dutch Origins Center.

Suzan Mazur: What is your current role and how does it differ from that of Jan-Willem Mantel's role as manager?

Frank Helmich: I'm involved, since January 2016, as chairman of the core group. I am still chairman of the core group.

When we applied for money, we got some money. But real work had to be done and we had other jobs as well. I still have another job.

So Jan-Willem does the day-to-day coordination and I handle interaction with the core group. I chair the meetings.

Suzan Mazur: Are you doing experimental research in your field of astrophysics/astrochemistry as well?

Frank Helmich: My expertise is currently bringing people together, making sure funding is available and that space instruments are built. In Europe when you build something for space, it involves a lot of member states and institutes. You have to build consortia to make space instruments. I'll show you some of the instruments in the tour later.

Suzan Mazur: Do you have any doubts that we live in a 3D reality? There's been a lot of discussion about it this year at Perimeter Institute, University of Southampton, University of Waterloo, Fermilab and other places.

Frank Helmich: I don't know.

Suzan Mazur: They're saying there's early evidence that we live in a 2D reality.

Frank Helmich: Does that change my way of life? Not yet, I would say.

Suzan Mazur: What are the plans for the Dutch Origins Center?

Frank Helmich: We've only received €2.5 million. That's not much, so we have to improve on that. What we did is for the first two, three years we appointed seven fellows who are going to work on the game-changing topics. We're going to build all kinds of small projects in which people can start to collaborate with each other and learn each other's language. We will have a symposium every one and a half years for the whole community. We'll also apply for European Union funding. Funding is crucial to keep researchers interested.

Suzan Mazur: The big data aspect is important.

Frank Helmich: Yes and no. There are parts of the Origins Center that have to do with sequencing and bioinformatics, but there are also things that need much, much less data. So in some parts you'll see it and in some parts you won't. The same is true for big science facilities. The exoplanet community, where my roots are more than anywhere else. They need very big telescopes—

Suzan Mazur: Are you optimistic about habitable exoplanets?

Frank Hemlich: Yes. There are so many planets in the galaxy, there must be habitable planets. That doesn't mean that there

is life there. I don't know, I really don't know. Probably there is. But there's no way I can prove it now. However, if we are able to find the right biomarkers, which we can't at the moment, and if we're able to build very large telescopes in which we can see the atmospheres and soil—we may be able to detect it. But this is decades away. [emphasis added]

Suzan Mazur: What would you say is unique about the Dutch Origins Center?

Frank Helmich: The number of disciplines involved. They run from astrophysics to cell biology and chemistry. This is very, very big. It's not being done to this extent at other places, as far as I know.

Suzan Mazur: The Dutch Origins Center seems to be lending a new seriousness to the effort.

Frank Helmich: That's my goal, yes. If we do it, we have to do it right. What has surprised me is the enthusiasm of the scientists: Hey, this is something new, something that we have never tried before. And there is a platform on which we can do it.

Suzan Mazur: It's not a way to get money for basic research.

Frank Helmich: Without money, it fails. The Dutch science and research agenda is about getting money, let's be fair about it. But that is what is needed in The Netherlands to maintain and expand the high level of research.

Chapter 31

Who's Who at the
Dutch Synthetic Cell Symposium

Marileen Dogterom, Chair
2018 Dutch Synthetic Cell Symposium

"We received a grant of €19M from the Netherlands Science Foundation last summer for our synthetic cell development project. The award went to 15 working groups—15 groups working in this area is substantial. We will probably appoint 30-80 PhD students. But some of our labs also have national grants and so the 15 groups could each include 10 to 20 researchers.

The 15 PIs have already individually been working on aspects of synthetic cell development. But for the first time there is proper funding for tackling larger scale problems."
—**University of Groningen biochemist Bert Poolman**, in conversation with me in 2017

The Netherlands is a small country of 17 million people. With a GDP of roughly $850B, it is 18th in world economies. Not counting the narco economy, that is—estimated at $3.4B—money Dutch police report is being laundered in real estate, travel, hospitality and other industries. Nevertheless, it is a model state with a GDP per capita of $50,000, 5% living below poverty and with AAA Fitch and S&P ratings. A year or so ago the Dutch government, responding to public interest in origins of life, allocated €2.5 million to establish an Origins of Life Center and €19 million for a synthetic cell development program.

Scientists in The Netherlands have now tapped some of the €19M to organize the country's "1st International Symposium on Building a Synthetic Cell." The bottom-up meeting takes place August 28-29 at Delft University of Technology, where 32 speakers take the stage to present their perspectives. Half are Dutch, half from assorted countries. Two philosophers are in the mix, two chivalrous knights, and lots of fresh faces.

The symposium's chair is Marileen Dogterom, a Delft University biophysicist who also chairs Delft's bionanoscience department besides running the Dogterom lab, which looks at cytoskeleton "assembly, force generation and organization." Dogterom is a professor at Leiden Institute of Physics as well. She is a winner of the 2018 Spinoza Prize, The Netherlands' highest scientific award (€2.5M).

Dogterom describes the cytoskeleton:

> *"The cytoskeleton is a dynamic polymer system, it is constantly changing shape. So it is different than for example a human skeleton. The microtubules (tubular proteins that form the cytoskeleton, ed.) generate forces by growing and shrinking. The same microtubules also help with cell polarization, making a cell's front look different from its back. A cell needs this for example to be*

able to walk. So the cytoskeleton also has to do with the spatial organization of the cell."

Co-organizers of the event are: Gijsje Koenderink, Pascale Daran-Lapujade, and Wilhelm Huck—one of the chivalrous knights.

It's interesting that the conference is taking place at Delft, which is also home to a neutron and positron research center. Delft is part of LENS (League of Advanced European Neutron Sources), a consortium of countries using neutron scattering to probe and measure matter, including inside living cells—with the most sophisticated facility in Sweden (48% complete).

But the questions: Why build a synthetic cell? and What is life? continue to reverberate.

The late Carl Woese, who was awarded the Leeuwenhoek Medal by the Royal Netherlands Academy of Arts and Sciences (1992), opposed the idea of making a synthetic cell, telling me in a 2012 interview weeks before he died that he thought the push for a synthetic cell was all about "Power" and scientists "thinking they're God."

Indeed, the Germans have appointed Peter Dabrock—who chairs the German Ethics Council (a government advisory group)—to oversee "challenges at the interface of science and society," including synthetic cell development. However, as a Protestant theologian, Dabrock's appointment has generated criticism.

Stanford University biochemical engineer Drew Endy at the recent National Science Foundation synthetic cell gathering in Alexandria, Virginia questioned whether making a synthetic cell wasn't simply giving a name to what scientists have already been working on for years. Endy was a presence not only at the Alexandria synthetic cell meeting, but at the Bavaria synthetic cell conference last summer in Ringberg Castle and is a speaker at Delft as well. Coincidentally, he has an honorary doctorate from Delft. He's also on *Esquire* magazine's list of "The 75 most influential people of the 21st century."

316

The Dutch conference promo never actually defines life. It does, however, address why the country has decided to build a synthetic cell. It repeats the mantra that the initiative is all about trying to understand how life works, adding that part of the plan is to "gain insight" into what the conditions were that first enabled life to emerge on Earth, which may also be relevant elsewhere in the universe. *Plus* the Dutch, like most invested parties, have an interest in seeing spinoffs from the research.

Motive-wise, nothing really new here. What is new is the Dutch drive to get the job done. To show they mean business, they've invited some pretty serious scientists to the Delft discussions.

Among the big name presenters from the Netherlands is University of Groningen biochemist Bert Poolman. Poolman is a principal investigator in the Dutch synthetic cell initiative and was introduced to me last October while I was in North Holland by Jan-Willem Mantel, coordinator of the Dutch Origins Center.

Another key speaker is Christophe Danelon at Delft, who has been working on a minimal cell for some years. The Danelon Group wants to "reconstitute four cellular modules":

— DNA replication
— vesicle growth through lipid biosynthesis
— compartment division
— regulatory genetic circuits

Of considerable note among the Dutch presenters is Cees Dekker, who in 2014 was decorated by King Willem-Alexander for his "pioneering work of great social relevance": Knight of the Order of the Netherlands Lion. Cees Dekker is a physicist at Delft whose research interests include the biophysics of DNA and synthetic cells.

Cees Dekker, with Delft biophysicist Nynke Dekker—another symposium speaker—co-founded the university's bionanoscience department (they are not otherwise related).

Nynke Dekker's lab is investigating the "key cellular process of nucleic acid replication from a biophysical perspective in viral, bacterial, and eukaryotic systems."

Wilhelm TS Huck is both a presenter and a Delft conference organizer. Huck was decorated by King Willem-Alexander earlier this year with the civilian order of chivalry: Knight of the Order of the Netherlands Lion. He is a professor of physical organic chemistry at the Institute for Molecules and Materials, Radboud University Nijmegen. Huck has been developing "artificial cells on the basis of tiny droplets the size of a picolitre."

In 2016, Huck was awarded the Spinoza Prize. He's also a member of the Simons Collaboration on Origins of Life (project: "the influence of molecular structure on dynamics of complex reaction networks"). In addition, Huck serves as vice president of the scientific advisory board of MaxSynBio—the Max Planck program on synthetic cell development.

According to physicist Eberhard Bodenschatz, director of Max Panck Institute for Dynamics and Self-Organization, Gottingen, who addressed the NSF synthetic cell meeting in May—the Dutch and Max Planck synthetic cell initiatives are very similar, except that the Dutch have now added a genome to their synthetic cell scheme and the Germans have not. The Germans want to see how far self-organization will take them.

"Extraordinary professor" Pieter Rein ten Wolde, from AMOLF (Dutch Foundation for Fundamental Research on Matter), will also share highlights of his research at the Delft gathering. His Biochemical Network group at AMOLF is looking to "unravel the design principles" of biochemical networks through database analyses, theory and computer simulation. PR ten Wolde thinks cellular copy operation can be mapped onto a computational copy operation. On his web page he points out that cyanobacteria clock components have to be synthesized every cell cycle. Ten Wolde would like to "develop minimal models of the cell cycle." He thinks these "can be exploited in the design of synthetic cells that need to grow and divide."

Another symposium presenter from Holland who I interviewed last October while in Groningen, is engineer-turned-systems biologist Matthias Heinemann. Heinemann describes the Dutch synthetic cell initiative this way:

> *"A lot of biology has to do with control mechanisms, with oscillation, with feedback, and these are all things engineers know how to deal with. An engineer actually does biotechnology, and biotechnology is to some extent metabolism. Some think metabolism came early in evolution. This is what I'm investigating now, metabolism.*
>
> *If you look at this map of chemical reactions, which take place in every single cell—1,000 to 1,500 chemical reactions. This map that anyone during their biochemistry studies has had to suffer through. This is our field of research now.*
>
> *In trying to understand how life first came about, we look at how food molecules are taken up in existing cells and then processed. How energy is extracted. How new cells are synthesized. We're trying to learn what the principles are behind this network. What in evolutionary terms governs this network. Nothing makes sense without evolution. . . .*
>
> *What I mentioned earlier—metabolism could be responsible for introducing some cell dynamics and these dynamics could then lead to a growth and division cycle. We're studying this with existing cells but in the effort together with Bert Poolman we also will try to mimic this in a synthetic system. As we build the synthetic cell, we'll try to introduce oscillations to get the cell to split. It's a two-way approach. Dissecting and studying*

existing cells—how they do it—and trying to rebuild this in a synthetic cell."

Tom de Greef, a professor of synthetic biology at Holland's Eindhoven University of Technology will conduct a masterclass at the symposium titled: "Engineering Bioinspired Molecular Networks and Synthetic Cells."

The de Greef research group is working on "bottom-up construction of basic cellular functions from well-characterized biological components, and the development of novel biological computing devices that can enhance signal-processing capabilities of natural and synthetic cells."

Radboud University presenter Carla Rita Palmerino is a philosopher and science historian on the faculty of philosophy, theology and religious studies.

Ramboud University philosopher Hub Zwart is also scheduled to speak. He's the author of 10 books and founder of ISIS (Institute for Science, Innovation and Society). His interest is in how scientific research challenges our understanding of life and "the place of human beings" in it.

Other Dutch speakers include: John van der Oost ("a pioneer of the CRISPR revolution")—as well as Arnold Driessen, Bela Mulder, Gijs Wuite (researching physics of life processes), Sander Tans, and Siewert-Jan Marrink.

On the international side—the committee was wise to invite as a keynote speaker NCBI-NIH's Eugene Koonin. Koonin is a mesmerizing personality with an H-index of 196 (that's higher than Charles Darwin's). In 2002, Koonin and NCBI colleague Kira Makarova identified the genetic region now known as CRISPR-Cas.

(By the way, Delft conference organizers refer to every international speaker as a "keynote speaker.")

Koonin has demonstrated the ability to unite various tribes of evolutionary science and articulate a way forward. And he has set the record straight on natural selection, even if his co-author(s) may be stuck in selfish Dawkins-speak.

Said Koonin in our 2017 conversation about "The New Evolutionary Biology":

> *"Perhaps making all these parallels between natural selection and artificial selection, the way Darwin does in his book, could be somewhat dangerous because in artificial selection there is someone who is selecting, even if unconsciously. In that respect, the evolutionary process is very different in nature where nothing is there to actually select. . . . No one in the mainstream scientific community now takes selection literally."*

Chemist John Sutherland, Medical Research Council/ Laboratory of Molecular Biology in the UK, is another of the high profile international speakers. Sutherland co-chairs the Simons Collaboration on Origins of Life and is probably best known for winning Harry Lonsdale's Origin of Life Challenge in 2012 along with University College London chemist Matt Powner.

Eors Szathmary, a Hungarian biologist from Eotvos Lorand University, will share his insights as well. Szathmary was one of the organizers of COOL EDGE 2013—the origins of life conference at CERN (which not even Ganesh was able to rescue)—and one of "the Altenberg 16." Szathmary collaborated with John Maynard Smith on two books: *The Major Transitions in Evolution*; and *The Origins of Life*.

Michael Jewett is a biochemical engineer and keynote speaker from Northwestern University. The focus of the Jewett lab is "designing, constructing, and modifying biological systems involved in protein synthesis and metabolism" using cell-free systems.

Developmental biologist Kate Adamala is a presenter from the University of Minnesota. Her protobiology lab is "building tools for studying and controlling biology using synthetic cells and protein engineering technologies."

Several presenters are from various Max Planck Institutes in Germany.

Petra Schwille is a biophysicist at MPI for Biochemistry, Martinsried (near Munich) working in cellular and molecular biophysics. She describes her lab's research on bottom-up minimal systems this way:

> *"Our ambition is to quantitatively understand living systems on the scale of individually active and interactive molecules such as proteins, lipids and nucleic acids. We primarily employ single molecule fluorescence microscopy and spectroscopy, supplemented by force microscopy to achieve resolution far below the diffraction limit."*

The research interests of presenter Joachim Spatz, director of MPI for Medical Research in Heidelberg, include cellular biophysics, materials science, cell biology, interface science and physics of soft matter.

Tobias Erb is a speaker from MPI, Marburg (Max Planck Institute for Terrestrial Microbiology). He is director and head of the department of biochemistry and synthetic metabolism there. The focus of the Erb lab is "understanding and applying fundamental design principles of metabolism." Studying metabolism in the living cell to "build novel, synthetic metabolism in a bottom-up fashion."

Cell and developmental biologist Mohan Balasubramanian is a keynote speaker from the UK's University of Warwick. He is currently investigating cytokinetic actomyosin ring structure, assembly and function, with funding from the Royal Society.

Balasubramanian described his research philosophy in an interview last year with Nida Siddiqui:

> *"I think research is about enjoying the process not waiting for the results. You can tell from talking to some people that they enjoy the process and if you do the process properly, you will get something."*

And he voiced these concerns:

> *"There is a big shift in how science is being done, nowadays it's a lot of collaborative science. When I started my Ph.D., it was very common to pick any of the top journals and find papers that have only 2 authors. There is a first author and the senior author. There were even papers that had one author. This was all possible those days. But if you look at papers now there are too many authors. The problem with that is it takes thirty human years to finish a project and there is a team of people and four joint first authors and a senior author. There aren't going to be enough jobs. The way science has evolved requires large teams to accomplish the jobs and many of them may not make it because to accommodate that many successful postdocs you need to quadruple the intake. It is only natural since people have to earn a living and have a good quality life. Other options, like an industry job, is becoming more and more common."*

An important talk at Delft representing the rapidly growing mechanobiology movement will be Allen Liu's. Liu is a mechanical and biomedical engineer at the University of Michigan. The Liu Lab's interests are "mechanobiology and mechanotransduction, bottom-up synthetic biology, droplet microfluidics, systems biology of endocytosis and cell migration."

Keynote Hagan Bayley is from the University of Oxford, where he is a professor of chemical biology. He also heads the Bayley Group at Oxford, whose research interests include: fundamental properties of ion channels and pores, single molecule chemistry and catalysis, printed tissues and tissue-like materials, among others. Bayley was one of the organizers of the 2017 synthetic cell meeting at Ringberg Castle.

Yannick Rondelez, a presenter from France's National Center for Scientific Research (CNRS/ESPCI) is investigating information processing chemical systems, *in vitro*. Rondelez describes cellular computing this way:

> *"The dynamical and information-processing properties of living cells, i.e., their ability to make decisions, sense their environment, maintain their integrity, memorize bits of information, interact, coordinate, etc. is indeed encapsulated in the topology and dynamics of their molecular networks."*

It's a large group and a landmark meeting, one whose proceedings should be live streamed over the Internet—like last February's Mechanics of Morphogenesis conference at Princeton—or at a minimum, talks videotaped and posted online as the NSF synthetic cell gathering's organizers were smart to do to garner public support.

Chapter 32

National Science Foundation Funds
Synthetic Cell Development

Vincent Noireaux — *photo courtesy V. Noireaux*

7/12/2018

Not to be outdone by Dutch, German and other Europeans now officially dabbling in synthetic cell research, America's National Science Foundation has thrown its hat into the ring on funding synthetic cell development, per its April 18, 2018 letter to colleagues inviting proposals on the design and engineering of synthetic cells and cell components ($100K for relevant conferences, $300K re multicomponent subsystems, and up to $1M for research on the "pseudo-cell"). In May, following its call for proposals, NSF co-sponsored a synthetic and artificial cells roadmap meeting in Alexandria, Virginia with a handful of

325

scientists already working in the field presenting and others in the audience looking to be educated.

Videos of the presentations are posted online and are well worth viewing.

One of the most substantive presentations was by Vincent Noireaux, a University of Minnesota physicist, whose lab I visited in 2014. Noireaux, a former protégé of Rockefeller University's Albert Libchaber, has been funded by DARPA (Defense Advanced Research Projects Agency) in recent years for his work on the minimal cell.

Libchaber told me at a 2014 meeting in his Rockefeller University office: "Vincent thinks he will have a minimal cell that can self-replicate within five years."

My interviews with both Vincent Noireaux and Albert Libchaber are featured in *The Origin of Life Circus: A How To Make Life Extravaganza*. Excerpts from the Noireaux interview follow my wrapup of the NSF Alexandria gathering.

Another key presenter at the NSF meeting was Clyde Hutchison, a biochemist and microbiologist known for his role in creating "Synthia" eight years ago at J. Craig Venter Institute. Hutchison reminded the audience that JCVI had already made a synthetic cell, further advising that he realized that claim irritates people. Hutchison then described what JCVI means by a synthetic cell:

> *"We have built a synthetic DNA genome and installed it in the cytoplasm of a living cell. This produces a cell controlled by the synthetic genome."*

Hutchison added:

> *"Someday it will be possible to assemble a cell from non-living components (ribosomes, tRNAs, enzymes, membranes, etc.) but this seems very difficult at present."*

326

He said the long-term goal is an atom model of the synthetic cell. Hutchison also announced that JCVI was collaborating on further development of the cell with Zan Luthey-Schulten's lab at the University of Illinois, Urbana-Champaign. Luthey-Schulten was one of the organizers of the NSF Alexandria workshop.

Eberhard Bodenschatz, a physicist and director of Max Planck Institute for Dynamics and Self-Organization in Gottingen, Germany gave the European perspective on synthetic cells. Bodenschatz said that the Max Planck Society (Max Planck Gesellschaft, a German non-profit association with a budget of €2B) is establishing a new institute on origins of life, and that five of the MPG schools will be offering MS and PhD degrees in the Matter to Life field beginning 2019.

Bodenschatz is hopeful that the Max Planck program on synthetic cell development, known as MaxSynBio, will be funded in 2020 at €25M through the following sources:

(1) "Biotechnologie 2020+" through BMBF (Federal Ministry for Education and Research)

(2) Max Planck Society (MPG)

(3) Core budgets of participating Max Planck Institutes (MPI).

He also emphasized that a dialogue with the public on synthetic cell development is critical and that Peter Dabrock, a theologian who sits on the Ethics Council of the German government, will oversee "challenges at the interface of science and society."

Bodenschatz defined a living system as "a nonlinear, open system with chemical diversity driven far from equilibrium that consumes energy and generates structure showing emergent collective behavior." He considers the cell a technical system.

Bodenschatz said that there was as yet no genome in the MaxSynBio approach to synthetic cell development, that scientists there wanted to see how far into development self-organization would take them. He added that the Dutch and Max Planck synthetic cell initiatives are very similar, except that the Dutch have now added the genome to their scheme.

[See my interview with Bert Poolman for more on the €19M Dutch synthetic cell program BaSyC.]

It is unclear how much China is spending on synthetic cell development, but surely Tetsuya Yomo's PI status at East China Normal University's Institute of Biology and Information Science means China is seriously investigating. Also, Bodenschatz in his presentation referred to his participation at a Shanghai workshop that preceded both the German and Dutch initiatives, the NSF Alexandria workshop, and last summer's Ringberg Castle symposium in Bavaria on building a synthetic cell—the latter featuring: Jack Szostak ("Why make synthetic cells?"), Bert Poolman, John Sutherland, Eberhard Bodenschatz, Drew Endy, Sheref Mansy, and Mary Voytek, among others.

There was some banter at the recent NSF gathering about the difference between a synthetic cell and an artificial cell with nothing resolved. . .

Vincent Noireaux's NSF talk on cell free expression laid out the basics on cell parts: information, compartment, metabolism—saying all three have to be successfully linked to make a synthetic cell. He listed various bottom-up synthetic cell systems scientists refer to and gave his take on a few of the systems:

(1) protocell/coacervate: origin of unicellular life, peptide, RNA, fatty acids

(2) artificial cell: cell-sized self-sustaining homeostatic compartment made of natural and artificial molecules

328

(3) minimal cell: synthesis of a self-reproducing cell-sized compartment, natural molecular machinery (transcription, translation, phospholipids).

Noireaux next focused on the technical aspects of creating a minimal cell and said the objectives were (a) recapitulation of some cellular functions, and (b) self-replication of a cell-sized compartment (200-400 genes required).

He also described various challenges in the information, self-assembly, and metabolism blocks. Noireaux termed self-organization a "poorly characterized process" and said we need more attention to cytoskeleton development. He also noted that understanding how to make liposomes with complex phospholipid mixtures is still very limited. And that gene regulation needs work, among other challenges.

Richard M. Murray, a Caltech professor of bioengineering, followed up with a five-systems breakdown in building a synthetic cell:

(1) spatial organization—cell wall and internal structure

(2) metabolic subsystem—power supply, important chemicals

(3) sensing & signaling—sense the local environment and communicate with other cells

(4) regulation & computation—maintain the internal state and control interactions, motion

(5) actuation—move in/affect environment (physical and chemical).

As an engineer Murray thinks replication is not so important in building a synthetic cell. Murray said it will be 30 years before the synthetic cell is developed and that no single lab can do it—it has to be a collaborative effort.

Noireaux made brief mention of a collaboration with Murray.

Drew Endy, a Stanford University bioengineer who *Esquire* magazine named one of the 75 most important people of the 21st century (along with Tiger Woods, Michael Milken, Arnold Schwarzenegger, Bill & Hillary Clinton *et al.*), and who participated in the Ringberg Castle syncell symposium in Bavaria, cautioned about leaving out the cultural aspect to making a synthetic cell.

Endy considers the job 80% technical and 20% "anthropological." He said making the cell would not be acheived just within academic circles. Endy also addressed motive in syncell development asking:

> ***"Are we simply going to invoke a name of building cells to do what we're already doing?"***

[emphasis added]

One scientist in the audience from the Marvel comics camp cheered on the notion of a synthetic cell escaping outside its environment. . .

Vincent Noireaux in final thoughts about the NSF Alexandria meeting voiced his confidence that there was already a lot in place on synthetic cell development. Indeed, one or two scientists in the room seemed bewildered by the briefing.

My chat with Vincent Noireaux on "How to Make a Minimal Cell":

"May 12, 2014

It was positively springtime in Minneapolis. Raining lightly, glistening, a bit windy. Following my non-direct flight from New York, the air was like a rush of Peter's Blend (a serious Bleecker Street roast).

I was excited by Vincent Noireaux's invitation to visit his lab at the University of Minnesota, his minimal cell lab. Noireaux offered to meet me at the airport. But since I'd never been to Minneapolis, I decided to make my own way into town, to explore.

Vincent Noireaux is 40ish, quick, with attractive blue eyes and an unmistakably-French smile. His PhD is in physics from France's Institut Curie.

As a postdoc, Noireaux collaborated with Albert Libchaber on a synthetic cell system, working in Libchaber's condensed matter physics lab at Rockefeller University. Libchaber is formerly a director of research at CNRS (French National Center for Scientific Research).

We met in Noireaux's office. In the grass outside his building are a pair of condensed matter sculptures Noireaux introduced me to, recent additions to the university landscape called *Spannungsfeld*, meaning "tension field."

The pieces are the creation of German quantum physicist-turned-artist Julian Voss-Andreae, now an Oregonian (or "Orygunian," as they say). The 10-foot tall male and female torsos each weigh 1.5 tons and are made of sliced steel and open space. Viewed from various perspectives, the figures appear to change form, from solid to hologram.

Voss-Andreae says the sculptures are "a metaphor for the counterintuitive world of quantum physics."

Inside Vincent Noireaux's office I notice a baby carriage. Noireaux informs me that his wife is a scientist as well. She's now finishing her PhD in physics at the University of Minnesota.

Over a Starbuck's coffee, Noireaux tells me he grew up in the French countryside. His father is a government official and his mother a banker.

On the day of my visit, Noireaux was in the middle of a move to the university's 3M building, to a spacious new lab, which I toured —featuring state-of-the-art equipment and windows looking out into the Minnesota sky. It's a minimal cell research facility largely funded by DARPA (Defense Advanced Research Projects Agency).

But first we took a spin through Noireaux's old cramped and windowless *E. coli* lab, the door posted BIOHAZARD.

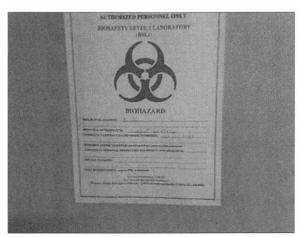

Photo, Suzan Mazur

Test tubes filled with fascinating liquid were being readied for transport. Noireaux noticed that a floor freezer was a bit ajar, and he quickly put a make-shift weight on top of the lid to close it. We next passed an innocent-looking white refrigerator that Noireaux opened to reveal shelves of tubes of much less innocent-looking stuff. We then proceeded out of the lab.

I didn't want to spend more time than necessary around the tubes, frankly, considering the biohazard sign. But I did wonder what DARPA's interest was in Noireaux's minimal cell project.

Noireaux says even he doesn't know what he might discover with his minimal cell research.

Noireaux works with a team of graduate students and one postdoc, Filippo Caschera, who he introduced to me in the room adjacent to the old lab. Caschera was busily organizing the move. He'd been a researcher in Venice, Italy at Norm Packard's company ProtoLife before coming to work with Noireaux and at Pier Luigi Luisi's minimal cell lab in Rome.

During our interview Noireaux described his current work on the minimal cell and also mapped out who some of the other synthetic cell players are.

Suzan Mazur: Can we walk through the three types of synthetic cells? And would you tell me at what stage of development you are with your system?

Vincent Noireaux: I am now finishing a review with my postdoc associates in the lab. What we see are the following three approaches to making a synthetic cell.

First is the protocell, which is about origin of life. It involves creating a self-reproducing unicellular entity with the basic molecules of life, including molecules for the membrane, ions, some genetic information like RNA.

The second approach is the minimal cell. The minimal cell is made of natural molecules and components. It's more sophisticated. Machineries such as transcription and translation are used to execute the DNA programs, to try to create a self-reproducing unicellular system. It's known now that approximately 200-400 genes are necessary to make a minimal cell that would be able to reproduce itself.

The third approach is the artificial cell. I define artificial cell as a synthetic cell system that incorporates non-natural molecules and components. I can give the example of block copolymers, which look like phospholipids and self-assemble into membranes. Eventually it is thought artificial cells can be made from them.

In my laboratory here at the University of Minnesota, we're working on minimal cells. We have developed a cell-free transcription-translation system to execute large DNA programs *in vitro*.

Suzan Mazur: Cell-free.

Vincent Noireaux: It's *in vitro*. There's just no cell there. We extract the molecular machineries (for transcription and translation) to express DNA programs. We developed recently what we call the cell-free transcription-translation toolbox, which allows us to express relatively complicated DNA programs.

The largest one we've executed so far is a natural DNA program. We just did a demonstration to challenge the system with the genome of a virus, a virus from bacteria—bacteriophage. This system is approximately 60 genes. It's still not the 200 to 400 genes needed for a minimal cell, but we demonstrated that the system we developed can take or execute very large DNA programs.

This electron microscope image is a picture of the system. You can see the phages that are made after a few hours entirely synthesized from the genome of these viruses. So we really have a system now. It's a liquid solution, where you put some DNA in it and the DNA is expressed. We are able now to make very well defined living entities, even though it's a virus and needs a host. It's a complex, self-assembled information-based system.

Suzan Mazur: Do you consider a virus living?

Vincent Noireaux: It's a very good question. It does require a host. It reproduces through a host. So whether it's living or not is a little bit debatable.

We have developed this system, which we call a cell-free transcription-translation platform, that allows us to execute DNA programs in vitro. We are returning now to the minimal cell. We want to encapsulate the system into liposomes and execute DNA programs that encode for essential functions of living cells.

What we do is take free cells and extract the complex machinery to express DNA. We remove everything, all of the genetic information of the cells, and we have all of these molecules we then use to express DNA that we synthesize in the laboratory. We can encapsulate that into liposomes.

Suzan Mazur: In trying to get it to self-reproduce, how close do you think you are? And what is the problem at this point in getting it to self-reproduce?

Vincent Noireaux: That's a very good question. The problem is. The cell is made of three parts [draws diagram]: information, metabolism, and there is self-organization. Each of these parts is made of molecular machineries, each of these parts is essential to make a cell.

The problem we have is to understand how these parts talk together. The real problem is the integration of these three parts in a compartment. Information is the DNA program, its genetic composition and its regulation. Metabolism is energy or the nutrients, at least at the beginning. And self-organization occurs with expression of proteins, which are able to make very specific assemblies and structures in specific locations. It is a real problem integrating these three parts in a container and coordinating their actions.

I have been working a lot on information and a system to express DNA. In the past few years, this has developed nearly to a system.

We've also worked to develop a system that can express protein for a very long time based on energy. Our platform is now more robust energetically.

Finally there is self-organization. We're trying to understand how when some proteins are expressed together, it is possible to make very specific structures.

In a sort of test before the minimal cell, we are looking at phages. In a certain amount of time, minutes or hours, you get something that is incredibly well defined. There are many things related to cells that we understand with this system, which recapitulate all of the fundamental steps of genetic information and its expression.

336

So you have information, you express a bunch of molecules, and they create something perfectly well defined. The phage in this case is a crystal, it's a crystal with DNA inside it.

The ultimate goal of what we are doing is the minimal cell, but first we have to understand the relationship between information and self-organization. Where we are right now is that we have the most versatile and powerful cell-free transcription-translation system reported so far for synthetic biology applications.

Suzan Mazur: So time-wise where are you with development of a minimal cell that can self-reproduce?

Vincent Noireaux: It may be early to give an estimation of how many years. We have a system which we think is relatively close to a minimal cell.

Suzan Mazur: How does recent creation of an organism with an expanded genetic code intended for use in the drug industry affect your current research, if at all?

Vincent Noireaux: For now, this work is relatively far from what we do. The current concern for us is to develop genetic regulation that will coordinate the expression of the genes. How to make a synthetic genome that works.

Suzan Mazur: Your interest is also in the minimal cell for use in drug delivery, I understand. In light of current thinking about top-down evolution, that evolution happens top down—tissues, organs, cells—and systemically, that it is not gene-centered—how do you think that plays out regarding human exposure to these future drugs.

Vincent Noireaux: If we get a minimal cell, we can engineer it for specific application such as drug delivery or use it as a factory to synthesize new drugs. First, what is the state of the art right now in building a minimal synthetic genome? It is still difficult to make genetic circuits of a few tens of genes with predictable behavior. So we are relatively far, in that sense, from the minimal cell of 200-400 genes.

Does this work have ethical problems. Is it dangerous?

Suzan Mazur: Yes, that's my question. Is it dangerous if it's used to produce drugs people are taking?

Vincent Noireaux: I think we are relatively far from such achievements. The synthesis of a real minimal cell that can self-reproduce presents more potential ethical problems than the applications that would come after.

Suzan Mazur: Could drugs made via the minimal cell using natural DNA prove more problematic once in the bloodstream than, say, a vaccine made using synthetic nucleotides?

Vincent Noireaux: Here I do not have the elements to answer this question.

Suzan Mazur: But if the minimal cell is used to produce drugs that people are taking—

Vincent Noireaux: Yes. You can think about that. Synthetic DNA really depends on what you do with it and where you express it.

My work is more about natural DNA in a container for the minimal cell. The first minimal cells able to reproduce themselves will still be relatively fragile mechanically. They're not going to have the real robustness of a cell as we know it. They're not going to be dangerous, in the sense that they will certainly not be competitive.

Suzan Mazur: What I'm referring to is the epigenetic factor— evolution that's top-down and systemic—organs, cells, tissues— not gene-centered. What could happen with the introduction into the human bloodstream of these drugs?

Vincent Noireaux: Your point is good definitely. If we have a minimal cell, how quickly is it evolvable? How quickly can it diverge and become something very robust? That is completely unclear what can happen.

Suzan Mazur: It's down the road and would have to go through all kinds of trials.

Vincent Noireaux: Exactly. Trials and engineering after that. Absolutely.

Suzan Mazur: Who would you say the key protocell, minimal cell, artificial cell players are?

Vincent Noireaux: Protocell, I would say Jack Szostak at Harvard. Pier Luigi Luisi and all the family of Luisi, Pasquale Stano et al. at the University of Rome3—they do both protocell and minimal cell.

[**Note**: Pier Lusi Luisi advises the Luisi lab is winding down due to lack of funding.]

Vincent Noireaux: There's the group of Steen Rasmussen at the University of Southern Denmark. They do modeling and both protocell and minimal cell.

Suzan Mazur: I interviewed both Rasmussen and Luisi. I haven't interviewed the Japanese researchers, like Tetsuya Yomo at Osaka who's working on the minimal cell. Albert Libchaber mentioned a former student of his, Yusuke Maeda now at Kyoto University, also working on minimal cell and protocell. I saw Maeda's Princeton Origins presentation last year.

Vincent Noireaux: There is also Takuya Ueda at the University of Tokyo. Ueda does minimal cell systems. There's Sheref Mansy of the University of Trento in Italy, as well as Christophe Danelon in The Netherlands at Delft University of Technology.

Suzan Mazur: One of your associates here was formerly a researcher at Norman Packard's ProtoLife lab, wasn't he?

Vincent Noireaux: Absolutely. Filippo Caschera. He was a postdoc at ProtoLife and got his PhD at the University of Southern Denmark. He was working with Steen Rasmussen and others.

Also, there's Pierre-Alain Monnard at the University of Southern Denmark.

The third synthetic cell is the artificial cell. The artificial cell is when you have synthetic components. More soft-matter people. Daniel Hammer at University of Pennsylvania is one scientist working on the artificial cell.

Suzan Mazur: There is also the Simons Foundation and its research team on origins of life. Actually, I think Sheref Mansy is part of that collaboration.

Vincent Noireaux: Our work here on the minimal cell is related to the origin of life but on a slightly more sophisticated level where we really try to understand the minimum genetic system. It's also a question of physics, how physically to make a self-reproducing entity.

Suzan Mazur: Research on origin of life is being increasingly privately funded meaning the research can be done more quietly. However, less public scrutiny may be a problem when the research is origin of life/protocell development.

Vincent Noireaux: I don't think there is a danger here, major results would be published. It is nice and essential that foundations support basic science."

Chapter 33

America Needs a Citizens Panel on Ethics & Synthetic Cell Development

"Meeting this challenge requires careful exploration of the social and ethical dimensions of such research."—**National Science Foundation**

11/25/2018

L et's cut to the chase—following is my list of individuals who could comprise an effective citizens panel on ethics & US synthetic cell development: **Noam Chomsky, Ralph Nader, Catherine Austin Fitts, Roger Morris, Phyllis Bennis, Barbara Ehrenreich, Arianna Huffington, Alvin Poussaint, Jaron Lanier, Elizabeth Holtzman**.

The National Science Board's quarterly meeting takes place this week—November 28-29—in Alexandria, Virginia. It is a public one and is being webcast. The meeting should be of interest to all since there are Big Doings at NSF regarding synthetic cell development. NSF is currently soliciting preliminary proposals for a program it calls: "Understanding the Rules of Life: Building a Synthetic Cell—An Ideas Lab Activity."

It has set a submissions deadline of December 28, 2018 for preliminary proposals. To see whether you qualify as a proposer, see NSF Program Solicitation (NSF 18-599), linked here.
NSF describes its interests this way:

> *"The ability to design and manufacture synthetic cells has significant implications for the scientific and economic enterprise of the United States. The synthesis of viable cells from non-living molecules and materials can open the door to the production of functional biomaterials and improved biofuels, large scale chemical synthesis, non-silicon-based computing, novel soil engineering, and medical and pharmaceutical advances, to name just a few possibilities. The study of synthetic cells, and of the processes used in their creation, can also provide a window on the origin and evolution of life on Earth and, potentially, provide insight into extraterrestrial life."*

NSF says the preliminary proposals submitted will be handled by a cross-disciplinary team of NSF program directors. Plus a panel of external reviewers (likely anonymous) who will advise on selection of proposers and proposals.

Proposers who make the first cut will participate in an Ideas Lab on synthetic cell development, February 25-March 1, 2019.

Following the Ideas Lab, another cut takes place. Applicants passing that screening will be asked to submit a full proposal—by May 13, 2019. Ultimately, NSF will award $10M in research funds to four to six individuals.

Unlike the way the Lonsdale Origin of Life Challenge was conducted, NSF has indicated that reviewers are being barred from receiving research funding.

However, there are two screeching issues here. One, unfortunately, is the very nature of the NSF itself—which science and technology historian David F. Noble described to me this way:

> *"By about 1943-44, there was a discussion about what the postwar scientific establishment would look like. . . .Vannevar Bush and his friends put together a counterproposal calling for a "National Research Foundation"—which became more or less what we have in today's National Science Foundation.*
>
> *The Vannevar Bush et al. legislation said essentially that science would be funded by the taxpayer but controlled by scientists. Again, scientists—this is important to emphasize—are not simply scientists, but scientists and the corporations they work for."*

The other issue is, of course, the ethics of synthetic cell development. NSF says it cares about the "social and ethical dimensions of such research." So who gets to say what synthetic cell research meets society's approval?

I think creating a responsible US citizens panel is urgent.

Eberhard Bodenschatz, a physicist and director of Max Planck Institute for Dynamics and Self-Organization in Gottingen, Germany, outlined his country's approach on ethics and synthetic cell development at an NSF synthetic cell meeting earlier this year.

Bodenschatz noted that a dialogue with the public is critical and announced that Peter Dabrock, a theologian who sits on the Ethics Council of the German government, will oversee challenges at the interface of science and society there.

Obviously, the German model can never work in America since we have a constitutional wall between church and state.

As of now, the NSF plan is to "educate" the American people about synthetic cell development after selections are quietly made by insiders who we don't know. This approach cannot remain unchallenged. We need a citizens panel. Further, David F. Noble's comments regarding the very nature of the National Science Foundation also need urgent public attention.

Part 4

Is It or Is It Not a 3D World?

Chapter 34

Niayesh Afshordi on Holographic Universe Media Spin & the Iranian Brain Drain

Photo, courtesy Niayesh Afshordi

"By the mid-1970s it [Iran] had become a showcase of development among the Third World countries, boasting one of the highest rates of economic growth and a superior record of social services. It had developed the critical mass of educated people needed for takeoff in science and technology. It was also making steady progress in fields ranging from women's rights and environmental protection to intercultural and cross-cultural communication to literacy and lifelong education, among others. As a result of these and other changes the country was a "brain-gainer" in 1975, attracting educated workers to its growing economy, a situation then unprecedented in the Third World. The new Islamic regime . . . turned the brain gain into brain drain."—**Gholam Reza Afkhami**, *The Life and Times of the Shah*

Astrophysicist Niayesh Afshordi is a native of and grew up in post-revolutionary Iran. In our conversation that follows about the physics of the early universe, Afshordi also comments on post-revolutionary Iran's brain drain. His own scientific career is a case in point.

(I can attest to progress on women's rights and "intercultural and cross-cultural communication" in mid-1970s pre-revolutionary Iran.)

Niayesh Afshordi graduated in 1999 at the top of his class with a BA in physics from Tehran's Sharif University of Technology. During his undergraduate years he was a gold and silver medalist in national and international physics Olympiads. After graduation he promptly left Iran for more opportunity in the West and postgraduate studies at Brown University, receiving his PhD in astrophysics in 2004 from Princeton University. He was a postdoctoral fellow at Harvard University's Institute for Theory and Computation. Afshordi now teaches at Canada's Perimeter Institute—one of the world's leading theoretical physics centers—as well as at University of Waterloo, considered the MIT of Canada.

But it hasn't been easy for Afshordi outside Iran either, even as a distinguished scientist. Afshordi says although he doesn't have as many immigration problems now, it has been difficult for him when applying for visas to go anywhere—to international scientific conferences, to visit national labs, even to visit the US where he received his PhD. He says he knows of many Iranian academics here in the West who have "those sorts of problems."

Some of Niayesh Afshordi's scientific awards include: Buchalter Cosmology Prize (2015, with Elliot Nelson); Professor M.K. Vainu Bappu Gold Medal (from the Astronomical Society of India, 2008, and in 2011 jointly with Nissim Kanekar); 1st Place, National Collegiate Physics Olympiad (1999, Iran); Silver Medal,

27th International Physics Olympiad (1996, Norway); Gold Medal, 8th National Physics Olympiad (1995, Iran) (partial list).

Aside from his current positions at Perimeter and Waterloo, Afshordi has taught at Guelph-Waterloo Physics Institute, and at Princeton, Brown, and Sharif universities, among others. He's been a guest lecturer at Harvard University and at the University of Waterloo.

His research focus is astrophysics, cosmology and fundamental physics. Since there has been considerable media spin that our universe is a vast hologram, citing a study (still ongoing) by Afshordi, and Kostas Skenderis and colleagues at the University of Southampton, I asked Niayesh Afshordi if he would give me his personal perspective about the evidence. I reached him recently at Perimeter Institute for comment.

Suzan Mazur: Your undergraduate degree in physics is from Iran's top science school, Sharif University of Technology. Why don't we hear more in the West about scientific research in Iran, aside from reports about Iranian nuclear technology?

Niayesh Afshordi: That's a very good question. I suppose the reason is that nuclear research—which is really technological, rather than scientific—people care about that because of its political and military implications. Nuclear research is separate from the vibrant scientific atmosphere prevalent in the top universities in Iran that doesn't make for the sexiest headlines.

The generation of scientists coming up in Iranian universities is not to be underestimated. There are already a significant number of Iranian academics at Western universities.

Of particular note, our friend Maryam Mirzakhani was the only woman ever to win the Fields Medal [2014]—considered the Nobel Prize of mathematics. She did her bachelor's degree at Sharif University, the same school where I did my undergrad work. Maryam was most recently at Stanford. Sadly, she died last year, at age 40.

People who do come to the West from Iranian universities may not necessarily work on the most headline-grabbing topics. A lot of them are actually here in the West because of various geopolitical and financial conditions. They can't be very productive in Iran. So a lot of us are here in the West, and some of us are very successful.

Suzan Mazur: Who owns the rights to scientific research done in Iranian universities?

Niayesh Afshordi: That's a good question. For most of my academic life I've been outside Iran. I did limited research as an undergrad in Iran. As far as I know, in Iran the rights for academic scientific research not involving profit, belong to the scientists themselves.

If someone works at the atomic agencies, that's a separate story. I don't have too much insight into it. . . .

Suzan Mazur: Why did you choose Canada as your base following your doctoral studies at Princeton and your postdoc at Harvard?

Niayesh Afshordi: I applied for a faculty position at many places, as did my wife. The place where we could both find a job was here in Canada. Canada was our best option.

Suzan Mazur: Is your wife a physicist also?

Niayesh Afshordi: Yes, she's a physicist.

Suzan Mazur: There at Perimeter Institute and University of Waterloo?

Niayesh Afshordi: She has an affiliation with both Perimeter and Waterloo, yes.

Suzan Mazur: What is her name?

Niayesh Afshordi: Ghazal Geshnizjani.

Suzan Mazur: Some of Perimeter's funding has come from the Templeton Foundation.

Niayesh Afshordi: That's right.

Suzan Mazur: Is your current research funded by Templeton?

Niayesh Afshordi: No.

Suzan Mazur: How close is the goal of combining Einstein's theory of relativity and quantum physics? Something Kostas Skenderis at the University of Southampton has described as a new paradigm for physical reality.

Niayesh Afshordi: We don't know. Physicists have been chasing this goal for the past 80 years. We'd like to think that we're closer than before. There have been new insights, theoretical and observational insights. But whether those are real, it's difficult to say.

Suzan Mazur: Your holographic universe research has been widely touted as "the first observational evidence that our universe could be a vast and complex hologram." Would you say that that is an accurate description?

Niayesh Afshordi: I think that's a little bit of an exaggeration. It is the first possible holographic description of our observed universe. There is evidence but it's not necessarily very strong evidence.

Suzan Mazur: You've also said that we are living in 3D:

> *"I can jump up and down, I can go back and forth, I can go left and right. There are three dimensions out there. I can again say that with confidence."*

350

But Leonard Susskind has said it's not clear which is the 3D reality, this one we think we're experiencing or the one out there in space. Would you comment?

Niayesh Afshordi: Yes. These are not inconsistent statements. The thing is we have a perception for everyday life. That perception may be complete and useful for our applications, like if I want to say, drive to work or drive home, or eat food, and basically everything else in everyday life that I'm interested in—the three-dimensional description of the universe is a good description.

However, there could be applications in very extreme circumstances. For example, very close to the Big Bang or Black Holes the three-dimensional description of the universe is not a very useful description. There could be other descriptions that are more useful. I can make more predictions using those descriptions. It all basically comes down to the difference between the fundamental reality and the practical reality.

For practical reality of our everyday life, three dimensions seems to be sufficient and accurate. But for the fundamental reality, it's very hard to tell and we don't know. We don't really have access to the fundamental reality of space and time. That's the question of quantum gravity, the question that has eluded us for the past 80 years. What is the fundamental reality of space and time? There are various theories but there is no definite conclusion about that.

Suzan Mazur: Despite the fact that the Fermilab Holometer experiment did not find evidence of the space-time jitter it was looking for, Fermilab astrophysicist Craig Hogan—who first envisioned the project—said he nevertheless continues to regard space-time as jittery, made of waves. And so he's now reconfigured Fermilab's instrument to probe further. Do you share Hogan's perspective? And what instruments are you relying on for your measurements?

Niayesh Afshordi: I do share the qualitative perspective that space-time is made out of jitters. In a sense that's been the lesson of quantum mechanics, that everything we perceive around us is jittery. Quantum mechanics has been very successful in describing the universe on small scales. That's how we have cell phones. Computers. Internet. Everything is based on quantum mechanics around us. Quantum mechanics essentially is a jittery description of reality because everything is uncertain and fluctuating.

The problem is how it applies to gravity. That's the part that different people disagree on. I think Craig Hogan's perspective is a minority one. Most people don't share Hogan's particular thinking about the geometry of space. But everybody in the mainstream of theoretical physics believes, and physics for that matter, as far as I know, everybody believes that the smallest scale is jittery. The question is exactly what probes of that jitteriness we can use.

I have a different approach, which is less controversial. I look at the light that comes from the Big Bang, at cosmic background radiation. The light that surrounds us. Its temperature is something like -270° Celsius [-454° Fahrenheit]. Most cosmologists think this is the light that came from the Big Bang and the most direct evidence we have from the Big Bang.

Suzan Mazur: Where are your measurements coming from?

Niayesh Afshordi: The measurements are coming from NASA's WMAP and the European Space Agency's Planck satellite. The newer one is the ESA's Planck satellite.

Suzan Mazur: But your holography collaboration with the University of Southampton is an ongoing research project?

Niayesh Afshordi: It is. But I've kind of decoupled from it. My former student, Elizabeth Gould, is now a postdoc there. She's working on the project.

Suzan Mazur: I interviewed James Simons for my 2014 book on origin of life and asked him to comment on the Fermilab experiment. He was surprised to hear about the Holometer probe and told me he continued to think we live in 3D. However, in 2016 the Simons Foundation committed $10 million to further investigate the holographic principle. How does what you've been doing at Perimeter and Waterloo differ from what Simons is exploring?

Niayesh Afshordi: The Simons holography collaboration you're talking about is clearly different from the Fermilab probe, although they're both rooted in holography.

Suzan Mazur: I'm referring to the "It from Qubit: Quantum Fields, Gravity and Information" Simons collaboration. Matthew Headrick is deputy director of the project, which involves 18 scientists.

Niayesh Afshordi: I do know about that program. "It" means everything including gravity and "Quibit" is quantum information. Rob Myers from Perimeter is actually part of that team.

As I said, both the Fermilab and Simons Foundation-funded programs are rooted in holography but "It from Qubit" is more theoretical in the sense that it doesn't have specific experiments it is testing.

The Simons collaboration is more a mathematical construction that relates theories that have gravity to theories that don't have gravity. It is basically an idea in mathematical physics. The thinking is there is some mathematical equivalence between theories that have gravity and theories that don't have gravity but have information in some sense.

Suzan Mazur: Even though you have "decoupled" from the holography research, do you see this as an emerging field, much like origin of life emerged a half dozen years ago with Harry Lonsdale's philanthropy?

Niayesh Afshordi: I think it's been an emerging field of research for the past 10 years. It's basically been happening for the past 15-20 years. Probably 20 years is more accurate. It was started by Juan Maldacena, who's now in Princeton at the Institute for Advanced Study. So it's been ongoing and has taken various shapes and forms.

Suzan Mazur: Maldacena is also one of the Simons Foundation investigators on It from Qubit. As is Susskind.

Niayesh Afshordi: This idea of It from Qubit. Where it's going to go in the future is hard to say. I personally think physical theories have to connect with data for them to actually be physical. So if it doesn't make a connection with observation or experiments, then at some point it becomes irrelevant.

Suzan Mazur: Is that why you've stepped back, "decoupled"?

Niayesh Afshordi: I have been working on a part of this that is connected with data. It's something I've been working on with Elizabeth Gould and Skenderis. So that part could survive, depending on how the data goes. The thing about connecting with data is that the data may confirm your theory or rule out your theory. If the theory is ruled out, it of course becomes irrelevant and we move on.

What is dangerous is that some theories can't be tested, can't explain anything and can only survive as zombies. I avoid these. I try to work on theories that connect with observation, that can be tested by observation that either confirms or rules them out. That is how you can make meaningful progress.

Suzan Mazur: Great. Thank you. Is there a final point you'd like to make?

Niayesh Afshordi: When it comes to the origins of the universe, there are lots of ideas that are out there. I don't think any of us are really committed to any of them. Some might be more committed than others. I personally, for example, have five or six different theories for the Big Bang and don't have any ideological commitment to any of them.

At the end of the day the question is, can data confirm one of them or will data rule out all of them? Then we have to move on to something different. That's roughly the goal for us as cosmologists and physicists. To go out, test hypotheses, rule out the ones that don't agree with data and keep the ones that can objectively explain the universe.

Chapter 35

Onward!—Into Holographic Noise: A Chat with Fermilab's Craig Hogan

Craig Hogan portrait, courtesy Fermilab

5/3/2018

Craig Hogan is obviously a trailblazer. He was part of the High-z Supernova Search team that discovered dark energy, two of whose members were awarded the 2011 Nobel Prize in physics for the breakthrough. And measured in productive scientist years, he is somewhat still a pup. So Hogan, who serves as director of Fermilab's Center for Particle Astrophysics has plenty of time to find the holographic noise he's been looking for, for a half dozen years or so, having now reconfigured his original holometer space probe instrument that DOE invested $2.5M in. Craig Hogan is no quitter, he's pressing on, as he tells me in the interview that follows:

"[I]t's not fair to say that it's time to give up because there are very few experiments, and our experiment is the only one of its kind . . . I think you should give us a little bit of time to look for it."

Hogan says that his main motivation is "this principle of holographic information" and that he and his team have adjusted the experiment to now be "sensitive to rotations."

Hogan has a point about his experiment being the only one of its kind. The field is rife with theory and often comes down to showmanship. Theoretical physicist Leonard Susskind's antics may be the most flagrant.

As widely reported, Susskind, a co-inventor of the holographic principle, threatened to slit his own throat if Hogan found holographic noise. Susskind once threatened me saying that if I ever published the transcript of our 20-minute taped telephone conversation he agreed to, in which he said that everything he knew about evolution he learned from reading Richard Dawkins' book and then proceeded to describe two other giants of biology as nut cases, that he would—. He never finished the sentence, never said specifically what he'd do if I published it. Ironically, another leading theoretical physicist I interviewed told me he based part of his cosmology theory on the thinking of one of the biologists Susskind trashed in the interview.

I first contacted Susskind as a followup to his statement at the 2008 World Science Festival regarding a biological and evolutionary element in physics. Said Susskind at WSF: "I wouldn't underestimate the biological elements to it also or the evolutionary element to it," and "what we have to get down to is what the DNA is in the universe."

But back to hands-on science. Hogan's holometer was inspired by the interferometer that Nobel laureate Albert Michelson invented over a hundred years ago, which was essentially made of mirrors and a light beam splitter.

Hogan's holometer was built with two interferometers designed to split incoming laser light. The plan was to get the two interferometers in their cosmic probe to simultaneously "jitter," which would confirm quantum uncertainty in space-time. Hogan and his team have now, as mentioned, moved some of the holometer parts around to get a "different form of holographic noise."

Craig Hogan wears several hats. Since 2008, he's been an astronomy and astrophysics professor at Enrico Fermi Institute and at Kavli Institute for Cosmological Physics, University of Chicago, as well as director of the Center for Particle Astrophysics at Fermi National Accelerator Laboratory.

Prior to Chicago, for a decade and a half, Hogan's base was the University of Washington, where he taught astronomy and physics, chaired the department and served as University of Washington's Vice Provost for Research, as well as Divisional Dean of Natural Sciences at the school's College of Arts and Sciences. He taught astronomy at the University of Arizona for five years before that and was an astronomer at the university's Steward Observatory.

Some of his awards include the 2015 Breakthrough Prize in Fundamental Physics (co-recipient; $3M awarded to Craig Hogan as a member of the High-z Supernova Team split with 50 other scientists for their "most unexpected discovery that the expansion of the universe is accelerating"); Gruber Cosmology Prize (co-recipient, discovery of dark energy, 2007); Alexander von Humboldt Research Award (1999-2008); Distinguished Scientist, Fermilab (2004); Discovery of the Year, *Science* magazine (1998, as a member of the High-z Supernova Team for the discovery of dark energy) (partial list).

Hogan has chaired and been a member of NASA's Astrophysics Subcommittee as well as its Space Science Advisory Committee. He was also part of NASA's Roadmap teams (2005; 2001-2002). From 2001-2011 Hogan was a US member of LISA (Laser Interferometer Space Antenna) International Science team looking for gravitational waves. In 2009, he was elected a Fellow of the American Academy of Arts & Sciences and the American Physical Society, among other professional honors.

Craig Hogan grew up in California and attended public high school. His BA is in astronomy, *summa cum laude*, from Harvard University and his PhD in astronomy from King's College, University of Cambridge. He was a postdoctoral fellow at Cambridge, University of Chicago and at California Institute of Technology.

He is a co-founder of the Large Synoptic Survey Telescope Corporation, and author of the book *The Little Book of the Big Bang*, featuring a foreword by Sir Martin Rees, his PhD advisor at Cambridge. Rees has been quoted as saying:

> *"Craig has forged unusually original and versatile theoretical insights into astrophysics. If you look at any number of subjects—from dark energy to how the Universe began—you'll find the earliest papers are from Craig."*

Our interview follows.

Suzan Mazur: You haven't found the quantum jitter you were probing for with the holometer and now have new instruments you're using to probe for "rotational quantum twists of space." Is that right?

Craig Hogan: Yes. In fact, the new instrument is almost exactly the same as the old one. The only difference is that we shifted some parts around so the light beams have a different configuration. It's designed, like you said, to be sensitive to rotations, which the first one was not.

Suzan Mazur: The rotational quantum twist of space would tell us that real space is not a continuum?

Craig Hogan: Well, yes. It doesn't have an infinite amount of information like an infinitely divisible space would. That's sort of just the tip of the iceberg. What it really is telling you is a lot of things.

People sometimes say there's no such thing as absolute space in relativity. But actually there is. There is very much an absolute local inertial frame and that's the one that isn't rotating.

No matter how small a piece of space you go to, you can tell whether you're spinning around or not because of the centrifugal force if you spin around. But the existence of that is something that might not actually be exact. As you go to smaller scales the definitions of directions, things we're used to as properties of space, might just dissolve into a quantum system.

Suzan Mazur: Thank you. You've said the holometer will be a template for a whole new field of experimental science. My understanding is that your view of geometry in space-time is a minority view. Would you comment?

Craig Hogan: Some of the things we're looking for are completely standard. My main motivation for it is this principle of holographic information, which is very widely believed in the community of black holes and quantum gravity.

The thing that isn't agreed upon is what effects that should have on an experiment. Nobody knows. And so we're just looking to see.

What we know is that the standard theory leaves something out. Everybody agrees with that. It leaves out something important, large scale. Everybody agrees with that. We know that from the behavior of black holes and from the cosmological constant. So the only disputed thing that is controversial is the idea that maybe that thing that we leave out on large scale is something we might actually be able to measure.

Suzan Mazur: The current thinking is that space-time is emergent, it's 2D sheets encoding a 3D environment?

Craig Hogan: That's a very widely held view. There are a lot of differences among people as to what is meant by emergence. What is generally agreed upon is that there is missing information, which means there have to be extra correlations. But nobody knows how it works.

However, it's not like anybody actually has a theory that predicts that we won't see something in the experiment. If we see something, it doesn't actually disprove anybody's theory. Even though some people are saying that it will. But they don't actually make predictions. It's a very difficult field that way.

Suzan Mazur: Leonard Susskind has said it's unclear whether the 3D we think we're experiencing is here or out there in space. What are your thoughts about that?

Craig Hogan: In a way we know that it's everywhere because the structure of space and time is built on light cones. Surfaces containing information connect all events at the speed of light. So, what you regard as here and now, the edge of the now extends forever at the speed of light into the future and the past.

Again, it's currently standard thinking in quantum mechanics that if you do a measurement at one place in the universe, that instantly affects things happening elsewhere—acausal correlations. That's been proven in many experiments in quantum mechanics. We know in quantum physics that nothing ever happens at a definite place and time—there is no such thing as locality. It has to be defined by physical measurement. All this is very weird but, in effect, totally non-controversial.

Suzan Mazur: Thank you. There is criticism that the holographic investigation has been going on for almost 20 years, kicked off by Juan Maldacena and that there's very little evidence so far, despite the bold headlines. That at some point in scientific investigations if the data doesn't correlate with the experiment as modeled, it's time to move on.

I gather you don't share that perspective. You've said you're only at the beginning of the investigation. Do you see this as an emerging field like origin of life, spawning an increasing number of virtual research hubs in various parts of the world?

Craig Hogan: That's very interesting. It's true this holographic idea has been around even before Maldacena. The basic idea goes back to the 1970s and black hole entropy and Stephen Hawking. But it's not fair to say that it's time to give up because there are very few experiments, and our experiment is the only one of its kind. It's not like there's a worldwide program of experiments testing this stuff. I think you have to try to look for it before you give up. We haven't really been looking that long. We have a small team working on this for less than 10 years. I think you should give us a little bit of time to look for it.

If it isn't there, we'll know that within a year or two. And we'll move on. Then maybe somebody else will try again.

Suzan Mazur: You're the only team with specific instruments probing.

Craig Hogan: Yes, for this particular type of thing, for this particular effect.

Suzan Mazur: So you don't you see your initiative beginning to inspire other experiments and other research centers.

Craig Hogan: It will depend on whether we're successful. If we get a null result from the experiment we have, it should be able to go well beyond the Planck length of sensitivity. If we don't see anything, that's basically the end of it. If we do, then there will definitely be significant followup.

Suzan Mazur: How close is the goal of combining Einstein's theory of relativity and quantum theory? Something that's been described by Kostas Skenderis at University of Southampton as being a new paradigm for physical reality.

Craig Hogan: I'm not sure that a single goal is well defined. There are several fundamental contradictions between the model of space-time that we use, Einstein's theory of relativity, and quantum mechanics. I think we can expect to circumvent some of those fairly soon and not others. It won't be completely solved for a long time.

Suzan Mazur: How does this focus intersect with current research into origin of life? There's no real consensus on what life is. Does this throw an additional wrench into the investigation of origin of life?

Craig Hogan: **Of course I'm not really a specialist in biology. But in my view, it's the behavior of atoms and molecules. Details are necessary to fill in, but that's basically what it is.**

Those are all quantum systems—the atoms and molecules. It's true that we don't know how much inherently quantum mechanical behavior that we're talking about, how important that is to life. Some people think it is. It's just not that clear what the dependence is. [emphasis added]

Suzan Mazur: But you think the 3D existence is real that we're living in.

Craig Hogan: It's 4D, of course. Three dimensions of space and one of time. We've known for 100 years that they're not really separate, time and space. So probably time is connected with one of the space dimensions. In that sense the four dimensions are really three dimensions. That's where the holographic idea comes from. You are kind of down one dimension because of the fact that time and space are interrelated in a certain way. Nothing ever moves faster than the speed of light. That's built into the system.

363

Suzan Mazur: Is Templeton also funding, in part, the new aspect of your investigation?

Craig Hogan: We used the Templeton money to fund our graduate students working on the experiment that we're now just finishing up. We've reconfigured our instruments to be sensitive to rotations—to a different form of holographic noise—without spending any extra money. So we're not looking for new funding yet. We will be, if we get a result.

Chapter 36

"Three Dimensions of Space"?—D'Arcy Thompson Letter to Whitehead

10/25/2017

With researchers earlier this year at several universities—University of Southampton (UK), University of Waterloo (Canada), Perimeter Institute (Canada), INFN, Lecce (Italy) and the University of Salento (Italy)—publishing findings in the journal Physical Review Letters that we live in a 2D, i.e., a holographic universe, it was interesting to come across biologist/mathematician D'Arcy Wentworth Thompson's 1918 letter to philosopher/mathematician Alfred North Whitehead in a recent exhibition of Thompson's work at the University of Dundee in which Thompson addresses the issue of "Three Dimensions of

Space." Thompson and Whitehead had developed a rapport some years earlier, as students at Cambridge.

The three-page typewritten letter was loaned to the Dundee exhibit by the University of St Andrews (the two schools Thompson called home). According to University of Dundee museum curator Matthew Jarron, who organized the three-day event at Dundee and St Andrews commemorating the 100th anniversary of the publication of Thompson's book On Growth and Form, Whitehead's response to Thompson unfortunately has not survived.

Thompson's letter follows (*letter photo, Suzan Mazur*).

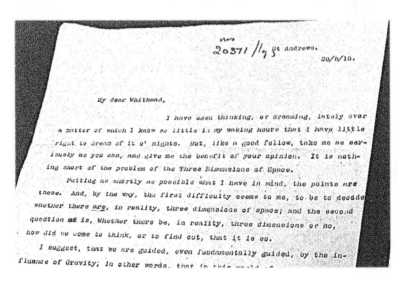

"St Andrews.

20/5/18.

My dear Whitehead,

I have been thinking, or dreaming, lately over a matter of which I know so little in my waking hours that I have little right to dream of it o'nights. But, like a good fellow, take me as seriously as you can, and give me the benefit of your opinion. It is nothing short of the problem of the Three Dimensions of Space.

Putting as shortly as possible what I have in mind, the points are these. And, by the way, the first difficulty seems to me, to be to decide whether there are, in reality, three dimensions of space; and the second question is, Whether there be, in reality, three dimensions or no, how did we come to think, or to find out, that it is so.

I suggest, that we are guided, even fundamentally guided, by the influence of Gravity; in other words, that in this world of ours we are always face to face with a vertical axis, and with a plane (or apparently plane) surface perpendicular to it. In other words, the right angle assumes a very special importance, and, consciously or unconsciously, we refer everything in space to trihedral coordinates.

Now suppose, on the other hand, that we were of so minute a size (or lived in a medium so dense) that gravity would have no sensible hold upon us; and suppose, owing to our minute size, that we were mainly under the influence of other, say molecular, forces. Then, to begin with, we should know nothing about a vertical, and care nothing about a right angle. And suppose, in the next place, that we lived in some sort of 'close-packed' or crystalline medium, say a tetrahedral one, we should never dream of three-dimensional space (unless perhaps after long mathematical investigation), but we should automatically refer everything to tetrahedral coordinates. In short, we should solemnly believe that we lived in a four-dimensional space.

So, paradox or no paradox, I seem to be driven to the conclusion that there is a quibble, or even a fallacy, underlying our definition of Space, or of Dimensions, (or perhaps both). Perhaps that 'dimensions'

2.

are not necessarily rectangular: or that perpendicularity, inter se, is not a fair condition to postulate of them. That the Space which actually exists is quite independent of dimensions; and that, by appropriate transformations we may ascribe to it as many as we please.

Of course, you may then say at once that even my quasi-molecular mathematician would learn, in time, that three-dimensions would suffice for his purposes, i.e. if he saw any good reason for using as few as possible. Well and good, but does that in any way prove that we have a right to say there are, in reality, three dimensions; is it anything more than a mathematical figment, an elegant formula.

It is something like Helmholtz's theory of Colour-vision: where H. showed that we account for all our phenomena by postulating three fundamental colours, or three fundamental sets of sensory cells. Nobody doubts it; but the physiologists have been ever since wondering, and arguing whether there actually are these three: in short, whether because this is the simplest possible hypothesis, it is necessarily the true explanation.

Another point that comes into my head, with reference to the case in general, is an old and simple saying of Tait's. He used to say that, given a symmetrical individual in symmetrical space, how on earth could you ever teach him what right and left meant. He would obviously have no right and left and space itself has, obviously, no right and left. And so, I come back to my query. Has Space really three dimensions; or is this only a convenient figment of terrestrial, and large and clumsy, mathematicians?

I put this, very much more briefly, to Larmor,- who simply swept me aside, with a story that 'If you fix a body in space by two points, it will always come back, at length by rotation, to the same position as before'. I can't see, for the life of me, that this answers my point. I think I have read in Clifford, of elliptical space in

368

which it doesn't follow in the same way. It seems to me that even if I fix it by only one point, then given perfect freedom otherwise, I may safely assert that it will still come back to the self-same position if I give it time enough.

3.

Besides, I don't know how to fix my body by two points in space. It reminds me of a friend of mine who wrote, and printed an article in Mind containing the remarkable phrase, 'Let us lay down some fixed line in space, as for instance a line from London to York'. .
. . . .

Kindest regards to your Wife and you. I hope to look you up some time next month.

Ever yours faithfully,

[DWT]"